mathematics for electronics and electricity

Prepared by the Staff of
National Radio Institute, Washington, D. C.

HAYDEN BOOK COMPANY, INC.
Rochelle Park, New Jersey

17 18   PRINTING

80 81 82 83 84 85   YEAR

Preface

Mathematics for Electronics and Electricity is written for the technician or technical student who needs a practical knowledge of mathematics as it is specifically related to electronics. Each topic is introduced and explained in terms of its electronics application. Learning is then reinforced by the presentation of example problems which are worked out and explained in detail.

The text was originally prepared by the National Radio Institute as a part of its comprehensive home study course in the principles of electronics. Thus, the contents of this book have been evaluated by thousands of students who found it acceptable from the standpoints of coverage, presentation, and technical accuracy.

The book begins with a complete review of arithmetic, from counting through the operations of addition, subtraction, multiplication and division. Fractions and decimals are then taken up. The use of decimals in multiplying and dividing in powers of ten is discussed and directly related to the conversion of electronic units. As examples, the changing of megacycles to kilocycles, and microampere to amperes are demonstrated. Several practice problems, complete with answers, are then given. The topic "percentage" is tied in with electronics by means of examples in finding resistor tolerances. Numerous dc circuit problems are given for practice in applying basic mathematics to electronics.

Next, the basic operations that are used in solving elementary ac circuit problems are treated. This section covers squares and square roots, ratio and proportion, positive and negative numbers, and vectors. In each case, a completely practical approach is taken in the presentation, and every effort has been made to relate each topic to its electronics applications. A number of practice problems related to basic ac circuits are presented.

The reader is later introduced to some more powerful mathematical tools which will enable him to solve complex circuit problems. Algebra is introduced with the application of the rules of arithmetic to combinations of letters and symbols. Equations are defined, and systematic methods for setting up and solving electronics problems are given. The "J" operator is presented with examples of its application in solving complex impedance problems. Many problems are given which furnish practice in applying algebra and the "J" operator to practical circuits.

So that the student can more quickly solve vector problems, basic trigonometry is introduced. The topics of angles, triangles, trigonometric functions and coordinate systems are presented in that order. The construction and application of several types of graphs which are widely used in electronics are discussed. Many short-cuts that are useful in speeding up and simplifying circuit calculations are presented. Practical circuit problems requiring the use of trigonometry in their solution are given.

The binary number system, which is the "language" of most digital computing systems, is discussed. The conversion of decimal numbers to binary and binary numbers to their decimal equivalents are covered. The arithmetic processes of addition, subtraction, multiplication, and division in the binary system are treated. The reader is then introduced to Boolean Algebra by a discussion of the basic logic operations and the laws of combination. Logic circuits such as AND, OR, NOR, and NOT gates are covered singly and in various combinations.

The material presented in this book has been student tested. However, widespread use and evaluation in this edition will probably reveal areas where improvement is needed. Your comments and criticisms are invited.

NATIONAL RADIO INSTITUTE

Washington, D.C.
July 1963

Contents

CHAPTER ONE

DC Circuit Calculations

1-1. Introduction

ONE of the first things that is explained to anyone learning electronics is Ohm's Law. This is the basic law covering the relations of voltage, current and resistance in electrical circuits. In addition to being one of the most basic of the fundamentals of electronics, it is also one of the important rules or laws. Whether it be industrial electronics, radio communications, or electronics engineering, this law, which states that "the current flowing in a circuit is equal to the applied voltage divided by the resistance" will be used and applied over and over again.

Ohm's Law can be expressed much more simply by using the symbols for current, voltage, and resistance in the formula: $I = E \div R$. This is a mathematical expression of the law using symbols instead of words.

Most of the rules or laws of electronics, or of any other science for that matter, are expressed as formulas for two reasons. One reason is that these simple mathematical expressions of the laws are much easier to memorize. The other reason is that they automatically provide a workable relationship of the laws for use in calculations. Thus, once you have learned the formulas, you not only have learned the rules, but also have them expressed properly for use in circuit calculations.

One of the best things about formulas is that they can be rearranged to find the particular quantity that we want to know. For example, the formula for Ohm's law, $I = E \div R$, is used when we know the voltage and resistance and want to find the current in circuit. We also learned that another way of saying the same thing is to state that $E = I \times R$ or more simply, $E = IR$. This manner of expressing the basic formula is very handy when we know the current and resistance and want to find the voltage.

By still another rearrangement, we can state the formula so that we can easily find the resistance by saying R = E ÷ I. All three of these statements of Ohm's Law say exactly the same thing. They are simply arranged in different ways for convenience in making circuit calculations.

We are able to change these formulas around to suit our purposes by applying some very basic rules of mathematics. In electronics, we must learn quite a few formulas to perform certain calculations so that we can understand how the circuits work and what may be wrong with them. Of course, the formulas can be rearranged depending on what we want to find and what we already know. Obviously, if we had to learn not only all the formulas but all the different forms of the formulas as well, we would have to do a lot of memorizing.

This would be impractical because we can easily learn a few of the basic laws of mathematics and then change the formulas to suit our own purposes. By doing this, we need to learn only one form of each formula, plus the few rules for changing formulas. In this way, mathematics becomes a useful tool, both in studying and working in the electronics field.

Of course, this is only one of the many reasons why a little mathematics is very useful to anyone who is making a career of electronics. For example, to use the formula, I = E ÷ R, we must know how to divide. When we say that E = IR, we must know how to multiply in order to use the formula. We will also find that we

constantly need to add and subtract.

Also, although we usually don't stop to realize it, a formula such as Ohm's Law and its rearrangements is actually a basic form of algebra. When we get into AC circuits, we will need to know a little about angles and triangles too. These first few sections in mathematics will enable you to use these simple, but very helpful, mathematical tools.

These sections in mathematics may be a review, but they are so complete that, even if you have never had any math at all, you will be able to understand any mathematical problems in electricity and electronics that come along. The sections have been devised to teach mathematics from the standpoint of usefulness in electricity and electronics.

In this first chapter, there is a complete review of arithmetic from counting to fractions and decimals. Examples and problems include circuit applications to help you learn how to make calculations in DC circuits. It may seem rather simple; however, you should read it all to make sure you remember it. Also, we have put in a few short cuts which you probably didn't learn in school and presented some of the material in a special way to help you later in your study of computers.

If mathematics has always bothered you before, don't be discouraged by the fact that you have to study it now. We present it very simply, and having a practical use for it makes it even easier to understand and remember. Let's begin by taking a look at our numbering system.

1-2. Arithmetic Review

There is nothing much more useful to us in our daily life or in electronics than basic arithmetic. Through this simple medium, we are able to count, make change, and separate similar things from each other.

For example, let's consider the circuit in Fig.1-1.

In this circuit we have a battery and a switch to supply five resistors and a light bulb through a fuse. We know this because we have learned to recognize these symbols and know what they mean. However, suppose we want to talk about just one of the resistors. Which one? Well, let's take the one closest to the switch. This is not too difficult to designate with words. Now, suppose we want to pick out the one closest to the light on the switch side of the battery to talk about. This still is not too hard to do. Now, how about "the one between the two resistors that are between the switch and the light"?

This is a very simple circuit compared to the circuitry of an amplifier or control system. Suppose we had to designate all the parts in a circuit by using words when we were trying to study or repair complex circuits. It certainly would be very awkward to use such a crude method. If we simply

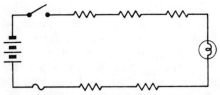

Fig. 1-1. Simple circuit without number designation.

add numbers to the circuit as shown in Fig.1-2 we can designate all the parts

so that there will be no question as to what we mean. How many times do we stop to realize just how important numbers are?

Our Number System

The number system which we use every day was originally based on the

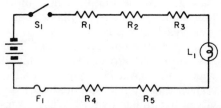

Fig. 1-2. Simple circuit with numbered parts.

number of fingers (including the thumbs) which we have on two hands. These ten items are called digits and are represented by the characters 1, 2, 3, 4, 5, 6, 7, 8, 9, and 0. What seems almost like a miracle is that with these ten characters we can write any number, no matter how large it may be. We will see when we explain decimals, later in this lesson, that with these same ten characters we can write any number, no matter how small it may be.

The ten digits, when written by themselves, have the values from zero to 9. But, when they are combined, as in the number 3947, they assume position values. Starting at the right, we say that 7 is in the "units" place— it has the value of 7 units. The 4 is in the "tens" place and represents 4 tens, or 40. The 9 is in the "hundreds" place and means 900, and the 3 is in the "thousands" place and denotes 3000. As you know, we read this number as "three thousand, nine hundred, forty (that is, 4 tens), seven."

The zero is used for any position where a denomination is missing, as in 4057 (read 4 thousand, fifty-seven) where it is used to show that this number has no entry in the hundreds place.

When a number contains many digits, it is customary to start at the right of the number and point off groups of three digits each with commas, reading toward the left. This groups the numbers into units, thousands, millions, billions, etc., where each group is a thousand times as large as the one to its right. This has a double advantage in that it makes the number easy to understand, and much simpler to read. Given a number like 12987632, compare it with 12,987,632 for simplicity. In this form, we would read it as "twelve million, nine hundred eighty seven thousand, six hundred thirty two."

Fig.1-3 is a chart showing how numbers up to billions are related. The next group of three digits to the left would be trillions, etc. In this way, our number system provides an easy way of keeping track of quantities in

0	1	2	3	4	5	6	7	8	9
1	2	3	4	5	6	7	8	9	10
2	3	4	5	6	7	8	9	10	11
3	4	5	6	7	8	9	10	11	12
4	5	6	7	8	9	10	[11]	12	13
5	6	7	8	9	10	11	12	13	14
6	7	8	9	10	11	12	13	14	15
7	8	9	10	11	12	13	14	15	16
8	9	10	11	12	13	14	15	16	17
9	10	11	12	13	14	15	16	17	18

Fig. 1-4. Basic addition table.

either very small or very large amounts.

Addition

Addition is a technical name for a process which is as old as counting. It is something you do every day, especially when you spend money. If you buy a pilot lamp for fifteen cents, a connector for a dime, and a fuse for a nickel, you realize almost at a glance that these three items will cost you thirty cents. Your own experience with this simple example will illustrate that you can add only "like" things, in this case "cents." The result of addition is called a sum or total.

Successful written addition involves only a repetition of the sums of numbers from zero to 9. If you find that you do not remember these combinations too well, you can get back into shape by practicing with the addition table given in Fig. 1-4.

To find the sum of two digits like 7 and 4, we look up the 7 in the first row, and the 4 in the first column, as shown by the arrows. Where the

BILLIONS, MILLIONS, THOUSANDS, UNITS

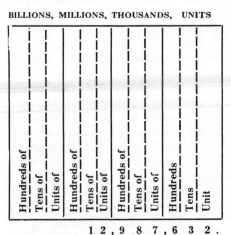

1 2 , 9 8 7 , 6 3 2 .

Fig. 1-3. Basic number chart.

column and the row meet is the sum, 11, which is marked by the box. Note that if you take the column headed by 4 and the row which begins with 7, you also get the same result, 11. We can say either 7 + 4 or 4 + 7 because both are equal to 11. From this, we can see that when adding, the order in which we take the numbers does not matter.

If you have a number of large items to add, such as your grocery bill, you will need to write them in a careful column. Neatness is always important! Then, we perform the process of repeated addition of the digits as in the tables.

Let's suppose that you have a number of resistances in series in a circuit. You learned that the total resistance of a series circuit is equal to the sum of all the separate resistances. This is a practical application of addition in electricity and electronics.

Seven resistances, all in ohms, are in series in a circuit. Find the total resistance, R_T, if the separate resistances are 3046, 2974, 8263, 5007, 1278, 6035, and 9707 ohms, respectively.

First, we will set the numbers down in good order, as shown in Fig. 1-5. We start our addition with the right hand

```
      3046
      2974
      8263
      5007
      1278
      6035
      9707
        40   Sum of the Units
       270   Sum of the Tens
      2000   Sum of the Hundreds
     34000   Sum of the Thousands
     36310   TOTAL
```

Fig. 1-5. Adding large numbers.

column which is the units column. Starting at the bottom and working up, we say: 7 and 5 is 12, 12 and 8 is 20, 20 and 7 is 27, 27 and 3 is 30, 30 and 4 is 34, 34 and 6 is 40. Then we write the 40 under the tens and units columns.

With a bit of practice you will find yourself omitting some of the detail and saying only the totals such as, 12, 20, 27, 30, 34, 40. If you find you are actually saying these numbers aloud, practice until you can do addition like this without even moving your lips.

Next, we add the items in the tens column. Reading only the totals as we go along from the bottom we have: 3, 10, 16, 23, 27. Since 27 tens is 270, we enter that number in the proper columns.

Starting at the bottom of the hundreds column we read the totals 7, 9, 11, 20, and since 20 hundreds is 2000, this is our next entry. Similarly, in the thousands column, we read, 9, 15, 16, 21, 29, 31, 34, and we enter 34,000 in the proper columns. The sum of these partial sums is our total: 36,310.

This method of addition shows every step of the process, but it involves extra writing. We generally practice so that we can perform the addition using the "carry" system. This is how we do it.

The sum of the units column is 40, so we enter the zero in that column and write a 4 at the top of the tens column. We have indicated this "carry" in Fig. 1-6 with a small 4, just above the 4 at the top of the tens column. Notice that this is the same addition that we did in Fig. 1-5, we are just doing it a little differently.

The sum of the tens column, including this carried 4, is now 31. Accordingly, we enter the 1 in the tens column and the 3 is entered above the hundreds column as a "carry." The sum of the hundreds column is now 23, including the carry, so we place the three under this column and insert the 2 at the top of the thousands column. The thousands now add up to 36, which is entered in its proper place and we have our total 36,310.

In our additions, we perform the operations from the bottom upward. It is a good check to start at the top and read downward. If you get the same result both ways, you may feel sure that your sum is correct.

In many cases, the numbers you add will not have the same number of digits, as shown in Fig. 1-7. In this case, when you add, if there is no figure to be added, treat it like a zero. Thus, in the example shown in Fig. 1-7, after the digits column is added up to 19 you enter 9 and carry 1 to the tens column. Then, as you add the tens, notice that there is no entry in front of the 5.

This blank space is the same as a zero, leaving only 2, 5, 4, and the carry of 1 to be added in the tens column. This gives a total of 12.

The 2 is entered in the tens column and the 1 is carried to the hundreds column. Then, in adding the hundreds column, blanks appear before 5, 22, and 47, leaving only 8, 2, 9, 3, and the carry of 1 to be added, giving a total of 23 for this column.

The 3 is entered in the hundreds column and the 2 is carried to the thousands column, giving us a total of 11 for the thousands column. Both of these digits can be entered since there is no more addition to do. Thus, our answer or total is 11,329.

$$
\begin{array}{r}
2\ 1\ 1 \\
3300 \\
47 \\
905 \\
250 \\
22 \\
6800 \\
5 \\
\hline
11,329
\end{array}
$$

Fig. 1-7. Adding numbers with different amounts of digits.

Here are several practice problems for you to work out. Copy the problems on a separate piece of paper and compare your answers with those we give.

(1)		(2)		(3)	
	296		4729		470
	926		2065		2
	112		1001		120
	211		1234		56
	876		4567		—
	555		6543		

$$
\begin{array}{r}
2\ 3\ 4 \\
3046 \\
2974 \\
8263 \\
5007 \\
1278 \\
6035 \\
9707 \\
\hline
36,310
\end{array}
$$

Fig. 1-6. Addition using system of carrying.

(4) 47,000
   220
 1,000,000
    15
  6,800
     7

(5) 820,000
    33
   1,080
    27
  500,000
   604

Answers: (1) 2,976; (2) 20,139; (3) 648; (4) 1,054,042; (5) 1,321,744.

Subtraction

Subtraction is just the opposite of addition. Given the sum of two numbers and one of the numbers, subtraction asks, "What is the other number?" Thus, if 36 is the sum of two numbers and 21 is one of them, the other must be 15, since 21 + 15 is equal to 36.

Another way of saying the same thing is "what must I add to 21 to make 36?" The 15 is called the *difference* between 36 and 21, and it is written 36 − 21 = 15. The two dashes (equal sign) are a mathematical symbol that means "equal to."

Since addition and subtraction are so closely related to each other, the addition table can also be a subtraction table. Suppose you want to find the difference between 16 and 9. First, find the column marked 9 and follow it until you find the number 16. Then go to the left in this row and you will find the difference, 7, at the left end of the row. Let's do a subtraction problem in detail.

Find the difference between 5832 and 2386. This would be written 5832 − 2386, which is the mathematical way of stating the problem. You will remember that 5832 is equal to 5000 + 800 + 30 + 2, and that 2386 is equal to 2000 + 300 + 80 + 6. The difference can be found by determining the following simple dif-

ferences and then combining them:

5000	800	30	2
−2000	−300	−80	−6

Starting at the right, we cannot take 6 from 2 so we borrow 10 from the 30 in the tens column. This leaves 20 there and gives us 12 in the units column as follows:

20	12
−80	−6
	6

It is plain that we have a 6 for the units place in our difference since 6 and 6 make 12. Now, let's look at the tens place. We have to find the difference between 20 and 80, and we have to borrow 100 from the hundreds to do it. This leaves 700 there and gives us 120 from which we can take 80. This will leave us a difference of 40 in the tens column as shown below:

5000	700	120	12
−2000	−300	−80	−6
3000	400	40	6

The other two columns offer no difficulty, so we simply take 300 from 700 which leaves us 400. Then 2000 from 5000 leaving 3000. Now, we combine the differences as follows:

  6
  40
 400
3000
————
3446

Thus, we see that 5832 − 2386 equals 3446.

In actual practice we usually shorten the work as shown in Fig.1-8. First, we set down the larger number and put the smaller number directly under it. Then we draw a horizontal line under the smaller number. We start at the right and say we cannot take 6 from 2, so we borrow 1 ten from the tens, leaving a 2 there. See how we have crossed out the 3 and placed a small 2 in its place in the tens column. Of course we can now take 6 from 12 which is equal to 6.

Similarly in the tens column we must borrow 100 from the next column leaving 700 there. We show this by striking out the 8 and replacing it with a small 7. Then, 8 from 12 is 4 for the tens entry. The other two places offer no complications and we again have the result 3446.

To test the correctness of a subtraction problem, add the difference to the number we subtracted. The

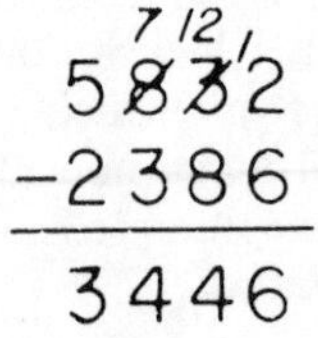

$$\begin{array}{r} 7\ 12 \\ 5\cancel{8}\cancel{3}2 \\ -2386 \\ \hline 3446 \end{array}$$

Fig. 1-8. Subtracting two numbers.

sum of these two must always add up to the number which we started with. In this case:

$$\begin{array}{r} 2386 \\ +\ 3446 \\ \hline 5832 \end{array}$$

Each of the numbers in a subtraction problem has a particular name. The one at the top that we subtract from is called the *minuend*. The one directly above the line is the one we subtract and is called the *subtrahend*. The result is the difference or the *remainder*. Here are several practice problems and their answers for you to work out.

(1) 5843
− 2951

(2) 8032
− 2417

(3) 7205
− 4313

(4) 32964
− 3497

(5) 121324
− 22496

(6) 403010
− 395347

Answers: (1) 2892; (2) 5615; (3) 2892; (4) 29467; (5) 98828; (6) 7663.

Multiplication

Suppose that we want to add 7 + 7 + 7 + 7. We say that we have 7 taken 4 times, or 4 times 7. Now, the sum of this addition problem is clearly 28. Hence, we can say that 4 times 7 is 28.

The sign "×" means multiplication and we write this 4 × 7, and read it "4 times 7." If we add 4, seven times, we will have 4 + 4 + 4 + 4 + 4 + 4 + 4 and we will find that we again have 28. You can see, therefore, that 4 × 7 = 7 × 4 because they are both equal to 28.

This illustrates a basic principle of multiplication. When multiplying, the order in which we take the numbers makes no difference in the result. The answer we get is called the product. As we have just seen, 28 is the product of 7 × 4. No doubt in your early days at school, you learned a large number of these products. In case you have trouble remembering them now, we have shown a multiplication table in   1-9. You can use this to review these basic products.

This is how we use the table. Locate a number (in multiplication they are often called factors) in the top row and read down the column. Find the other factor in the first column and read to the right along the row that it appears in. You will find the product where the row and the column meet.

In the chart, we have marked column 7 and row 4 with arrows and they meet at their product 28, which

*1	2	3	4	5	6	7	8	9	0
2	*4	6	8	10	12	14	16	18	0
3	6	*9	12	15	18	21	24	27	0
4	8	12	*16	20	24	28	32	36	0
5	10	15	20	*25	30	35	40	45	0
6	12	18	24	30	*36	42	48	54	0
7	14	21	28	35	42	*49	56	63	0
8	16	24	32	40	48	56	*64	72	0
9	18	27	36	45	54	63	72	*81	0
0	0	0	0	0	0	0	0	0	0

Fig. 1-9. Multiplication table.

agrees with what we have just explained. Also, notice that if we had taken column 4 and row 7 we would have found 28 again. This table gives us an easy way to practice reviewing the products of numbers from 1 to 9. Knowing these products is important because if you are sure of the product of any one digit times another digit in this basic table, you will have no trouble in finding the product of any two numbers no matter how large they may be.

In the table, the numbers that run down diagonally from left to right are starred (★). These numbers (1, 4, 9, 16, 25, 36, 49, 64, and 81) are the products of 1×1, 2×2, 3×3, 4×4, 5×5, 6×6, 7×7, 8×8, 9×9. We call the products of two numbers that are exactly alike, "squares." Squares are sometimes written 1^2, 2^2, 3^2, etc. In other words, 6^2 means 6×6.

This is a very common way of indicating that one number should be multiplied by itself and is used throughout mathematics. In fact, squares are so common that you should certainly memorize the squares of all the numbers from 1 to 10. Many

people, even those not working with mathematics very much, work out and learn the squares of all the numbers from 1 to 25.

The products given in the table in Fig.1-9 are the products of one digit multiplied by another digit. All other problems in multiplication are of two kinds. Either one factor is a single digit and the other has more than one digit, or both factors have more than one digit.

Let's examine a problem such as 7×932. You know that 932 means $900 + 30 + 2$. Therefore, 7×932 means the sum of 7×900 and 7×30 and 7×2. There are three ways of writing this same product, as shown below.

(A)	932	(B)	900
	932		900
	932		900
	932		900
	932		900
	932		900
	932		900
	———		30
	6524		30
			30
			30
			30
			30
			30

(C) $\quad 7 \times 900 = 6300$
$\qquad 7 \times 30 \;\; = \;\; 210$
$\qquad 7 \times 2 \;\;\; = \cdot\; 14$
$\qquad\qquad\qquad ———$
$\qquad\qquad\qquad 6524$

2
2
2
2
2
2
2
———
6524

We can add 932 seven times as shown at A; or we can add 900 seven times, 30 seven times, and then 2 seven times as shown at B. Still another way is to multiply 900×7, 30×7 and 2×7 and then add up the three products as shown at C. Each of these methods gives us the same answer.

In actual practice we write the problem:

$$932$$
$$\times 7$$

Then, we multiply the digit in the units column, or:

$$2$$
$$\times 7$$
$$\overline{14}$$

Next, we multiply the tens and enter this product as:

$$30$$
$$\times 7$$
$$\overline{210}$$

Finally, we multiply the hundreds and enter this product:

$$900$$
$$\times 7$$
$$\overline{6300}$$

Now we can add all these products to obtain the final answer:

$$14$$
$$210$$
$$6300$$
$$\overline{6524}$$

It is generally more convenient to total our answer as we go along as shown in Fig. 1-10. This we do by recording the 4 in the first step and "carrying" the 1. This 1 is entered above the 3 in the tens column. There it is *added* to the product we obtain by multiplying 3 by 7 (3 × 7 = 21). Notice that we do *not* add the 1 to the 3 before we multiply; we add the 1 to the 21 *after* we multiply and get 22. The 2 in the digits place is written in the product line under the 3. The 2 in the tens place is written over the

9 to remind us to add it to the next product.

The last multiplication is 7 × 9 which gives us 63. To this is added the 2 we carried over from the last multiplication.

Since there is no further multiplication to do, we enter both the 5 and the 6. We would carry the 6 to the thousands column if there were more multiplication. In this manner, we can multiply 932 by 7 and get our answer directly. We eliminate writing out the extra steps as we did before.

Remember that the "carry" is added to the product after we multiply. It does not change the number over which it is placed. With practice, you will be able to add these "carrys" after you multiply without writing them down.

Now suppose that both factors have several digits as in the problem 327 × 849. This is the same as saying 7 × 849 plus 20 × 849 plus 300 × 849. This will give us three products which we can add together.

849	849	849
× 7	× 20	× 300
5943	16980	254700

Notice that multiplying a number by 20 is the same as multiplying it by 2 and adding a zero at the right. Multiplying by 300 is the same as multiplying by 3 and adding two zeros to the right of the product.

$$\begin{array}{r} 2\,1 \\ 932 \\ \times 7 \\ \hline 6524 \end{array}$$

Fig. 1-10. **Multiplication using carry and simultaneous addition.**

The sum of these three products is the product we are looking for:

$$5943$$
$$16980$$
$$254700$$

$$327 \times 849 = 277623$$

With a little practice you will soon find it easy to multiply by a single digit at a time and your multiplication will look like this.

$$849$$
$$327$$

$$5943$$
$$1698$$
$$2547$$

$$277623$$

Here we have omitted the zeros in each step and have moved the partial product one place to the left each time. It is customary to set the larger number over the smaller one and do the work as shown.

Starting at the right we have $7 \times 849 = 5943$. Then $2 \times 849 = 1698$ which we set over one space to the left. Then $3 \times 849 = 2547$ which is set over one space farther to the left. Finally, the sum of these three numbers is the product.

Notice that each time we multiply 849 by one of the digits in the lower factor, the first number of each product that we enter is placed exactly below the digit in the lower factor. Thus, when we multiply 849 by the 2 in the tens column, the first entry of the product (8) is lined up beneath the 2. Likewise, when we multiply the 849 by the 3 in the hundreds column, the 7 is entered directly below the 3. You will need to practice this type of work with great care for a single slip will give you an incorrect result.

You will recall that current times resistance equals volts ($I \times R = E$), and that volts times amperes equals watts ($E \times I = P$). Here are some problems for you to work out using these formulas. Given the circuit and resistance, find the voltage and wattage.

Circuit 1. current (I) in amp. = 26
  resistance (R) in ohms = 217
Circuit 2. current (I) in amp. = 15
  resistance (R) in ohms = 328
Circuit 3. current (I) in amp. = 23
  resistance (R) in ohms = 197

First, multiply the resistance by the current to find the voltage. If you do this properly you should have:

Circuit 1. voltage (E) in volts = 5642
Circuit 2. voltage (E) in volts = 4920
Circuit 3. voltage (E) in volts = 4531

Now, multiply the voltage you have found for each circuit by the current in that circuit to find the wattage:

Circuit 1.
  power (P) in watts = 146,692
Circuit 2.
  power (P) in watts = 73,800
Circuit 3.
  power (P) in watts = 104,213

Division

The process known as division is just the reverse of multiplication. You remember that a product is the result of multiplying one number by another. In division, we are given the product of two numbers and one of the numbers and asked to find the other number. Thus, if we are given a product 56 and a number 7, we are asked what number multiplied by 7 equals 56. If you have learned your multiplication table, you know that 8 times 7 is equal to 56. Therefore, 8 is the number that we have been asked to find.

In division, the product that we

are given is called the *dividend*. The number we divide by is called the *divisor*. The number we are asked to find is known as the *quotient*. The symbol for division is ÷. Whenever we see this symbol we know that it means "divided by." Thus, we would write the above problem which says 56 divided by 7 equals 8 as:

$$56 \div 7 = 8$$

Here, 56 is the dividend, 7 is the divisor, and 8 is the answer or quotient. Two other ways of indicating division for the same problem are $56/7 = 8$, or $\frac{56}{7} = 8$.

Since the process of division is just the opposite of multiplication, we can use the multiplication table in Fig.1-9 for a division table if we learn how. First, we locate the divisor (the number we want to divide by) at the head of a column. Then we follow down the column until we come to the dividend. Then we follow to the left along the row that the dividend is in until we come to the first column. The number in the first column in the same row as the dividend will be our quotient.

For example, for $56 \div 7 = 8$, we locate the column headed by the number 7. Then we go down that column until we find the dividend which is 56. Then we go left along the row the dividend is in until we come to the first column where we find the number 8. Thus,

$$56 \div 7 = 8$$

Of course, this table shows only the exact products of two digits. If the number you wish to divide is not one of these products, you will not find a complete quotient. For example, if we wish to divide 58 by 7, we will not be able to find the number 58 in the 7 column. Therefore, we will go

down the 7 column until we find the number that is closest to 58, but smaller. In this case it will be 56. Following to the left of the 56 row, we find the quotient 8. However, we must consider the difference between 58 and 56 which is 2. Thus we say that $58 \div 7 = 8$ with a remainder of 2.

We frequently need to know this sort of an approximate answer in a division problem as we shall see later. If you have been practicing with your multiplication combinations and are now fairly expert with them, you will not need to go to the table very often.

Now that we have learned how to use the table to find the answer to simple division problems, let's see how this process can be expanded to divide larger numbers. One of the easiest types of division problems is one in which the number we are dividing by is a single digit. Suppose we have the problem $732 \div 3$. Here, the dividend has three numbers and cannot be found in the division table.

The first thing we do is set down the divisor 3 as shown in Fig.1-11A. Then we make a short vertical line after the 3 and write the dividend immediately after the vertical line. Next, we draw a line over the dividend starting from the vertical line and continuing to the right until the dividend is completely covered. As we find each number of the quotient, we will set it down in order above this line until the division is completed and we have the complete answer. Remember, that neatness in the set-up of any mathematical problem is important to speed and accuracy.

Now that we have the number set up in standard division form, let's go ahead and solve it. Remember, we want to know what number multiplied by 3 will give us 732. Therefore, the first thing we do is divide three into seven. We say to ourselves, "How many times does 3 go into 7?" By looking in the table in Fig. 9, or by calling on our memory if we have learned the basic table, we find that 2 times 3 is 6, and 3 times 3 is 9. Since 9 is more than 7, we go to the next smaller number which is 6. Thus, 3 will go into seven 2 times with a remainder.

We write 2 above the line directly over the 7, indicating that 3 goes into seven 2 times. Then we write the product of 3 × 2, which is 6, right under the 7 as shown in Fig. 1-11B. We draw a line under the 6 and subtract the 6 from the 7, giving a remainder of 1.

Now, notice that we have actually been dividing 700 by 3 although we have only been concerned with the first number 7. Therefore, our remainder when we divide 700 by 3 is really 100 instead of just 1, and our quotient is 200 instead of 2. Also, the number that we want to divide is 732 not just 700. Consequently, our full remainder at this time is our actual remainder of 100 plus 32, or 132 as shown. Now, we must divide this reminder by 3 and add the answer to our quotient of 200.

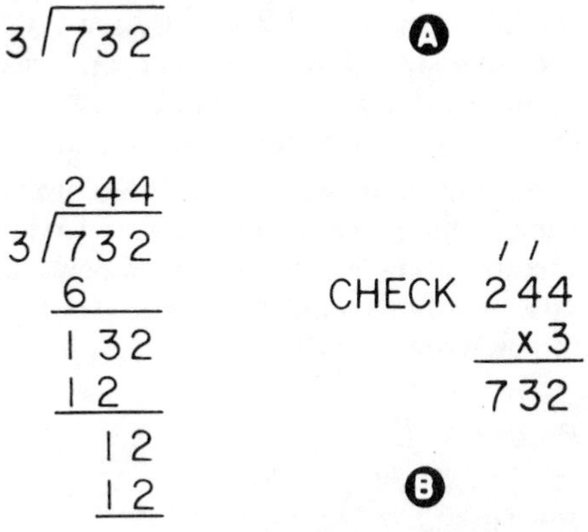

$$3\overline{)732} \qquad \text{A}$$

However, in our next step, we don't worry about the whole 132 any more than we were concerned with the whole 732 in the first step. First, we consider the 1 by itself. It is obvious that 3 won't go into 1 alone, so we look at the 1 and the 3 together, which make 13. Checking our table, we find that there is no number multiplied by 3 which will give exactly 13, but 3 times 4 make 12, which is the next smaller product of 3 times a number. Therefore, we write the 4 above the line in the space for our quotient next to the 2. Then we enter the product of 3 times 4 (12) directly under the 13 and subtract to find our remainder.

Since 12 from 13 leaves a remainder of 1, we write this down as shown. However, since we actually had an original number of 132 instead of 13, we bring the 2 down also, making our complete remainder 12. We can look at our division of 13 by 3 as if we were dividing 130 by 3 and got a quotient of 40 instead of 4 and a remainder of 10 instead of 1.

In our quotient, we have the number 24 which is really 240 since we have actually divided 732 by 3 which has given us an answer of 240 with a remainder of 12. Now we perform the last step which is to divide the 3 into the remainder of 12 as shown. This gives us another 4 which we place in the quotient as shown and we have no further remainder. We now have a complete quotient because there is nothing left to divide so we know that 732 divided by 3 is 244. We can check or prove our answer by multiplying 244 by 3 to make sure that we get a product of 732.

Now let's try another problem for practice. This time we will handle our remainders a little differently. Instead of bringing down the whole remainder each time, we will bring down just the

$$\begin{array}{r} 244 \\ 3\overline{)732} \\ \underline{6} \\ 132 \\ \underline{12} \\ 12 \\ \underline{12} \end{array} \qquad \begin{array}{r} \text{/ /} \\ \text{CHECK } 244 \\ \underline{\times 3} \\ 732 \end{array}$$

B

Fig. 1-11. Setting up a division problem, A; working a division problem, B.

part of it that we are going to use for each division. This is the way we usually perform division problems because it saves us writing down numbers each time that we won't use. This also helps us to know exactly where to put the numbers in our quotient as we find them as we shall see when we work the problem.

First we state our problem: Divide 43467 by 7. Then we set the problem down in the proper manner for division as shown in Fig. 1-12 and work it out. Let's go through it step by step to make sure we understand it.

When we try to perform the first step of division, we see that 7 won't go into 4. So, we take the first two numbers, 43, and we see that 6 × 7 is 42 and therefore 7 will go into 43, six times with a remainder. We enter the 6 in the quotient, but we place it above the 3. In effect, we already have a 0 above the 4 because we saw that 7 wouldn't go into 4. We don't usually write this zero down, we just indicate it by placing the 6 over the 3. This is a good example of how important neatness and order can be.

Next, multiply the divisor by this 6 and enter the product (42) under the first two numbers of the dividend (43). Take the difference to get the remainder (1), and bring down the 4 from the dividend to get 14 for the next step of division. Notice that we

didn't bring down the whole remainder this time, just the 4 which we need. 7 goes into fourteen 2 times, so enter 2 in the quotient over the 4 and beside the 6. Multiply the divisor by this 2, entering the product below the 14.

The number we enter here this time is also 14, so the remainder is zero. We still bring down 6 for the next step, but 7 won't go into 6 so we enter a zero in the quotient after the 2. We must enter this zero because a zero between two digits in a number indicates position value. The first zero we got wasn't important because there was no number in front of it.

Since 7 won't go into 6, we have to bring down the 7 from the dividend, making 67. 7 will go into sixty-seven 9 times, with a remainder. Enter the 9 in the quotient beside the zero and multiply the divisor by 9. The product is 63, which is subtracted from 67 to get a remainder of 4. 7 won't go into 4, and there are no more numbers to bring down, so 4 is a final remainder. Thus, the answer of 43,467 divided by 7 is 6209, with a remainder of 4. This remainder is sometimes written in the quotient as 4/7, showing that we were unable to divide 4 by 7.

To check this answer, we multiply the quotient 6209 by the divisor 7 to get 43,463. Then we add our remainder of 4 to this product and get our original dividend of 43,467.

Now practice with these three problems, and check your answers to be sure they are right. Be very neat in your work to avoid writing a number in the wrong column.

```
  06209         CHECK 6209
7/43467              x 7
  42               43463
  14                 +4
  14               43467
  67
  63
   4
```

Fig. 1-12. Another division problem.

Problems:

(1) Divide 3248 by 7.

(2) Divide 40,734 by 3.

(3) Divide 9627 by 8.

Answers: (1) 464; (2) 13578; (3) 1203 with a remainder of 3.

Now that we have learned how to do a problem with a single digit for a divisor and a large number of digits in the dividend, let's look at some problems where both the divisor and the dividend contain several digits. For example, consider the problem of 803,368 ÷ 274. We go at this just the way we did with a single divisor except that we have no multiplication table for the number 274 so we make one.

```
274 x 1 =  274              2932
274 x 2 =  548      274 /803368
274 x 3 =  822              548
274 x 4 = 1096             2553
274 x 5 = 1370             2466
274 x 6 = 1644              876
274 x 7 = 1918              822
274 x 8 = 2192              548
274 x 9 = 2466              548
```

Fig. 1-13. Division with several digits in divisor and dividend.

We do this by multiplying 274 by each number from 1 to 9 as shown in Fig. 1-13. First, we multiply 274 by 1 and list this product. Then we multiply 274 by 2, 3, 4, etc. and list their products until we have a list of products of 274 and all the numbers from 1 through 9. Now we set up our problem for division as shown.

Next, we start at the left of the dividend and look to the right until we find a number larger than our divisor 274. In this problem we find an 8, then a 0, and then a 3, giving us 803 as the first number larger than our divisor. By looking at the table we have made we see that this is larger than two times the divisor which is 548, and smaller than three times the divisor which is 822. So, we enter 2 in the quotient directly above the 3

in 803. We now place 548 (274 × 2) under the 803 and subtract it from 803, which leaves 255. Now we bring down the fourth figure of the dividend and get the number, 2553, and find the largest of our products that will go into it.

The table shows that 9 × 274 is 2466, so we enter 9 in the quotient above the 3 and subtract 2466 from 2533. This leaves us 87 for a remainder and we bring down the 6, giving us 876 for the next number to divide. 3 × 274 is 822 which we will subtract from the 876, leaving a remainder of 54. We enter the 3 in the quotient.

Bringing down the final 8 gives us 548 for the final dividend. Since this is exactly 2 × 274, we subtract from 548 and have a zero remainder. Of course, we must enter the 2 in the quotient which is now 2932. The check consists in showing that 274 × 2932 is actually the dividend 803,368 by performing the multiplication.

Notice that we only used a few of the numbers out of our table of the products of the divisor. We used 2 times 274, or 548; 9 times 274, or 2466; and 3 times 274, or 822. All the rest of the table wasn't used. Consequently, if you know your multiplication well enough you may want to omit making the entire table. We can do this by multiplying the divisor by only the numbers we need to solve the problem.

Let's try a problem without making a products table for the divisor and see how it is done. Suppose we want to divide 73,276 by 437. First, we set up the problem in the usual manner as shown in Fig. 1-14. Then, starting at the left of the dividend we look to the right until we find a number larger than 437. In this problem it is 732.

Now we look at 4, which is the first

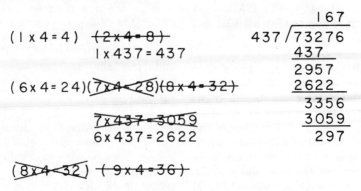

Fig. 1-14. Estimating the quotient numbers in division.

number in our division, and ask ourselves how many times it will go into seven. Since two times four is eight, which is larger than 7, four will obviously go into seven just once. Therefore we estimate (an intelligent guess) that 437 will certainly not go into 732 more than once. Thus, we enter 1 in our quotient directly above the 7 in our dividend and subtract 1 × 437 or 437 from 732. Our remainder is 295.

This remainder allows us to check our first estimated quotient number. If the remainder is smaller than the divisor, we are right. However, if the remainder comes out larger than the divisor we are wrong because we could have multiplied our divisor by a larger number than we did. When this happens, we try the next larger number to see if it will work.

If the product of our estimated quotient number and our divisor is so large that we can't subtract it, we are also wrong and will have to try a smaller number for our quotient. In this problem we are right, because our quotient number 1 and our divisor 437 give us 437 for a product which is small enough to subtract, and the remainder which we get is smaller than the divisor.

Now, we bring down the 7 from the dividend and see how many times 437 will go into 2957. We make an estimate the same as we did before. The first number of our divisor is 4. We say to ourselves "how many times will 4 go into 29?" 7 times 4 is 28 which is smaller than 29, and 8 × 4 is 32 which is larger than 29. Therefore we will multiply 437 by 7 to see how it works. We find that this gives us 3059 which is larger than 2957, so we can't subtract. This means that 7 was really too large even though it looked as if it might work.

Now, we try 6, which is the next smaller number. We find that 6 × 437 = 2622 which is small enough to subtract from 2957. When we do subtract, we see that our remainder, 335, is smaller than the divisor 437, so 6 meets both requirements and can be entered in our quotient beside the 1 and above the 7.

Now we bring down the 6 from our dividend and try to estimate how many times 437 will go into 3356. We immediately see that 8 × 4 is 32 which might work. However, if we look at our complete product of 7 × 437 which we found but couldn't use in the previous step, we can see that by subtracting it from 3356 we will certainly get less than 437 because 3356 − 3059 is going to be about 300, certainly less than 437! Therefore we won't bother to try 8 × 437 as a trial product because the product of 7 × 437 which we have already found satisfies the problem.

If we had forgotten or misplaced our product of 7 × 437, it wouldn't do any harm to try 8 × 437. We would quickly find out it wouldn't work and then we would try 7 anyway. However, as you can see, we saved the trouble of trying 8 by keeping track of our 7 × 437 trial product even though we couldn't use it the time we found it.

Getting back to our problem, when we subtract 3059 from 3356, we get a remainder of 297 which is satisfactory so we enter 7 in our quotient. Since we have no more numbers to bring down, our full quotient is 167 with a remainder of 297. We can check this in the usual way by multiplying 167 × 437 and then adding our remainder 297 to the product. If we have done our division correctly, we should get our original dividend of 73,276.

Division is a good way to test or improve your ability with numbers, since it also uses the processes of addition, subtraction, and multiplication. If you can get all the following drill problems right, the chances are you won't have much trouble with any of the four basic processes: addition, subtraction, multiplication, and division.

Problems	Answers
26,708 ÷ 793	33, remainder 539
386,921 ÷ 8076	47, remainder 7349
270,414 ÷ 498	543
4000 ÷ 3571	1, remainder 429
423 ÷ 72	5, remainder 63
8,926,104 ÷ 678	13,165, remainder 234

Rules of Order

So far we have learned how to add, subtract, multiply, and divide. These are all very basic mathematical operations which we will use over and over again in the study of electronics. In learning how to do these operations, we have been concerned with just one operation at a time. In actual practice we will find a need to do several, or perhaps all of these operations in order to find the answer to one problem.

While it may not seem at first glance that there is anything special about this, most of the time there will be a definite order in which we should do them. For example, take a simple problem like "what is 10 × 5 + 2 equal to?" Let's look at this closely.

If we do the multiplication first and then the addition, we get 10 × 5 = 50, then we add the 2 and find the answer 52. However, if we look at the problem and say 5 + 2 equals 7 and then 7 × 10, we come up with an answer of 70. As you can see, there is quite a difference between our first answer of 52 and our second answer of 70. Thus, the order in which we do a problem is quite important.

Let's take another more practical operation that we might find in our work in electronics. In the circuit shown in Fig. 1-15, we have a voltage supply of 100 volts and two resistors. One resistor is 10 ohms and the other is 40 ohms. Now the current in the circuits will be equal to the voltage divided by the resistance. Let's state the problem mathematically:

$$I = E \div R$$
$$I = 100 \div 10 + 40$$

Which operation do we do first? We know from our lessons on Ohm's Law that we are dealing with a total voltage of 100 volts. Therefore, we will be finding the total current, and naturally we will want to divide our total voltage by the total resistance. For this reason we add the two resistances first to get $10 + 40 = 50$ ohms and then divide 100 by 50 to get a current of 2 amperes.

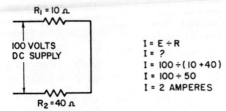

R₁ = 10 Ω

100 VOLTS
DC SUPPLY

R₂ = 40 Ω

$I = E \div R$
$I = ?$
$I = 100 \div (10 + 40)$
$I = 100 \div 50$
$I = 2$ AMPERES

Fig. 1-15. Practical circuit where rules of order are important.

We did it this way because we know something about electronics. Ohm's Law states that total current = total voltage divided by total resistance. We also know that the total resistance is equal to the sum of all the resistances. Therefore, in our problem although we might not be aware of it, we actually thought this way:

$I_T = E_T \div R_T$, but
$R_T = R_1 + R_2$, so we keep the two resistances together by enclosing them in parenthesis to get:

$$I_T = E_T \div (R_1 + R_2).$$

Then we substituted to get:
$$I_T = 100 \div (10 + 40)$$
Thus, $I_T = 100 \div 50$
$$= 2 \text{ amps}$$

However, suppose someone without any knowledge of electronics or mathematics other than how to add, subtract, multiply, and divide, saw this problem. What would they do to this example of:

$$I = E \div R$$
$$I = 100 \div 10 + 40$$

They might do it the way we did, or they might do it as follows:
$$I = 100 \div 10 = 10$$

Then say
$$10 + 40 = 50 \text{ amperes.}$$
Or, they might say
$$I = 100 \div 40 = 2\tfrac{1}{2}$$
then
$$2\tfrac{1}{2} + 10 = 12\tfrac{1}{2} \text{ amperes.}$$

As you can see, both of these answers are wrong. To prevent mistakes like this, universal rules have been established for writing out problems and solving them. These rules automatically and quickly show the order in which the operations should be performed. These are called the Rules of Order and they ensure that everyone everywhere will always know in what order to tackle a problem.

The rules of order are very easy to learn and must always be followed. Always start at the left of a problem and work towards the right and do all the multiplication and division in the order in which they occur. Then go back to the left of the problem and again work to the right, doing the addition and subtraction.

By following these rules there is no possibility of coming up with a wrong answer due to working the wrong operations at the wrong time. A problem such as:

$$57 + 63 \times 85 - 51 \div 17$$

can only have one answer. We start at the left and multiply 63×85 to get 5355, then we divide 51 by 17 to get 3. Then we rewrite our problem, inserting these answers and get:

$$57 + 5355 - 3 =$$

Now we start at the left and do all our addition which gives us $57 + 5355 = 5412$, then we subtract 3 from 5412 to get our answer of 5409. Since these rules are universally accepted, anyone seeing the problem would do it exactly the same way.

Quite often, occasions will arise in which we want to ensure that the addition or subtraction is done first, like in our circuit problem in Fig. 15. In order to do this, we enclose those operations, which must be done first, in parenthesis ( ) as follows:

$$I = 100 \div (10 + 40)$$

Whenever we see numbers enclosed like this, we do the operations within the parenthesis first. When they are complete, we take the parenthesis away and then do the remaining operations in accordance with the standard rules. For example:

$$2 \times 250 \div (15 + 35) - 5$$

would be done as follows:

First, we do the operations in the parenthesis: $(15 + 35) = 50$, and then rewrite the problem putting 50 in place of the $(15 + 35)$ and it becomes:

$$2 \times 250 \div 50 - 5$$

Referring to our regular rules of order, we now multiply 2×250 to get 500. Then we divide 500 by 50 and get 10. Then we subtract 5 from 10 and get our answer, 5. Once again, there is no possibility of getting the wrong answer if we follow the rules of order. However, as you can see, if we didn't have any rules to follow we could get several different answers.

Sometimes we need to do two or more things in a special order. For this reason we also use brackets [ ] which are really just a different kind of parentheses to indicate which comes first. Thus we might have a problem $5 \times 300 \div [2 \times (15 + 35)] + 20 - 5$. Here we do the operations within the parentheses, $(15 + 35) = 50$ and rewrite the bracket operation, replacing the $(15 + 35)$ with 50 to get $[2 \times 50]$.

Then we do the operation inside the brackets to get $[2 \times 50] = 100$. Now we rewrite the whole problem replacing everything inside the brackets with 100 and leaving the brackets out as: $5 \times 300 \div 100 + 20 - 5$. By following our rules, we start at the left and multiply 5×300 to get 1500, then we divide this 1500 by 100 to get 15. Now we do our addition and subtraction: $15 + 20 - 5 = 35 - 5 = 30$ to find our final answer.

Since these rules of order are so important, let's state them again. First we do all the operations within the parenthesis. Second, if we have one parenthesis within another, we do the operations inside the small parenthesis first and then do the operations within the next larger parenthesis, etc. When the parenthetical operations are all out of the way we remove the parentheses, replacing the data within them with the answers we got. Then we rewrite our problem and start at the left and work toward the right doing all the multiplication and division in the order in which it occurs. Then we return to the left and work to the right doing the addition and subtraction in the order in which it occurs to get our answer.

Practice doing the following sample problems until you are sure you have learned the rules.

1. $25 + 16 \times 3 - 28 \div 7$
2. $5 \times (11 - 8) + 3 \times (7 - 5) \div 2$
3. $4 + (5 + 2) \times 20 - (10 - 6) \div (7 - 5)$
4. $3 \times 500 \div \left[2 \times (28 + 22) \right] + 25 - 6$

Answers: (1) 69; (2) 18; (3) 142; (4) 34.

1-3. Fractions

In the simple circuit shown in Fig. 1-16, we have 100 volts applied to a circuit containing 100 Ω total resistance. This means that we will have a current through the circuit of one ampere and a voltage drop across the resistances of the circuit equal to the applied voltage of 100 volts.

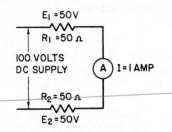

Fig. 1-16. One hundred volts divided into two equal parts or halves.

However, in this circuit we do not have a single resistance equal to 100 ohms. Instead, we have two resistances of 50 ohms each which makes up the 100-ohm total resistance. Therefore, our voltage drop of 100 volts does not occur as one voltage, it occurs as two drops of 50 volts across each resistor.

In a case like this, where we have two equal voltage drops of 50 volts that add up to a total voltage of 100 volts, we often say that each drop of 50 volts is equal to one half of the total voltage. Just what do we mean when we say one half of something? First, we mean that the "something," in this case 100 volts, is split up into parts. Further, since we have only two parts and they are equal, we mean that the whole 100 volts is split up into two equal parts. Thus, when we say one half of a hundred, it is like saying one of two equal parts of a hundred or, more simply we mean 100 ÷ 2.

Likewise, in a circuit such as the one shown in Fig. 1-17, the total voltage drop of 90 volts is split up into three equal parts of 30 volts each. This is

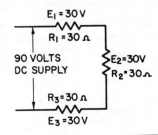

Fig. 1-17. Ninety volts divided into three equal parts or thirds.

just the same as saying that the voltage is split into thirds and one drop of 30 volts is equal to one-third of the total or 90 ÷ 3. You will recall from the section on division that we can also write 100 ÷ 2 or 90 ÷ 3 as $\frac{100}{2}$ or $\frac{90}{3}$, respectively. Whenever we split anything into parts we call the parts *fractions*.

Thus, $\frac{100}{2}$ is a fraction and $\frac{90}{3}$ is also a fraction. Now these particular fractions can easily be worked out by performing the actual divisions so that $\frac{100}{2}$ is 100 ÷ 2, or 50; and $\frac{90}{3}$ is 90 ÷ 3, or 30. When they are worked out like this, 50 and 30 actually become whole numbers in themselves because they each represent an individual voltage drop. However, when we consider them as part of the total voltage drop, they are both fractional parts of something and therefore they are also fractions.

When we want to represent "50 volts of 100 volts" or "30 volts of 90 volts" as fractions we would write them as $\dfrac{50}{100}$ or $\dfrac{30}{90}$, respectively. The fraction 50 can be written more simply by dividing both the top of the fraction 50 and the bottom of the fraction 100 by the same number. For example, if we divide 100 by 50 we get 2 for an answer, and if we divide 50 by 50 we get an answer of 1. By placing the 1 in place of the 50 and the 2 in the place of 100, our fraction becomes $\dfrac{1}{2}$, or one-half. Thus, $\dfrac{50}{100}$ can be changed to $\dfrac{1}{2}$ or, as we say, "one half" by dividing both the top and bottom of the original fraction by 50. In the same way, we can write $\dfrac{30}{90}$ more simply by dividing both 30 and 90 by 30. This gives us $30 \div 30 = 1$ and $90 \div 30 = 3$. Then by replacing 30 with 1 and 90 with 3 we have the fraction $\dfrac{1}{3}$, which we pronounce "one-third." This fraction $\dfrac{1}{3}$ and the fraction $\dfrac{1}{2}$ which we found previously are the simplest forms of the original fractions. We call this process of changing a fraction to its simplest form "reducing" the fraction.

Thus, in the circuit in Fig.1-16 either one of the voltage drops can be considered in several ways. They can be considered as one-half of a hundred which we write mathematically as $\dfrac{1}{2}$ of 100. It can be considered as $\dfrac{50}{100}$ which we can reduce to one-half ·or $\dfrac{1}{2}$, or it can be considered as $\dfrac{100}{2}$

which is equal to 50. Now, these are all just different ways of saying the same thing.

Likewise. any one of the drops in the circuit in Fig.1-17 can be expressed as $\dfrac{1}{3}$ of 90, $\dfrac{30}{90}$ which equals $\dfrac{1}{3}$, or $\dfrac{90}{3}$ which equals 30.

We also have many other fractions. In fact, just as there is no limit to the largest number we can write by using combinations of the digits from 0-9, there is no limit to the smallest part of something that we can write by using the same digits. Just as $\dfrac{1}{2}$ means a whole something divided into two equal parts and $\dfrac{1}{3}$ means something divided into three equal parts, we can write $\dfrac{1}{6}$, which means that a whole something is divided into six equal parts. We can continue in this way indefinitely. For example, $\dfrac{1}{64}$ means one of 64 equal parts; $\dfrac{1}{128}$ means one of 128 equal parts, and $\dfrac{1}{2465}$ means one of two thousand four hundred sixty five equal parts of something.

Notice, however, that a fraction by itself does not mean anything specific. For example, $\dfrac{1}{2}$, $\dfrac{1}{3}$, $\dfrac{1}{128}$, or $\dfrac{1}{2465}$ are fractions, but until we say what they are fractions of, we don't have any idea what they are equal to. $\dfrac{1}{2}$ of 50 volts is 25 volts, but as we have already seen, $\dfrac{1}{2}$ of 100 volts is 50 volts so a fraction to indicate anything definite must be accompanied by the whole something that we are talking about. Thus, we always say $\frac{1}{2}$ of a gallon, or $\frac{1}{3}$ of a quart, $\frac{1}{128}$ (pronounced one, one hundred twenty eighth) of an ounce, $\frac{1}{5}$ of the voltage, etc.

There are two parts to every fraction. There is the top part written above the line which is called the *numerator*, and there is the bottom part below the line called the *denominator*. The number in the numerator always tells us how many parts we have, and the number in the denominator tells us the size of the parts. Just as we can have $\frac{1}{3}$ of a gallon, it is also possible to have two $\frac{1}{3}$'s of a gallon which we would write $\frac{2}{3}$ of a gallon. The two indicates that we have two parts of a gallon and the 3 indicating that each part equals $\frac{1}{3}$ of a gallon.

There are also two kinds of fractions. One kind is called a *proper* fraction and always has a numerator (the top) that is smaller than the denominator, (the bottom). Thus, $\frac{1}{3}$, $\frac{1}{2}$, $\frac{4}{7}$, and $\frac{5}{128}$ are all proper fractions because their denominator is larger than their numerator. The other kind of fraction is called an *improper* fraction. An improper fraction is one in which the numerator is larger than the denominator, such as $\frac{100}{50}$, $\frac{100}{2}$, $\frac{755}{4}$, etc.

Both proper and improper fractions can be added, subtracted, multiplied, and divided just like any whole number. After all, it is possible to have several halves of something, or several fifths of something which we might want to add or subtract from each other. The basic operations with fractions are much the same as with any whole number, but there are certain rules that we must follow. In this section of the lesson we will learn the rules and see how to apply them.

Adding Fractions

In adding fractions, we must remember one of the basic rules of any addition problem. Only like things can be added together. We can add any number of volts to any other number of volts. We can also add ohms to ohms and amperes to amperes, but we cannot add ohms to amperes or volts. The same rule applies to fractions except that we have an additional item of similarity to consider.

The denominators of fractions must be alike if we are going to add them. For example, $\frac{1}{2}$ of a gallon can be added to another $\frac{1}{2}$ of a gallon to get a whole gallon. $\frac{1}{3}$ of a gallon can be added to another $\frac{1}{3}$ of a gallon to get $\frac{2}{3}$ of a gallon. Thus. fractions of like things with like denominators can be added together very simply by adding their numerators. Thus:

$$\frac{1}{2} + \frac{1}{2} = \frac{1+1}{2} = \frac{2}{2} = 1$$

$$\frac{2}{3} + \frac{1}{3} = \frac{2+1}{3} = \frac{3}{3} = 1$$

$$\frac{1}{3}+\frac{1}{3}=\frac{1+1}{3}=\frac{2}{3}$$

$$\frac{1}{5}+\frac{3}{5}=\frac{4}{5}$$

$$\frac{12}{64}+\frac{13}{64}=\frac{12+13}{64}=\frac{25}{64}$$

$$\frac{55}{137}+\frac{67}{137}=\frac{55+67}{137}=\frac{122}{137}$$

Now we have just seen that all fractions with like denominators can be added together by adding their numerators. However, fractions with unlike denominators could not be added. While this is true, we can arrange fractions with unlike denominators in a way so that they can be added by making their denominators all alike. This is called finding the lowest common denominator.

Finding a Common Denominator. When we first started our discussion of fractions, we discovered that we could "reduce" a fraction such as $\frac{50}{100}$ to a fraction of $\frac{1}{2}$ by dividing both the numerator and the denominator by the same number. In this case, the number was 50 because with both the numerator and denominator of $\frac{50}{100}$ divided by 50 we got $\frac{1}{2}$. When we did this, we realized that either $\frac{50}{100}$ or $\frac{1}{2}$ meant exactly the same thing. Since either of these two ways of writing the fraction is correct, the two fractions must be equal. Thus, by dividing the numerator and the denominator by the same number, we have not changed the value of the fraction.

If this is true, we must also be able to multiply the numerator and the

denominator of a fraction by the same number without changing its value. 50 times both the numerator and denominator of $\frac{1}{2}$ is $50 \times 1 = 50$ and $50 \times 2 = 100$, or $\frac{50}{100}$. From this we can see that we can either multiply or divide the numerator and the denominator of a fraction by the same number without changing the value of the fraction. Accordingly, a fraction such as $\frac{1}{2}$ might be written in any one of several ways as follows:

$$\frac{1}{2}\times\frac{2}{2}=\frac{2}{4}, \frac{2}{4}\times\frac{2}{2}=\frac{4}{8},$$

$$\frac{1}{2}\times\frac{3}{3}=\frac{3}{6}, \frac{4}{8}\times\frac{4}{4}=\frac{16}{32}$$

$$\frac{16}{32}\times\frac{100}{100}=\frac{1600}{3200}$$

All these fractions are exactly equal to $\frac{1}{2}$ because they can all be reduced to $\frac{1}{2}$.

Likewise, we can change a fraction such as $\frac{1}{3}$ to any of the following fractions:

$$\frac{1}{3}\times\frac{3}{3}=\frac{3}{9}, \frac{1}{3}\times\frac{2}{2}=\frac{2}{6},$$

$$\frac{2}{6}\times\frac{5}{5}=\frac{10}{30}, \text{ etc.}$$

Let's see how this will help us in adding fractions. Suppose we want to add $\frac{1}{2}+\frac{1}{3}$. Since their denominators are not alike, we know that we can't add them as they are. However, suppose we change $\frac{1}{2}$ to $\frac{3}{6}$ which we can do by multiplying both the numerator and denominator by 3. Then, if we also change $\frac{1}{3}$ to $\frac{2}{6}$ which we can do by multiplying both numerator and denominator by 2, we now have two fractions which have the same denominator. They are $\frac{3}{6}$ and $\frac{2}{6}$ and they can be added together in the usual way to get $\frac{3+2}{6}$ or $\frac{5}{6}$. We have changed $\frac{1}{2}$ and $\frac{1}{3}$ to fractions with the same denominator so that they can be added without changing the values of the fractions themselves. $\frac{3}{6}$ is exactly the same as $\frac{1}{2}$ and $\frac{2}{6}$ is exactly the same as $\frac{1}{3}$. Added together they make $\frac{5}{6}$ or five-sixths.

When two fractions have the same denominator, we say they have a common denominator. When we change two or more fractions to equal fractions having the same common denominator so that we can add them, we call it finding the common denominator. Let's try a few more examples. For example,

$$\frac{1}{5} + \frac{1}{3} + \frac{4}{5} =$$

By reviewing our multiplication, we see that 15 is the first number that both 3 and 5 can be divided into. Therefore 15 will be the lowest common denominator. 5 goes into 15 three times so we must multiply both the numerators and denominators of $\frac{1}{5}$ and $\frac{4}{5}$ by 3 to get $\frac{3}{15}$ and $\frac{12}{15}$. Then we see

that 3 has to be multiplied by 5 to make 15 so we change $\frac{1}{3}$ to $\frac{5}{15}$. Now, we have three fractions that can be added together. They are $\frac{3}{15} + \frac{12}{15} + \frac{5}{15}$ which, when their numerators are added, equal $\frac{3+12+5}{15}$ or $\frac{20}{15}$. Thus, the sum of $\frac{1}{5} + \frac{1}{3} + \frac{4}{5} = \frac{20}{15}$.

Here is another example:

$$\frac{1}{2} + \frac{2}{7} + \frac{1}{14}$$

Both 2 and 7 will go into 14 so 14 is our lowest common denominator. Therefore, we change $\frac{1}{2}$ to $\frac{7}{14}$ and change $\frac{2}{7}$ to $\frac{4}{14}$ and we have $\frac{7}{14} + \frac{4}{14} + \frac{1}{14}$ which we can add to get $\frac{12}{14}$. Now $\frac{12}{14}$ can be reduced by dividing both parts or members of the fraction by 2 to get $\frac{6}{7}$. We usually reduce a fraction to its simplest form when we finish adding fractions. Thus,

$$\frac{1}{2} + \frac{2}{7} + \frac{1}{14} = \frac{12}{14} \text{ or } \frac{6}{7}$$

Sometimes it is a little difficult to see exactly what the lowest common denominator of a group of fractions is. This is especially true when we have a lot of fractions to add and the denominators are all different. One way to find a common denominator that is sure to work is to multiply all the denominators together and use the product as the common denominator.

Thus, in adding $\frac{1}{7} + \frac{1}{3} + \frac{2}{5}$, we can find a common denominator by multiplying $7 \times 3 \times 5$. This denominator would be 105 and is sure to be divisible by the denominator of each of the fractions.

Now, we have to divide the denominator of each of our original fractions into 105 to determine how much we must multiply the numerator by so that we won't change the value of our fractions. 7 goes into 105 fifteen times so $\frac{1}{7}$ is changed to $\frac{15}{105}$. 3 goes into 105 thirty-five times, so $\frac{1}{3}$ is changed to $\frac{35}{105}$. 5 can be divided into 105 twenty-one times so $\frac{2}{5}$ becomes $\frac{42}{105}$. Now we add the numerators to get $\frac{15 + 35 + 42}{105}$ or $\frac{92}{105}$ which is the sum of $\frac{1}{7} + \frac{1}{3} + \frac{2}{5}$.

Now let's add the following fractions:

Problems	Answers
$\frac{1}{2} + \frac{1}{3} + \frac{1}{12}$	$= \frac{11}{12}$
$\frac{3}{4} + \frac{1}{16} + \frac{1}{8}$	$= \frac{15}{16}$
$\frac{1}{4} + \frac{1}{8} + \frac{3}{12}$	$= \frac{5}{8}$
$\frac{1}{3} + \frac{3}{7}$	$= \frac{16}{21}$
$\frac{1}{5} + \frac{2}{9} + \frac{3}{11}$	$= \frac{344}{495}$

$$\frac{1}{7} + \frac{3}{14} + \frac{2}{7} + \frac{1}{4} = \frac{25}{28}$$

Subtracting Fractions

Subtracting fractions is just the reverse of adding fractions. All the rules that apply to the addition of fractions apply to subtraction. First, the fractions must be parts of like things and they must have the same denominator in order to subtract them. If they don't have a common denominator, we must find the lowest common denominator for them. We do this in exactly the same way we did for addition.

When we are subtracting one fraction from another, we subtract only the numerators and when we have finished our subtraction, we always reduce the answer as much as possible.

For example, $\frac{5}{6} - \frac{1}{6} = \frac{4}{6}$ or $\frac{2}{3}$. To subtract $\frac{1}{3}$ from $\frac{1}{2}$, we find the lowest common denominator which is 6. This makes our fraction $\frac{3}{6} - \frac{2}{6} = \frac{1}{6}$. As you can see, since we have learned to subtract whole numbers and add fractions, we have nothing really new to learn for subtracting fractions.

However, for practice, subtract the following fractions to make sure you understand how to do them.

(1) $\frac{4}{5} - \frac{1}{2}$ (2) $\frac{7}{10} - \frac{3}{5}$

(3) $\frac{7}{8} - \frac{1}{9}$ (4) $\frac{11}{12} - \frac{1}{3}$

Answers: (1) 3/10; (2) 1/10; (3) 55/72; (4) 7/12

Multiplying Fractions

When we learned to multiply earlier in this lesson, we discovered, for instance, that 2×3 was the same as either adding 3 to itself or adding 2 three times. Thus, we arrived at the conclusion that finding the product of two numbers was a simple way of performing tedious repeated additions. All we had to do in order to perform this repeated addition quickly was to learn the simple multiplication table for the digits from 1 to 9. Once we had done this, we discovered that we could multiply any two numbers no matter how large they were.

We also learned that 2×3 was the same as saying two taken three times. The same rules apply to multiplying fractions. However, due to the very nature of fractions, we must pause to look at them closely in order to see this. For example, $\frac{1}{2} \times \frac{1}{2} = \frac{1}{4}$. This is true because we have a simple rule for multiplying fractions which states that the numerators are multiplied together to get the numerator of a new fraction whose denominator is equal to the two original denominators multiplied together. Thus, $\frac{2}{3} \times \frac{1}{2}$ is equal to 2×1 equals 2 which is the numerator of the new fraction, and 3×2 which equals 6 is the denominator of the new fraction. Our new fraction is $\frac{2}{6}$ which can be reduced to $\frac{1}{3}$. Therefore, $\frac{2}{3} \times \frac{1}{2} = \frac{1}{3}$.

Now the rule that we have stated is true, and if you learn it you will never have any trouble multiplying fractions. However, it may seem strange that in both examples of multiplying fractions, we wound up with a smaller fraction than that we

started with. How can this be true if multiplication is really repeated addition?

The reason is quite simple and we will have no trouble seeing why if we stop to analyze what we're actually doing. When we multiply 2×3 to get 6, we actually add 2 three times. When we multiply a fraction such as $\frac{2}{3} \times \frac{1}{2}$, we actually add $\frac{2}{3}$ to itself, but only $\frac{1}{2}$ times. We also can say we take $\frac{2}{3}$, one half times. Since any number times one is the number itself' we say we take the number once. If we multiply a number or a fraction by a fractional part of itself, we must take that number only the fractional number of times. A simple way to sum this all up so that it will be easy to remember is that when we say "multiplied by" or "times" when we deal with fractions we mean "of."

Thus, $\frac{1}{5} \times \frac{4}{10}$ is like saying $\frac{1}{5}$ of $\frac{4}{10}$. By multiplying the numerators together and the denominators together we get the new fraction $\frac{4}{50}$ which we usually reduce to $\frac{2}{25}$. We can also multiply several fractions at once.

For example, $\frac{2}{9} \times \frac{3}{4} \times \frac{5}{7}$ would be set up for multiplication like this:

$$\frac{2 \times 3 \times 5}{9 \times 4 \times 7} = \frac{6 \times 5}{36 \times 7} = \frac{30}{252} = \frac{15}{126} = \frac{5}{42}$$

Since the resultant fraction is reducible, it is usually possible to reduce some of the fractions by what we call division or cancellation, before we multiply. Thus, in a problem such as:

$$\frac{2 \times 3 \times 5}{9 \times 4 \times 7}$$

the first number in the numerator is 2 which can be divided into the second number in the denominator which is four. This would leave us:

$$\frac{\overset{1}{2} \times 3 \times 5}{9 \times \underset{2}{4} \times 7}$$

We can also divide the 3 in the numerator into nine in the denominator which leaves us:

$$\frac{\overset{1}{2} \times \overset{1}{3} \times 5}{\underset{3}{9} \times \underset{2}{4} \times 7}$$

Now when we multiply we have 1 × 1 × 5 or 5 in the numerator and 3 × 2 × 7 or 42 in the denominator and we get our answer $\frac{5}{42}$ directly. Thus, by cross division or cancellation before we multiply, we simplify the problem.

For practice, multiply the following fractions:

Problems	Answers
(1) $\frac{3}{4} \times \frac{2}{3} \times \frac{1}{5}$	(1) $\frac{1}{10}$
(2) $\frac{2}{7} \times \frac{9}{28} \times \frac{3}{4} \times \frac{4}{9}$	(2) $\frac{3}{98}$
(3) $\frac{3}{64} \times \frac{4}{5} \times \frac{3}{8} \times \frac{15}{27}$	(3) $\frac{1}{128}$
(4) $\frac{5}{28} \times \frac{4}{9} \times \frac{7}{15} \times \frac{3}{4}$	(4) $\frac{1}{36}$
(5) $\frac{9}{128} \times \frac{259}{300} \times \frac{46}{49} \times \frac{21}{37}$	(5) $\frac{207}{6400}$

Dividing Fractions

Like any other division, division of fractions is just the reverse of multi-plication of fractions. In division we have a fraction for our dividend and a fraction for a divisor and we are asked what number or fraction when multi-plied by the divisor will give a product that equals the dividend. If $\frac{1}{2} \times \frac{1}{2} = \frac{1}{4}$, then $\frac{1}{4} \div \frac{1}{2}$ must equal $\frac{1}{2}$. Likewise, if $\frac{2}{3} \times \frac{1}{2} = \frac{2}{6}$ or $\frac{1}{3}$ then $\frac{1}{3} \div \frac{1}{2}$ must equal $\frac{2}{3}$.

All we do to perform this operation is turn the divisor upside down (invert) and then multiply the two fractions. We actually cross-multiply the numerator of one fraction by the denominator of the other. In doing this, we keep the numerator and denominator of the product fraction, which will really be our quotient, in the same relative position as the dividend fraction numerator and denominator.

Thus, $\frac{1}{3} \div \frac{1}{2}$ becomes

$$\frac{1}{3} \times \frac{2}{1} \text{ or } \frac{1 \times 2}{3 \times 1} = \frac{2}{3}.$$

Likewise,

$$\frac{3}{7} \div \frac{5}{6} \text{ becomes}$$

$$\frac{3}{7} \times \frac{6}{5} = \frac{18}{35}.$$

If we don't wish to actually invert the second fraction, we can just cross-multiply, remembering to locate the numerator and denominator of the product fraction or quotient properly. We would do it like this:

$$\frac{4}{7} \diagdown \frac{2}{3} = \frac{4 \times 3}{} = \frac{12}{}.$$

Then,

$$\frac{\cancel{4}}{\cancel{7}} \cdot \frac{\cancel{2}}{\cancel{3}} = \frac{}{7 \times 2} = \frac{}{14}$$

and our quotient is $\frac{12}{14}$ or $\frac{6}{7}$.

Dividing all fractions is as simple as this. Try the following problems and check your answers with ours. Incidentally, the standard division check of multiplying the divisor by the quotient should always give you the dividend.

Problems	Answers
(1) $\dfrac{7}{8} \div \dfrac{5}{16}$	(1) $\dfrac{112}{40} = \dfrac{14}{5}$
(2) $\dfrac{9}{10} \div \dfrac{10}{64}$	(2) $\dfrac{576}{100} = \dfrac{144}{25}$
(3) $\dfrac{3}{4} \div \dfrac{1}{5}$	(3) $\dfrac{15}{4}$
(4) $\dfrac{7}{8} \div \dfrac{1}{64}$	(4) $\dfrac{448}{8} = \dfrac{56}{1}$

Mixed Numbers and Improper Fractions

We have learned that a fraction is said to be *proper* if the numerator is less than, or equal to, the denominator; all other fractions are *improper*. On this basis $\frac{2}{7}$, $\frac{5}{7}$, $\frac{4}{5}$, etc. are proper fractions and $\frac{10}{7}$, $\frac{15}{11}$, $\frac{35}{6}$ are improper fractions.

In the case of an improper fraction like $\frac{10}{7}$, we have two ways of writing it. We can leave it as an improper fraction or, since it is the same as saying 10 divided by 7, we can perform the division to get a quotient of 1 and a remainder of 3. We write this

as $1\frac{3}{7}$ and read as "one and three-sevenths." Such an expression as this is known as a *mixed number* because it is partly a whole number and partly a fraction.

Any mixed number may be written as an improper fraction by reducing the whole number to a fraction which has the same denominator as the fractional part of the mixed number and then adding the two together. This is done by thinking of the whole number as a fraction with denominator of 1. Next, we multiply both members of the whole number fraction by the denominator we are using. Then, we can add the fractional expression of the whole number to the fractional remainder in the mixed number to get the final improper fraction. Thus, we think of a mixed number such as

$$2\frac{5}{12} = \frac{2}{1} + \frac{5}{12}$$

$$= \frac{24}{12} + \frac{5}{12} = \frac{29}{12}$$

All rules for working with fractions hold for improper fractions as well as for proper ones. In any computation, it is usually wise to change all mixed numbers to improper fractions before proceeding with the work.

Here are some examples:

$$2\frac{3}{5} \times 3\frac{1}{13}$$

$$= \frac{13}{5} \times \frac{40}{13}$$

$$= \frac{13 \times 40}{5 \times 13}$$

$$= \frac{\cancel{13}^1 \times \cancel{40}^8}{\cancel{5}_1 \times \cancel{13}_1}$$

$$= \frac{8}{1} \text{ which equals } 8.$$

$$2\frac{3}{5} + 3\frac{1}{13} = \frac{13}{5} + \frac{40}{13}$$

$$= \frac{169}{65} + \frac{200}{65} = \frac{369}{65} = 5\frac{44}{65}$$

In division:

$$3\frac{3}{4} \div 3\frac{1}{8}$$

$$= \frac{15}{4} \div \frac{25}{8}$$

$$= \frac{15}{4} \times \frac{8}{25}$$

$$= \frac{6}{5} \text{ or } 1\frac{1}{5}$$

Summary

We have now gone through all the rules for operating with fractions and we can summarize our results for easy reference as follows:

(1) The PRODUCT of two or more fractions is a new fraction whose numerator is the product of the numerators of all the factors, and whose denominator is the product of the denominators of all the factors. Any whole number may be considered as a fraction with a denominator of 1. For instance, 127 means $\frac{127}{1}$.

(2) The QUOTIENT of two fractions is the product of the dividend times the divisor inverted (turned upside down).

NOTICE CAREFULLY that neither multiplication nor division of fractions require the use of a common denominator.

(3) To ADD fractions, they must be reduced to equivalent fractions with a common denominator; then their sum is the sum of the numerators divided by the common denominator.

(4) Similarly, to SUBTRACT one fraction from another, we use a common denominator and the difference is the difference of the numerators, divided by the common denominator.

(5) All results should be reduced to their simplest form by dividing both numerator and denominator by the largest common divisor.

1-4. Decimals

In our discussion of fractions, one idea that may have bothered you was that it was necessary to reduce the fractions to a common denominator before they could be added or subtracted. This also bothered mathematicians and scientists and led them to search for some method that would make it possible to express all fractions with denominators of ten, one hundred, one thousand, etc. The result is what we call the *decimal system*.

The results are fractions called "decimal fractions" or, quite frequently, just "decimals." Let's look for a moment at a simple example which is a part of your daily experience. You are acquainted with these coins: a cent, a nickel, a dime, a quarter-dollar, and a half-dollar. They are $\frac{1}{100}, \frac{1}{20}, \frac{1}{10}, \frac{1}{4},$ and $\frac{1}{2}$ of a dollar, or $\frac{1}{100}, \frac{5}{100}, \frac{10}{100}, \frac{25}{100},$ and $\frac{50}{100}$ of a dollar.

It is just second nature for us to write these as \$.01, \$.05, \$.10, \$.25, and \$.50. That is, \$1.25 means one dollar and twenty-five cents, or 1 and $\frac{25}{100}$ dollars. On this basis you easily add up such amounts as:

$$
\begin{array}{r}
\$3.25 \\
7.12 \\
2.84 \\
6.33 \\
\hline
\$19.54
\end{array}
$$

Just as we separate the dollars and cents (the cents are hundredths of a dollar), we can separate our whole numbers and our fractions with a point. This is called a *decimal point*, and we can write all our fractions with denominators of ten, one-hundred, one-thousand, etc. as whole numbers by learning to use this decimal point. To do this, we use the first place to the right of the point for tenths, the next for hundredths, the third for thousandths, etc.

In this fashion $1\frac{1}{10}$ becomes 1.1 and $1\frac{2}{10}$ becomes 1.2, $1\frac{1}{100}$ becomes 1.01, and $1\frac{1}{1000}$ can be written as 1.001. A table of the decimal representations of the fractions from $\frac{1}{10}$ to $\frac{1}{1,000,000}$ is shown in Fig. 1-18.

Since $\frac{1}{4}$ becomes $\frac{25}{100}$ if we multiply both members by 25, its value as a decimal would be .25. Similarly, $\frac{1}{8}$ becomes $\frac{125}{1000}$ if we multiply by 125, and thus $\frac{1}{8} = .125$ and $\frac{5}{8}$ would be

.625. We have no difficulty in changing ordinary fractions to decimal fractions if their denominators are factors of 10, 100, 1000, etc.

However, we run into difficulties with a simple fraction such as $\frac{1}{3}$. There is no whole number by which we can multiply the members to make the denominator 1000, or any other multiple of ten. The best we can do is come up with decimal numbers with a remainder of one third. Thus, $\frac{1}{3}$ becomes .3$\frac{1}{3}$, .33$\frac{1}{3}$, .333$\frac{1}{3}$, or .3333$\frac{1}{3}$, etc. when we try to make a decimal out of it.

The results we have just gotten by changing denominators to tenths, hundredths, thousandths, etc. can be obtained more quickly by a type of division which we shall now set up. Let's think of the fraction $\frac{1}{8}$. This indicates the division of 1 by 8. We shall set up an ordinary division problem with the divisor 8 and the dividend 1 followed by a decimal point.

Since zeros behind a decimal point have no value except for position purposes, we can write as many zeros as we wish to the right of the point. We shall write the quotient over the

.1	1/10	one-tenth
.01	1/100	one-hundredth
.001	1/1000	one-thousandth
.0001	1/10,000	one ten-thousandth
.00001	1/100,000	one hundred-thousandth
.000001	1/1,000,000	one millionth

Fig. 1-18. Decimal equivalents of fractions divisible by 10.

dividend in the usual manner, but we will place a decimal point over the point in the dividend. Thus, we have

$8\ \overline{/1.000}$. Now, following our regular rules for division we get:

$$8\ \overline{\smash{\big)}1.000}^{\ \ .125}$$

```
        .125
   8  /1.000
        8
      ____
       20
       16
      ____
       40
       40
      ____
```

It is evident that we obtain exactly the same result as we got with the more cumbersome method of reducing the fraction to a new fraction with 1000 for a denominator. Here are some other fractions:

$$\frac{1}{2} = 2\ \overline{\smash{\big)}1.0}^{\ \ .5}$$

```
          .5
 1
 _ = 2  /1.0
 2       10
       ____
```

$$\frac{5}{8} = 8\ \overline{\smash{\big)}5.00}^{\ \ .625}$$

```
         .625
 5
 _ = 8  /5.00
 8       48
        __
         20
         16
        __
         40
         40
        __
```

Each of these divisions came out exactly when carried out far enough.

However a fraction such as $\frac{1}{3}$ becomes:

```
        .333
  3  /1.000
       9
      __
      10
       9
      __
      10
       9
      __
       1
```

and the threes will keep on repeating as long as you keep on dividing.

Rounding Off Numbers. In changing the fraction $\frac{1}{3}$ to a decimal, it would be very undesirable to carry out many of these threes. Three or four of them would probably be enough for the accuracy of the work in electronics. Therefore, we have uniform rules for "rounding off" such a decimal. These rules are very simple:

(1) Determine the number of digits you wish to have in your rounded result.

(2) Zeros between the decimal point and the first figure which is not a zero are not counted.

(3) Write the number of digits you want in your result. These digits are called "significant figures." If the next digit is 0, 1, 2, 3, or 4 you have written the proper rounded off result. If the next digit is 5, 6, 7, 8, or 9 you increase the last entry in your rounding by 1.

Here are some examples: .0065738 with three significant figures is .00657 since the next digit is 3. With four significant figures it becomes .006574. Since the next digit is 8 we must increase the fourth digit, 3, by 1 and write .006574.

Problems: Write (1) 1/7, (2) 1/28, and 11/63 as decimals with three significant figures.

Answers: (1) .143; (2) .0357; (3) .175

These same rules for rounding off apply to whole numbers as well as to decimals, but it is necessary to fill any discarded places with zeros to the decimal point, thus, 657,300 with three significant figures is 657,000 and with two significant figures is 660,000.

Fig. 1-19 is a table showing the decimal values of a number of the common fractions in everyday use. The diagram shows you where they lie with respect to each other.

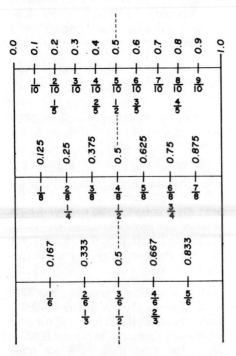

Fig. 1-19. Table of decimal equivalents of fractions.

Adding and Subtracting Decimals

The operations of addition and subtraction of numbers involving decimals are precisely the same as those involving whole numbers. In setting up the numbers, the decimal points must all be placed in a vertical line and the decimal point in the sum or difference will be in that same line. Here are several examples:

ADD	123.45	From	985.00
	23.41	Subtract	27.43
	2745.00		
	1.12		957.57
	.03		
	2893.01		

For practice, try the following:

(1) ADD	2543.67	(2) From	768.08
	100.24	Subtract	129.29
	78.29		
	2.27		
	.09		

ANSWERS:

(1) 2724.56   (2) 638.79

Multiplying Demicals

Multiplication of decimal numbers is the same as for any number except that we need a rule for determining the position of the decimal point in the product. This rule says that we count the number of decimal places in each factor. Then, starting at the right of the product we count off as many places to the left as the sum of the number of places in the two factors. Let's work out an example.

EXAMPLE: (232.7) × (4.89)

232.7   One decimal place
4.89   Two decimal places

20943
18616   1 + 2 = 3
9308

1137.903   Three decimal places

The denominator of the decimal part of the first factor is 10; that of the second factor is 100. Hence, by the rule of fractions, the denominator of the fractional part of the product will be 10 × 100 or 1000, which means that we have 3 decimal places in the product. Let us repeat the rule: In a product involving decimal fractions, there will be as many decimal places in the product as the sum of the number of places in the factors.

It is a good idea to try to approximate an answer in every problem as a check against what is sometimes a long and complicated procedure. In the example of the last paragraph you are roughly multiplying 230 by 5 and the answer should be roughly 1150. You will see that is a good approximation of the result we obtained and is a check on the position of the decimal point in the product.

There is another type of product in which one factor is a decimal without any whole number part, or perhaps both factors are of that kind, like (.0032) (.1273).

.1273
.0032

2546
3819

.00040736

To have 4 + 4 or 8 decimal places in the product we must place three zeros to the left of the five digits before we put in the decimal point.

Problems: (1) (43.56) × (125.3); (2) (.00763) × (1.095)

Answers: (1) 5458.068; (2) .00835485.

Dividing Decimals

To divide numbers involving decimals we remember that it does not change the value of the quotient of two numbers if we multiply both of them by the same number before we begin the division. Also, we will need to remember that if we multiply a number by 10, we move the decimal point one place to the right. To multiply by 100, we move the decimal point 2 places to the right, etc.

Before we start a decimal division we move the decimal place of the divisor to the right as many places as necessary to have it at the extreme right of the number. Then, we move the decimal point of the dividend the *same number* of places.

Here is an example of what we mean. If we wish to divide 632.823 by 2.13 we move the decimal point in the divisor two places to the right, making it 213, and move the decimal point in the same number of places to the right in the dividend, making it 63282.3. From this point the division is exactly like we have previously done except for fixing the decimal point in the quotient. It will always fall directly above the point in the dividend.

```
                297.1         CHECK
213. /63282.3               297.1
      426                     2.13

      2068                    8913
      1917                    2971
      ----                    5942
      1512                    ----
      1491                  632.823

       21.3
       21.3
```

You will notice that in the check we used the quotient times the unchanged divisor to get the original dividend. Here again you can get a good idea of your quotient by saying that the original divisor was about 2 and the dividend about 600, so that the quotient should be around 300. Let's stress the idea again that after you have moved the decimal point as we have indicated, the divisor will be a whole number and the point in the quotient will be directly over the new position of the point in the dividend.

It is rather common practice to write the divisor and dividend as given and then to indicate the new positions of the points with a larger point or caret ($\wedge$) instead of rewriting the entire problem. Suppose we wish to divide .000327 by 10.9. We set it up as follows, where we have indicated the new position of the point with a caret:

$$10.9_\wedge \overline{)\, \begin{array}{r} .00003 \\ .000327 \\ \wedge \end{array}}$$

$$327$$

In this example, to get the decimal point correctly placed, we have to introduce four zeros to the left of the 3 in the quotient.

Another type of problem occurs when the divisor is very small as in the division of 2.34 by .00078. It looks like this after we have moved the point 5 places to the right and have filled in all missing spaces in the dividend with zeros:

$$.00078_\wedge \overline{)\, \begin{array}{r} 3000 \\ 2.34000_\wedge \\ 234 \end{array}}$$

CHECK:
	.00078	5 dec. places
	3000.	0 dec. places
	2.34000	5 dec. places

You have probably noticed that when we have a small divisor and a relatively large dividend, the quotient is large. but the quotient is small if the conditions are reversed.

Multiplying and Dividing by Ten

One of the greatest advantages of the decimal system is that multiplication or division by 10, 100 (10 $\times$ 10, or 10^2), 1000 (10 $\times$ 10 $\times$ 10 or 10^3), or any power of 10 can be accomplished by simply moving the decimal point as many places to the right as there are zeros in the particular power of ten. Thus, to multiply a number like 2.35 by 1000, which is 10^3, all we have to do is to move the point three places to the RIGHT, filling in any vacant spaces with zeros, to get 2350.

Similarly, to divide by any power of ten requires only that we move the point to the LEFT. Thus, $3500 \div 10^3 = 3.5$.

Special Electronic Units. You will remember that the basic electric units —ampere, volt, farad, cycle, henry, watt, etc. are sometimes too large for convenient handling in electronics. In other cases, they are much too small. So, a set of 8 prefixes (handles) for measurement are used to remedy these situations. They are:

		Units
G	Giga	1,000,000,000
M	MEGA	1,000,000
k	KILO	1000
m	Milli	.001
μ	Micro	.000,001
n	Nano	.000,000,001
$\mu\,\mu$	Micro-micro	.000,000,000,001
p	pico	.000,000,000,001

For example, 3 megacycles (mc) = 3000 kilocycles (kc) = 3,000,000 cycles; and 5 microvolts (μv) =

.000,005 volts.

Since changing from one of these units to another involves multiplication or division by a power of 10, it can be accomplished by moving decimal points. In Fig. 20 we have placed the larger units in the left-hand column and the smaller ones in the right-hand column.

From	$\longrightarrow$	To
MEGA	3 places	KILO
KILO	3 places	UNIT
UNIT	3 places	MILLI
MILLI	3 places	MICRO
MICRO	3 places	NANO
NANO	3 places	MICRO-MICRO
MICRO	6 places	MICRO-MICRO
To	$\longleftarrow$	From
PICO	equals	MICRO-MICRO

Fig. 1-20. Electrical unit conversion table.

To determine how many places to move the decimal point in changing 37 megacycles to kilocycles, we move the point 3 places to the right as shown by the arrow to obtain 37,000 kilocycles. If we wish to change 37,000 kilocycles to cycles we must move the point 3 places farther to the right to obtain 37,000,000 cycles. On the other hand, to change 327 microamperes to amperes, we would move the point 3 places to the left to get .327 milliamperes and still three more to the left to get .000 327 amperes. Thus, 327 microamperes = .327 milliamperes − .000 327 amperes.

Remember that when we move the decimal point and there are spaces not filled by numbers, they must be filled with zeros.

Problems
Convert:
(1) 2.3 Kilohms to ohms
(2) 437,000 ohms to kilohms
(3) .023 Megohms to ohms
(4) 1.5 amperes to milliamperes
(5) 13,000 microamperes to amperes
(6) 3 Kilovolts to microvolts
(7) 1.28 Megacycles to Kilocycles
(8) 4000 cycles to megacycles
(9) 1690 Kilocycles to megacycles
(10) 3000 Microamperes to amperes

Answers
(1) 2300 ohms
(2) 437 K
(3) 23,000 ohms
(4) 1500 ma
(5) .013 amperes
(6) 3,000,000,000 μv
(7) 1280 Kc
(8) .004 mc
(9) 1.69 mc
(10) .003 amp

Percentage

Percentage is an item of everyday interest. It affects your income tax and your social security. It is also called "tolerance" in electronic work. Basically, the idea of percentage is very simple. *Percentage* is a fractional part expressed in hundredths. Thus, 5 percent means $\frac{5}{100}$ or .05. This is usually written as 5% (the symbol "%" stands for the word "percent"). Since 1 percent is equal to $\frac{1}{100}$ or .01, the sign "%" is also equal to $\frac{1}{100}$.

Since percentage is a type of fractional expression, it follows that any percentage must be in the same units as whatever you're taking a percentage of. Thus, percentage of dollars is dollars, of kilohms is kilohms, etc.

In the course of your work you may come across a statement like this: "The resistor has a value of 500 ohms, with a tolerance of 10%." Now, 10% of 500 ohms is $\frac{10}{100}$ of 500 ohms, or 50 ohms, and this means that the value of this resistor may be 50 ohms above or 50 ohms below its rated value of 500 ohms. That is, it lies between (500 − 50) ohms and (500 + 50) ohms, or between 450 and 550 ohms.

The amount that any piece of apparatus may vary from its listed value is called its *tolerance*. Since it is expensive to make parts with a very low tolerance like 1% or 2%, it is fortunate that almost all the parts used in commercial electronic apparatus have a reasonably high tolerance.

To find the percent that one number is of a second number, divide the first number by the second, and multiply the quotient by 100. Thus, to find what percent 2 is of 15, we divide 2 by 15 and multiply the answer by 100.

$$2 \div 15 \times 100 = \frac{2}{15} \times 100$$

$$= \frac{200}{15} = \frac{40}{3} = 13\frac{1}{3}\%$$

Therefore, 2 is 13-1/3% of 15. This can also be written $.13\frac{1}{3}$ or .133.

The other percentage operation you will find useful is how to find a given percent of a given number. For example, what number is 40% of 350? To find this number, we convert 40% to a decimal, and multiply 350 by the decimal. To convert 40% to a decimal we merely move the decimal point two places to the left and drop the % sign. Thus 40% = .40. Now, to solve our problem, we multiply 350 by .4. The answer is 140, which is 40% of 350.

Here are some problems for you to try.

Problems
(1) What percent of 105 is 35?
(2) What percent of 40 is 8? (3) What percent of 100 is 96? (4) What percent of 96 is 3? (5) What is 33% of 100? (6) What is 15% of 60   (7) What is 22% of 3-4/11 (8) What is 36% of 4286?
Answers: (1) 33-1/3%; (2) 20%; (3) 96% (4) $3\frac{1}{8}\%$; (5) 33; (6) 9; (7) .74; (8) 1542.96.

1-5. Solving Circuit Problems

Now that we have learned the operations of basic arithmetic, let's use some of them to solve some circuit problems.

Before we start on the problems, let's review several important facts and laws about circuits which should be familiar to us.
1. One of the most important is Ohm's Law. We learned three ways

of stating it mathematically. They are: $I = E \div R$, $R = E \div I$, $E = I \times R$, where the current is in amperes, the voltage in volts, and the resistance in ohms. Don't forget to change the values of current, voltage, and resistance to their proper values when using the formulas if they are measured in other units such as megohms or milliamps. Also, don't forget to convert your answers back into the units called for when you have finished the problem.

2. We should know the Power formulas that let us find the power consumed in watts when two of the other circuit conditions are known. These formulas are: $P = E \times I$, $I = \dfrac{P}{E}$, $E = \dfrac{P}{I}$. These formulas can be used when we want to find the value of either power, voltage, or current when the other two factors are known.

There is another formula for power when we know the value of current and resistance, $P = I^2R$. We can also use this formula as $I^2 = \dfrac{P}{R}$ or $R = \dfrac{P}{I^2}$ to find resistance or current when the power and the other factor are known. Still another version of the power formula is $P = \dfrac{E^2}{R}$. This can be rearranged to $E^2 = PR$ when we want to find voltage and know the resistance and power. We can find the resistance by using $R = \dfrac{E^2}{P}$ if we know the voltage and power.

Remember, in all of these power formulas, P = power in watts, E = voltage in volts, I = current in amperes, R = resistance in ohms. The formulas cannot be used unless the proper measuring units are used. Pay particular attention to this, as one of the most common errors electronics men make in circuit computations is multiplying the wrong units together.

3. Another important fact that we should remember is that the total resistance of resistors in series is equal to the sum of all the series resistors. Thus, $R_T = R_1 + R_2 + R_3 \ldots$ etc., when the resistors are in series.

4. We also know about resistors in parallel. When resistors are in parallel, the total resistance is always less than the smallest resistance. We have two formulas for finding the total resistance of resistors in parallel. We can use whichever one we think is the easiest. They are:

(1) $R_T = \dfrac{R_1 \times R_2}{R_1 + R_2}$

(2) $\dfrac{1}{R_T} = \dfrac{1}{R_1} + \dfrac{1}{R_2} + \dfrac{1}{R_3} \ldots$ etc.

When we use the first formula, we can find the total of only two resistances at a time. With the second formula we can find the total for any number at a time.

You will notice that some problems don't appear to give you enough information at first glance. Many times you will have to solve for resistance and then current to get volts. This need for finding intermediate answers to get the necessary facts to find the final answer is quite common in electronics.

Problems

1. What is the total resistance of a circuit that has a 35-ohm resistor in parallel with a 75-ohm resistor? Round off your answer to the nearest ohm.

ANS.   24 ohms

2. If we have a voltage of 120 volts applied to a lamp with a resistance of 100 Ω, how many watts of power will be consumed?

ANS.   144 watts

3. How many kilovolts does it take to force 6 amperes through a motor that has resistance of 400 Ω?

ANS.   2.4 kv

4. In the circuit shown in Fig. 1-21, the total resistance of the circuit is 335 ohms. What is the resistance of R2?

ANS.   110 Ω

5. If the current flowing through the circuit in Fig. 21 is 6 amps, what is the power in watts?

ANS.   12,060 watts

6. What is the maximum rated current-carrying capacity of a 500-ohm resistor marked: 500 ohms, 2000 watts?

ANS.   2 amps

7. If the power input to a radio receiver is 75 watts, how many kilowatt hours does the receiver consume in 24 hours of continuous operation?

ANS.   1.8 kw hours

8. If a vacuum tube that has a filament rating of .25 amps at 5 volts is to be operated from a 6-volt battery, what value of series-dropping resistor would we need?

ANS.   4 Ω

9. A relay with a coil resistance of 500 Ω is designed to operate when 200 milliamperes flows through the coil. What value of resistance must be connected in series with the coil to limit the current to this value if we operate the relay from 110 volts dc?

ANS.   50 Ω

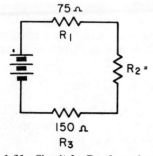

Fig. 1-21. Circuit for Problems 4 and 5.

10. If resistors of 3, 5, and 15 ohms are connected in parallel, what is the

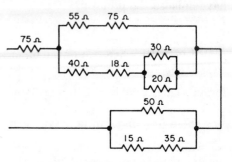

Fig. 1-22. Circuit for Problem 14.

total resistance?   Round off your answers to two decimal places.

ANS.   1.67 Ω

11. If 120 volts dc is applied to a 50 Ω resistor connected in series with two resistors of 50 Ω in parallel with each other, how much current will flow in the circuit?

ANS.   1.6 amps

12. If an ac generator delivers an effective voltage of 60 volts, what will the peak voltage be?

ANS.   84 volts

13. If an ac voltmeter that is used to measure a pure sine-wave voltage reads 85 volts, what will the peak-to-peak voltage be?

ANS.   238 volts

14. What is the total resistance of the circuit shown in Fig. 1-22?

ANS.   145.5 Ω

15. A 450 Ω resistor has a rated tolerance of ± 10%. When we measure it with an ohmmeter we find that it actually has a resistance of 410 Ω. Is it within its tolerance?

ANS. Yes

16. Three resistors in series have voltage drops of 36 volts, 24 volts, and 40 volts. What percentage of the total voltage is the 24-volt drop?

ANS. .24 or 24%

17. In the circuit shown in Fig.1-23, 450 watts of power are consumed. What is the voltage drop across R_1?

ANS. 90 volts

18. How many amperes of current flow through R_4 in the circuit described in Problem 17?

ANS. 1.5 amps

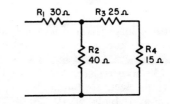

Fig. 1-23. Circuit for Problems 17 and 18.

1-6. Review Problems

1. A supply voltage of 120 volts is applied to three resistors in series. One resistor has a drop of 55 volts, another a drop of 30 volts. What is the voltage drop across the third resistor?

2. A 750-ohm resistor has a rated tolerance of ± 5%. When it is measured with an accurate ohmmeter, we find that the meter reads 697 ohms. Is the resistor (a) above, (b) below, (c) within its rated tolerance?

3. If 640 watts are consumed in a circuit with a total resistance of 160 ohms, how much current will flow in the circuit?

4. A current of 200 milliamps flows through a resistance of 1.6 K. What is the voltage drop across the resistor?

5. Find the answer to the problem $5 + 60 \times 3 \div 4 - 6$.

6. If 1/16 of the voltage applied to a circuit is dropped across a certain resistor, exactly what percentage of the total voltage does this represent?

7. What is the total resistance of the circuit shown at the right?

8. If 440 volts is applied to the circuit at the right, how much voltage will be dropped across the 35Ω resistor?

9. If a vacuum tube filament has a resistance of 20 ohms, and is rated at 250 milliamps, how much voltage should we apply so that it will draw its rated current?

10. The power consumed in a circuit is 160 watts. The voltage applied is 80 volts. What is the resistance of the circuit?

CHAPTER TWO

AC Circuit Calculations

2-1. Introduction

IN the chapter devoted to dc circuit calculations, you reviewed and studied many of the operations of basic arithmetic. You learned how important simple addition, subtraction, multiplication, and division can be in your work with electronics and electronic circuits. In this chapter you'll apply these same fundamental operations when solving ac circuit problems. However, as you know, alternating current reacts much differently from direct current in certain circuits. For this reason, you will have to expand your knowledge of basic mathematics in order to handle some of these conditions.

One of the first things you learned in dealing with alternating current is that the reactance of coils and capacitors causes the voltage and current to be out of phase with each other while any resistance tries to keep them in phase. Consequently, you cannot add

or subtract these ac circuit quantities without taking these phase differences into consideration. Although this might have seemed pretty difficult at first, you quickly learned that it could be done quite easily by using vectors to represent the phase relationships as well as the values. Then, by adding and subtracting the vectors, you were able to account for both the phase and the size of the circuit quantities.

While there is really no limit to the circuit solutions you can obtain by using simple vector measurement methods, they are very awkward and clumsy for the more complex circuits. For this reason, a number of simpler methods have been worked out to use in practical circuit solutions. Some of them involve square root, others use trigonometry, and one very common system uses a principle known as the j-operator. Like many other new subjects or methods, you will have to learn a few basic rules in order to use them with confidence and accuracy.

In addition to knowing how to do square root, you should be very familiar with dealing with positive and negative numbers. In this chapter we will discuss finding the square roots of numbers which is really just a special type of division. You will also study

positive and negative numbers, ratio and proportion, and then take a closer look at vectors themselves. Remember, you are not going to try to learn all there is to know about these subjects. You are simply going to look at them from the standpoint of their practical application in electronics.

2-2. Square Root

In the study of coils and capacitors, knowledge of doing the square root allows you to use a mathematical solution for finding the impedance in ac circuits. The formula for this method is

$$Z = \sqrt{R^2 + X^2}$$

where Z is the impedance, R is the resistance, and X is the total reactance. The reactance may, of course, be either the inductive reactance, X_L, capacitive reactance, X_C, or a combination of both X_L and X_C.

This is a very handy formula for finding the impedance and you will probably use it many times in your work with ac circuits. However, like many good methods of working out problems, it is of no use unless you know how to do square root. So let's take a look at this process which is known as finding the square root of a number. Even if you have already studied square root, it will still be a good idea to read this section to refresh your memory.

When you studied multiplication, you learned that the product of a number multiplied by itself was called a "square." You also learned a special

way of indicating the process of finding a square by placing a small "2" above and to the right of the number. Thus, 6×6 can be indicated as 6^2 or 136×136 as 136^2. Any other number times itself can be indicated the same way.

Many times in your work in electronics you will have the "square" of a number and will want to know the number. There is a special process of division that can be used to find the number that makes a square when multiplied by itself. Since the number that makes a square when it is multiplied by itself is sometimes called the "root" of a square, this special division process is called finding the "square root."

Let's make sure you understand this. A number multiplied by itself, or "squared," makes a product called a "square." The number that is squared is called the "root" of the square. The special division to find the root of a square is called finding the "square root."

Simple Square Roots

Now that you have seen what we mean by square root, let's look at a typical example and learn how to solve it. Suppose you are asked to find the square root of the number 576. What you want to know is: "What number will give a product of 576 if it is multiplied by itself?" The main difference between this and any other division problem is that here you are given only the product to work with. Instead of being given a product and one number and being asked what number when multiplied by the given number will equal the product, you are simply given a product and are asked to find the one number that can be multiplied by itself to give this product.

While this probably seems pretty difficult to do, it is really not hard at all. It is just a matter of learning a few rules and how to apply them. First, you must set the number up much as you would any other division problem as shown in Fig. 2-1A. However, you will notice that there is one major difference in addition to the fact that there is no divisor. This is the symbol that looks like a lopsided letter "V" that is in front of the dividend. It replaces the straight vertical line in a standard division symbol and is called a "radical" sign. This radical sign is the symbol for finding the root of a number and is always used in a square root problem.

In square root, just as in any other division, you do not tackle the whole number at once. You split it up into smaller numbers and work with the smaller numbers a few at a time. However, in square root you do it a little bit differently. You will notice that in Fig. 2-1B, we have placed a comma between the 5 and the 7. This breaks our number up into two numbers, 5

and 76. The method for breaking these numbers up in this way is quite simple. You merely start at the extreme right of the whole number and work toward the left, placing a comma after each group of two numbers. Thus, starting with the 6 and working towards the left we have our first group, 76, and then the 5. Since the 5 is the last number on the left in this particular problem, you have only two groups, one of which is a single number.

Grouping the numbers in this way under the radical sign completes the setup and you are ready to go to work. You will remember that in division you used a basic multiplication table containing all the products for various

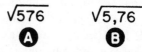

Fig. 2-1. Setting up a square root problem.

combinations of the numbers from 1 to 9. After you had a division problem set up, you tried various products to see which one would go into the dividend. In square root, you do much the same thing except that you need to know the squares of the numbers from 1 to 9. Fig. 2-2 shows the same multiplication table that you used in the first chapter. This table has all the squares of the numbers from 1 to 9 marked with stars. This table and these squares are all you need to work any square root problem.

Now, let's look at the problem again, as shown in Fig. 2-3A, where it is set up and ready to work on. Since we have broken the number up into two groups, and since the number 5 is alone in the first group, we consider the 5 by itself at first. We don't have a divisor to divide into the 5 to start with, so we must make one. We do this by determining the largest square that will go into 5. Looking at the table, we see that 2 squared is equal to 4 which is smaller than 5, and 3 squared is equal to 9 which is larger than 5. Since the square of 3 is larger than 5, the square of 2 is the largest perfect square that will go into 5.

Therefore, 4 becomes the first trial product and the 2, which is the square root of 4, is the first trial divisor. Now that we have found that 4 is the largest square that will go into 5, we place it under the 5 as shown in Fig. 2-3B. Then, we take the 2 which we squared to get the 4 and place it above the line over the 5 to indicate that it is the first digit of the quotient. This is also shown in Fig. 2-3B. Next, we subtract the 4 from the 5 to get the first remainder, which, in this problem, is 1, as shown in Fig. 2-3C. In this way, by finding the largest square that will go into the first group in our dividend, we have obtained the

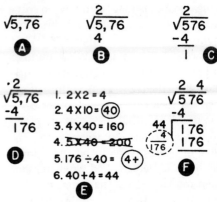

Fig 2-3. Steps in working out a square root problem.

first trial product, the first remainder, and the first digit in the quotient.

This first operation is the only time we have to worry about the squares of numbers when doing square root. As you can see, since we never have more than two numbers in any group, the largest number we can possibly have in the first group is 99, and 9 squared or 81 is the largest square that can go into 99 because 10 squared is 100. This is the reason that we never need more than the basic squares of the numbers from 1 to 9 in order to find the square root of any number. From now on, the problem becomes even more like regular division except for the way of obtaining the trial divisors and trial products.

Looking at Fig. 2-3D, you see that the next step is to bring down the next group of numbers, which is 76. Notice that we bring down the whole group, not just the 7. When we have placed the 76 beside the 1 as shown, we have a trial dividend of 176. Now we must learn the rule by which we establish the next trial divisor. To do this, we take the partial quotient of 2,

*1	2	3	4	5	6	7	8	9	0
2	*4	6	8	10	12	14	16	18	0
3	6	*9	12	15	18	21	24	27	0
4	8	12	*16	20	24	28	32	36	0
5	10	15	20	*25	30	35	40	45	0
6	12	18	24	30	*36	42	48	54	0
7	14	21	28	35	42	*49	56	63	0
8	16	24	32	40	48	56	*64	72	0
9	18	27	36	45	54	63	72	*81	0
0	0	0	0	0	0	0	0	0	0

Fig. 2-2. Basic multiplication table showing square of numbers from 1 to 9.

double it, and then multiply the result by 10.

Following this rule: the partial quotient is 2. If we double it, we get 4. Multiplying the 4 by 10 gives 40. Then we use the 40 as the trial divisor. Now we ask ourselves: "How many times will 40 go into 176?" We know that 4 times 40 is 160 which will go into 176 easily. Since 5 times 40 is 200 which is too large to go into 176, 4 is the number we want.

However, we are still not quite finished with the trial divisor. Before we can use it, we have one more step to do. After we have determined that 4 is the largest number of times that 40 will go into 176 we must then *add* the 4 to 40 as shown in Step 6 of Fig. 2-3E. This gives us 44 which we use as the final trial divisor as shown in Fig. 2-3F.

Now, we must multiply 44 by 4 to see if it will still go into 176. As you can see, 4 times 44 is exactly 176 and

we will have no remainder when we subtract. Since the trial divisor did go into 176 four times, the second number of the quotient is 4 and can be placed above the line over the second group of numbers. There is no remainder; therefore, the complete quotient is 24, which is the square root of 576. We can prove this by squaring 24 which will give the product of 576.

Although the process of finding the square root of a number is not really difficult, it does require a firm knowledge of some important rules. For this reason, we will work out another problem dealing with a larger square. Then, you will have a good review of the process as well as more practical experience. Remember, no matter how large the number may be, you proceed in exactly the same way.

Working Square Root Problems. Let's find the square root of 186,624.

First, set up the problem under the radical sign. Next, separate the num-

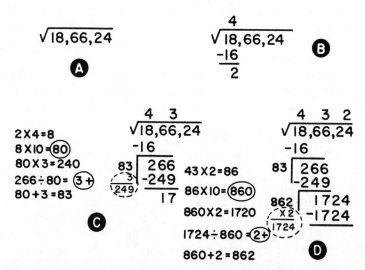

Fig. 2-4. Finding the square root of a six digit number.

ber into groups of two numbers, start-ing at the right and working toward the left, as shown in Fig. 2-4A. In this problem the radicand (the special name given to the dividend in square root) is divided evenly into three groups of two numbers each. Since the first group is the number 18, we find the largest square that will go into 18.

Looking at the multiplication table in Fig. 2-2, we see that the square of 4 is 16 and that the square of the next larger number, 5, is 25. Twenty-five is larger than 18, so 16 must be the largest even square smaller than 18. Therefore, we place the 16 under the 18 in our radicand and subtract, as shown in Fig. 2-4B. Since 4 is the num-ber that we squared to obtain this trial product, it is the first trial divisor and we place it in the quotient over the number 8 in the first group.

Next, subtract the 16 from 18 to get a remainder of 2. Then bring down the next group of two numbers, 66, and place them beside the 2. This gives a new number, 266, to use as the divi-dend for the next step, as shown in Fig. 2-4C. Next, you must determine the second trial divisor. Remember, dou-ble the existing quotient number, 4, to get 8, and then multiply by 10, which is 80 as shown. Then see how many times 80 will go into 266. For this particular problem, 80 will go into 266 three times, but not four. There-fore, we add 3 to 80, giving 83 as the second trial divisor. Now, multiply 83 by 3 to get the trial product of 249 which can be subtracted from 266. This subtraction gives a remainder of 17, which is shown in Fig. 2-4C. Since the trial divisor of 83 went into 266 three times, enter the 3 in the quotient above the line over the second group

of numbers, 66.

In this problem, we have still another group of two numbers left in our radicand, so we are not yet fin-ished finding the square root of 186,624. Therefore, we must bring the 24 down beside the 17 to give the divi-dend for the next step. As you can see in Fig. 2-4D, this gives 1724 and you must find a trial divisor for it so that you can find the next number for the quotient.

Proceeding as before, you take the partial quotient, 43, double it to get 86, and then multiply the product by 10, giving 860. You can see that 860 will go into 1724 only two times. Therefore, you add 2 to 860 giving 862 as the trial divisor. Now, multiplying 862 by 2 gives exactly 1724 and you can subtract without having any re-mainder. Finally, you place the 2 in the quotient above the 24 and you have the complete square root of 186,624, which is 432. You can check this, of course, by multiplying 432 by itself to see if the product is equal to the radicand you started with.

Although the rules for doing square root are a little different from those involved in other types of division, they are really no more difficult. Like anything else, it is a matter of prac-tice to become proficient at finding square roots. Most of us don't get this practice after we leave school, so we are likely to forget how to do it. How-ever, in electrical work, square root can be quite important. Let's try another problem.

In Fig. 2-5, we have set up the num-ber 7,306,209 to find its square root. Notice that the complete radicand contains seven numbers so that it can't be divided evenly into groups of two.

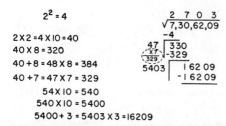

$2^2 = 4$

$2 \times 2 = 4 \times 10 = 40$
$40 \times 8 = 320$
$40 + 8 = 48 \times 8 = 384$
$40 + 7 = 47 \times 7 = 329$
$54 \times 10 = 540$
$540 \times 10 = 5400$
$5400 + 3 = 5403 \times 3 = 16209$

$$\begin{array}{r} 2\ 7\ 0\ 3 \\ \sqrt{7,30,62,09} \\ -4 \end{array}$$

$$\begin{array}{r} 47 \\ \overline{}\ 330 \\ -329 \end{array}$$

$$\begin{array}{r} 5403 \\ \overline{}\ 1\ 62\ 09 \\ -1\ 62\ 09 \end{array}$$

Fig. 2-5. Another square root problem.

Since we always start at the right hand end of the radicand, we form the groups as shown. In this way, a single number will be the first number to the right of the radical sign.

Now, we examine the number in the first group to find the largest square that will go into it. In this problem, the first group is only one number, 7, and the largest square that will go into it is 2^2, or 4. Thus, we place a 2 in the quotient or root, directly over the 7. Then we place the square of 2, which is 4, under the 7 and subtract, giving a remainder of 3.

Bring the next group, 30, down beside the 3. Then we double the root number, 2, which is 4 and multiply it by 10 for the next trial divisor. Now, we determine how many times 40 will go into 330. It looks as if 8 will work because $4 \times 8 = 32$. However, when we add 8 to 40 to get a trial divisor of 48, we find that $48 \times 8 = 384$, which is larger than 330. Therefore, we will have to try the next smaller number which is 7.

Notice that we don't multiply 48×7. We change the whole trial divisor of 48 to 47 and then multiply 47×7 which is equal to 329. In square root, we often have to reject trial divisors and use new ones that are smaller. Since 329 is smaller than 330, we place the 7 in the root and

subtract 329 from 330. This gives a remainder of 1 and we bring down the next group, 62, from the radicand, giving us our new remainder, 162.

Now, we double the two numbers in the root, 27, to get a new trial divisor which is 54 times 10, or 540. It is obvious at a glance that 540 will not go into 162. Therefore, we place a zero in the root above 62 and then bring down the next two numbers, which are 09. The remainder now becomes 16209.

Now we double the three numbers in the root, 270, to get the next trial divisor which is 540 times 10 or 5400. 5400 looks as if it will go into 16209 about 3 times. So we add 3 to 5400 to get 5403 and then multiply this number by 3 and get exactly 16209. Since we have no remainder, the problem is completed and we place the 3 in the quotient, or root, above the last group of numbers. Thus, we have found that the square root of 7,306,209 is 2703, which we can prove to be correct by squaring 2703 to see if we get the original radicand.

Imperfect Squares

So far all the answers have been the roots of perfect squares. Although this is convenient, it does not often happen in practice. There will usually be a remainder, which must be accounted for by making the root end with a decimal number or a fraction. For example, suppose the radicand for the last problem that you worked had been 7,306,976 instead of 7,306,209. If this had been the case, the problem would have worked along the same until you got to the last part of it, as shown in Fig. 2-6.

As you can see, the trial product of 5403 × 3 is equal to 16,209, but because the original radicand was changed, you now have a remainder of 767 when you subtract. This is not large enough so that it will increase the root by another whole number to make it 2704, but it does leave a fraction. If the need for accuracy is such that you want to carry the root of 2703 into its fractional part, you would continue the problem as shown in Fig. 2-6.

As you can see, you place a decimal after the last number in the radicand and then add a group of two zeros for each decimal place you want in the root. Notice that there are two zeros added for each decimal place in square root instead of only one zero as there is in regular division. In this particular problem, we have carried the answer to two decimal places and have added four zeros as shown.

After you have added the zeros in the radicand and the decimal point in both the radicand and in the root number, you continue in the same manner as before to find the new root

numbers. First, you bring down the first group of two zeros beside the remainder of 767 to give 76,700 for the next dividend. Then you double the existing root number, 2703, and multiply the product by 10 to get the trial divisor, 54,060. You can quickly see that this will go into 76,700 only once, so you add the 1 to it as shown. Then, since any number multiplied by 1 is the same number, you have 54,061 for the trial product. Place the 1 in the root.

Subtracting 54,061, you get a remainder of 22639. Bring down the next two zeros as shown. Now, double the quotient, multiply by 10 ignoring the decimal in the quotient. In other words, multiply 27031 by 2 to get 54062 and then multiply by 10 which is 540620. Then, continue as before to find the next root number, which is 4. As you can see, this gives a root of 2703.14 to two decimal places. Since we still have a remainder we do not have a perfect root, but except where extreme accuracy is needed, two decimal places in the answer are enough. Of course, if you do want more accu-

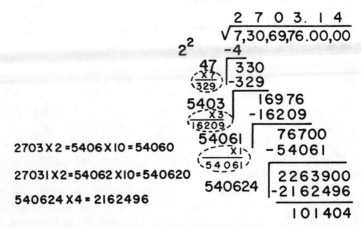

Fig. 2-6. An imperfect square root carried two places.

racy, you would simply continue in the same way, by adding two more zeros for each additional decimal place.

You can check your answer in the usual way by squaring the root to see if you get your original radicand. In this problem, if you square 2703.14, you get an answer of 7,306,965.8596. Although it is not exactly the same as the original radicand, because we did not have a perfect square to start with, it is close enough so that you can see that the root is correct to two decimal places, which is all we are interested in.

Fractions and Decimals

Many times in your work in electronics you will need to find the square root of a fraction or decimal. While the process for finding the roots of fractions or decimals is nearly the same as it is for whole numbers, there is one important thing to remember. The square root of a fraction or deci-mal will always be larger than its square. You will recall that the product of any two fractions or decimals is always smaller than either of the two numbers. Therefore, the square of any fraction or decimal must also be smaller than the numbers squared.

Finding the square root of fractions is usually very easy, because most fractions have small numbers in both the numerator and the denominator. Also, as you have already seen, finding the square roots of small numbers does not involve much work. The first thing to do to find the square root of a fraction is to reduce the fraction as much as possible. Thus, if you wanted to find the root of $\%_2$, you would first reduce it to $\%_6$, as shown in Fig. 2-7A.

Next, you separate the numerator and the denominator and find the square root of each one separately, using the same method that you learned for whole numbers. Thus, you would find the square root of 3 which is 1.732 to three places, as shown in Fig. 2-7B. Then you find the square root

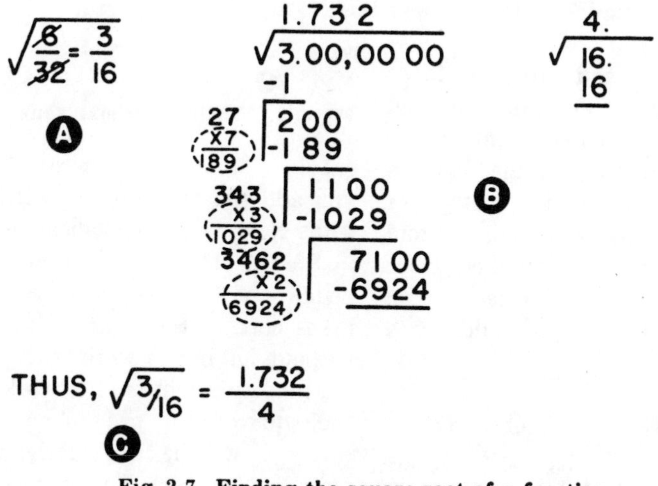

Fig. 2-7. **Finding the square root of a fraction.**

of 16, which is 4. Now you use the root of 3 as the new numerator and the root of 16 as the new denominator. Thus, the square root of $\frac{3}{16}$ is $\frac{1.732}{4}$ as shown in Fig. 2-7C. By using this simple method, you can find the square root of any fraction quickly and accurately.

In finding the square root of a decimal, you proceed exactly the same as for a whole number except in the grouping when you set up the problem. You still separate the decimal number in groups of two numbers, but with a decimal, you start at the decimal point and work to the right. Also, you must always have an even number of digits to the right of the decimal place. That is, each group must have two digits. Thus, to set up the decimal .961 for finding its square root, you proceed as shown in Fig. 2-8A.

After you have placed the number under the radical sign, you start at the decimal point and count two numbers to the right and place a comma between the 6 and the 1. Then you add a zero after the 1, so that the second group has two digits. If the number were .961235, you would place commas after the 6 and after the 2, as shown in Fig. 2-8B. The fact that you work from the decimal point to the right in the grouping of the digits is the only difference in the method of finding the square root of a decimal from that of a whole number. Once you have completed the setup, you proceed exactly as you would for a

$$\sqrt{.96,10} \qquad \sqrt{.96,12,35}$$

(A)   (B)

Fig. 2-8. Setting up a decimal for square root.

whole number. In Fig. 2-9, we have worked out the square root of two decimals. You should not have any trouble in following these examples.

Estimating Square Roots

Now that you have seen how to work out the square roots of numbers in detail, let's see how we can apply this process in ac circuits. Suppose, for example, that we want to find the impedance of the circuit shown in Fig. 2-10. By using the formula

$$Z = \sqrt{R^2 + X^2}$$

and substituting for the values of R and X, we have:

$$Z = \sqrt{50^2 + 60^2}$$

as shown in Step 2 of Fig. 2-10.

In working square root you must follow the rules of order just as in doing any other math. Therefore, the next thing you must do is to perform all the multiplication under the radi-

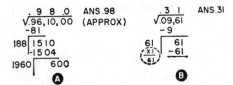

Fig. 2-9. Finding decimal square roots.

cal sign. This is shown in Step 3. Next, you add the two squares which gives 6100. Now, you can go ahead as shown in Step 4. This gives the circuit impedance of 78 ohms and automatically takes care of the phase relationships without having to work with vectors.

Many times, instead of working out the square root of problems accurately, it will be much easier to estimate the answers. For example, take the number 6436. You can see that 80 × 80 is equal to 6400 which gives a remainder of 36. For most purposes this would be close enough so we would use 80 as the answer.

Likewise, with a number such as 7548, you can see that it is more than 80^2 (6400), but less than 90^2 which is 8100. Therefore, it would be easy to

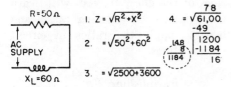

Fig. 2-10. **Using square root to find impedance.**

1. $Z = \sqrt{R^2 + X^2}$

2. $= \sqrt{50^2 + 60^2}$

3. $= \sqrt{2500 + 3600}$

guess that 84^2 might be close, since 7500 is a little less than halfway between 6400 and 8100. If we square 84, we will find that it is equal to 7056 which is somewhat less than 7548. When we are this far off in our estimate, the next number we would try

would probably be 86 or 87. Let's square 87 and see what we get.

$$
\begin{array}{r}
87 \\
87 \\
\hline
609 \\
696 \\
\hline
7569
\end{array}
$$

As you can see, this is very close. The difference between 7569 and 7548 is only 21, and unless you required extreme accuracy, you would just use 87 as the square root of 7548. By estimating in this way, you can come very close to the square root of any number with a little practice. For large numbers it is generally much easier than working out the root in detail. Try the following problems and see if you can get the answers we have shown.

Problems: (1) 625; (2) 11025; (3) 8094025;

Answers: (1) 25; (2) 105; (3) 2845.

2-3. Ratio and Proportion

There are many times in electronics work when we want to compare quantities. Sometimes we can simply say that something is either larger or smaller than something else, but usually this does not give us enough information. In electronics, as in any other scientific work, we generally need exact information as to sizes or quantities. For example, saying that one resistor is larger than another is not enough. We must know how much larger it is if we are going to use the resistors for anything practical.

Although we can subtract one quan-

tity from another to find out how much smaller it is, there are many times when even this type of specific information is not too useful. For example, suppose we want to compare the efficiencies of two electrical circuits. Let's say that one circuit has an input of 400 watts and an output of 300 watts, while the other has an input of 568 watts and an output of 426 watts. If we subtract the input from the output in the first circuit, we find that it has a loss of 400W — 300W or 100W. The second circuit. on the other hand, has a loss of 568W — 426W or

142W.

By subtracting this way, we find that the loss in the second circuit is 142 watts as compared to a loss of only 100 watts in the first circuit. However, we still don't know which circuit is the most efficient. We know that 42 watts more power is consumed in the second circuit, but since the input and output to this circuit are also larger, this does not tell us anything about its efficiency.

However, there is a method by which we can quickly and accurately compare the losses in the two circuits and determine their relative efficiencies. This is actually a form of division and is known as establishing ratios. For example, if we divide the output of the first circuit by its input and reduce the resulting fraction, we have:

$$\frac{300}{400} = \frac{3}{4}$$

This fractional value of $\frac{3}{4}$ tells us that three-quarters of the input power appears as useful output. The remaining one-quarter is the loss in the circuit.

If we do the same thing to the second circuit, we have $\frac{426}{568}$ which, reduced to its lowest possible form, is also $\frac{3}{4}$ because 142 will go into the numerator 3 times and into the denominator 4 times. Thus, the ratio of the output to the input of the second circuit is exactly the same as the ratio of output to the input of the first circuit. Their ratios are both ¾ and, therefore, their efficiencies are exactly the same. In other words, for every 4 watts we put into either circuit we

will get 3 watts output.

By establishing ratios in this way, we can make many accurate comparisons between various quantities. In addition, through a process known as proportion, we can use an established ratio to compute circuit values much more simply and quickly than we could in any other way. In this section of the chapter, you will learn the rules for establishing ratios and how to apply the ratios in circuit computations.

Establishing Ratios

When two quantities are compared by division, we call the ratio of the two quantities the "quotient." Thus, when we divided 426 by 568 and then reduced the resultant fraction to its lowest possible form, we had the ratio of $\frac{3}{4}$. We can write such a ratio as the fraction $\frac{3}{4}$, or we can use two dots as a ratio sign and write it 3:4. In either case, we say that the ratio is "three to four."

In establishing ratios for use in comparing quantities, we must always be sure to express the two quantities in the same units. For example, we can't compare 10 volts with 10 millivolts directly. We must either change the 10 volts to 10,000 millivolts or change the 10 millivolts to .010 volts before we can establish a ratio between them. Also, the quantities themselves must be of the same kind. We can't, for example, compare a volt with an ampere, or an ohm with a watt. However, there are many times when we can compare seemingly unlike quantities by changing both of them to a third quantity.

For example, suppose a motor's output is 5 horsepower and its input is 4 kilowatts. If we want to establish an output-to-input efficiency ratio for this motor, we can do it quite simply by converting our values. Horsepower is a measure of work done and there are approximately 750 watts in 1 horsepower. Thus, we can convert 5 horsepower to 5×750 or 3750 watts. We also know that 4 kilowatts is equal to 4000 watts. So, by converting both the input and the output to a common unit such as watts, we are able to establish the following ratio:

Given: Output 5 hp

Input 4 kw

Find: Efficiency

$$\text{Efficiency} = \frac{\text{output}}{\text{input}}$$

$$= \frac{5 \text{ hp}}{4 \text{ kw}} = \frac{5 \times 750}{4 \times 1000}$$

$$= \frac{3750}{4000} = \frac{15}{16} = 15:16$$

Thus, the efficiency of the motor can be expressed as the ratio of 15 to 16. If we prefer, we can change the ratio to a percentage value by dividing as follows:

$$
\begin{array}{r}
.9375 \text{ or } 93.75\% \\
16\overline{)15.0000} \\
\underline{144} \\
60 \\
\underline{48} \\
120 \\
\underline{112} \\
80 \\
\underline{80} \\
\end{array}
$$

In this way, we can express a ratio

as a fraction, a decimal value, or a percentage.

The rules for establishing ratios are quite simple. To find the ratio of two similar quantities:

1. Convert the quantities to the same units of measurement.

2. Form a fraction using the first quantity as a numerator and the second quantity as a denominator.

3. Reduce the fraction to its lowest possible terms.

4. If you wish, you can divide the denominator into the numerator to express the ratio as a decimal or as a percentage.

Proportion

Even though ratios are extremely useful for comparing similar quantities, they are probably even more useful as a computing tool. By setting certain ratios equal to each other in what is known as a proportion, we are able to make many shortcuts in circuit calculations. For example, suppose we had a circuit such as the one shown in Fig. 2-11 and wanted to know the voltage across R_2. Ordinarily, in a series circuit such as this, we would first find the current flowing through R_1 by using the formula $I = E_1 \div R_1$. Then, since the current is the same in all parts of a series circuit, we would find E_2 by multiplying I by R_2. However, by using ratio and proportion, we can find either the voltage across R_2 or the total voltage in one simple operation without ever knowing the current at all. Thus, ratio and proportion save time and work by eliminating the step of finding the current.

In order to use proportion, you have to remember only one simple rule.

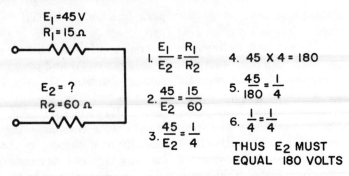

Fig. 2-11. Using ratio and proportion to solve for circuit values.

That is, a proportion is a mathematical statement that two ratios are equal. For example, refer back to the efficiency problem in the two circuits you studied earlier in this chapter. You recall that in the first circuit we had an efficiency of $\frac{300}{400} = \frac{3}{4}$. Likewise, in the second circuit the efficiency was $\frac{426}{568}$ which was also reduced to $\frac{3}{4}$. Thus, both of the ratios are equal and we can actually indicate this mathematically as

$$\frac{300}{400} = \frac{426}{568}$$

because when we reduce both fractions, we have $\frac{3}{4}$ on both sides of the equal sign. Thus, $\frac{300}{400} = \frac{426}{568}$ is a proportion because it contains two equal ratios.

Now let's see how we can apply this type of thinking to the circuit in Fig. 2-11. First, let's establish a resistance ratio for the circuit. We do this by dividing R_1 by R_2 to get the ratio $\frac{15}{60}$ or $\frac{1}{4}$. Now, let's find the current

in the circuit by dividing E_1 by R_1 and then find the voltage across E_2 by the method we are familiar with. If we do this, we find that:

$$I = E_1 \div R_1$$

$$= 45 \div 15 = 3 \text{ amp}$$

Then, $E_2 = R_2 \times I$

$$= 60 \times 3$$

$$= 180 \text{ volts}$$

If we now form another ratio from the voltages across E_1 and E_2, we will have $\frac{45}{180} = \frac{1}{4}$. Notice that this voltage ratio is exactly the same as the resistance ratio and, therefore, the two ratios must be equal. Accordingly, we can establish a proportion with the two equal ratios by stating them mathematically as:

$$\frac{R_1}{R_2} = \frac{E_1}{E_2}$$

or

$$\frac{15}{60} = \frac{45}{180}$$

or

$$\frac{1}{4} = \frac{1}{4}$$

All three expressions are proportions and say exactly the same thing.

Suppose we knew that the resistance and voltage ratios were equal to begin with. Actually, we can easily see that they would be because the voltage drops around a circuit must distribute themselves in accordance with the size of the resistances. If we had realized this, we could have set up our proportion as shown in Fig. 2-11 to begin with, and substituted all our known values as follows:

$$\frac{E_1}{E_2} = \frac{R_1}{R_2}$$

Substituting, we have:

$$\frac{45}{E_2} = \frac{15}{60}$$

This, of course, gives us what we call an "equation" that has one unknown value.

Now that we know that the two ratios are equal, we can find the value of E_2 quite simply. If we reduce the $\frac{15}{60}$ to its lowest form of $\frac{1}{4}$, we have:

$$\frac{45}{E_2} = \frac{1}{4}$$

Since one side of our proportion will reduce to $\frac{1}{4}$, the other side must also reduce to $\frac{1}{4}$ so the two sides can be equal. Thus, all we have to do is to replace the denominator, E_2, in our first ratio with a number that is equal to four times 45. Since $4 \times 45 = 180$, E_2 must be equal to 180 because $\frac{45}{180}$ is the only fraction with 45 as a numerator and 180 as a denominator

that will reduce to $\frac{1}{4}$ and we must be able to reduce both sides to $\frac{1}{4}$ in order to have a proportion.

Although this may seem a little complex at first, let's consider the following conditions which should clear it up. If 3 resistors cost 75 cents, we know that 6 resistors must cost $1.50. At the given rate, the cost of the resistors must depend only on the number bought. The more resistors we buy, the larger the cost will be. The fewer we buy, the less the cost will be. When two quantities depend on each other in this way, they are said to be in proportion.

We have already said that a proportion is a mathematical statement that two ratios are equal. In this problem, the two quantities that make up the ratios are the number of resistors, N, and the cost, C. Since the cost depends on the number of resistors bought, we can write a proportion.

First Purchase   **Second Purchase**

$N_1 = 3$ resistors $N_2 = 6$ resistors

$C_1 = \$.75$ $C_2 = \$1.50$

The ratio of the number of resistors is:

$$\frac{N_1}{N_2} = \frac{3}{6} = \frac{1}{2}$$

The ratio of the costs is:

$$\frac{C_1}{C_2} = \frac{75}{150} = \frac{1}{2}$$

Since the two ratios are equal, the proportion is written mathematically as:

$$\frac{N_1}{N_2} = \frac{C_1}{C_2} \text{ or}$$

$$\frac{3}{6} = \frac{75}{150} \text{ or}$$

$$\frac{1}{2} = \frac{1}{2}$$

This is an example of what we call a direct proportion. When two quantities depend on each other so that one increases as the other increases, or one decreases as the other decreases, they are said to be directly proportional to each other. This is what we mean when we say that the current through a fixed resistance is directly proportional to the voltage applied. As the voltage increases, the current increases, etc.

Notice that when we set up two equal ratios as a direct proportion, we must compare the two ratios in the same order. In other words, we used the quantities in the first situation, N_1 and C_1, as numerators, and the quantities in the second situation, N_2 and C_2, as denominators. Thus, they are in the same order because the second ratio, $\frac{C_1}{C_2}$, is patterned after the first, $\frac{N_1}{N_2}$. However, we could have written the proportion in the opposite form just as well. For example,

$$\frac{C_1}{C_2} = \frac{N_1}{N_2} \quad \text{or}$$

$$\frac{C_2}{C_1} = \frac{N_2}{N_1} \quad \text{or}$$

$$\frac{N_2}{N_1} = \frac{C_2}{C_1}$$

As you can see, it is not important which ratio is written first; neither is it important how the first ratio is written. However, in a direct proportion, the second ratio must always be written in the same order as the first.

Thus, the rules for setting up a direct proportion for two variables that depend on each other are:

1. Make a ratio of either one of the variables.
2. Make a ratio of the other variable in the same order.
3. Set the two ratios equal to each other.

Solving Proportions

In the first example of a proportion that we solved, we reduced the completed ratio to its smallest possible form and then found a number for the unknown in the incompleted ratio that would allow it to be reduced to the same form. While this is actually what we must do in order to find the solution for any proportion, there is a short cut which we can use that makes it quite easy. This short cut is called "cross-multiplication" and we will learn why it can be used later on. Right now, all we need to know is that it always works and learn how to use it.

For example, suppose we have a length of cable that is 78 ft. long and another length of the same kind that is 4 ft. long. We want to know how much the longer piece of cable weighs, but because it is bulky and hard to handle it will be difficult to weigh it. In this case, we could weigh the smaller length of cable and then set up a proportion and find the weight of the longer piece.

Let's say that the shorter piece weighs ten pounds. We would set up the proportion as follows:

$$\frac{L_L}{L_S} = \frac{W_L}{W_S} \quad , \text{ where}$$

L_L = length of longer cable
L_S = length of shorter cable
W_L = weight of longer cable
W_S = weight of shorter cable

Now, by substituting values, we have:

$$\frac{L_L}{L_S} = \frac{W_L}{W_S}$$

$$\frac{78}{4} = \frac{W_L}{10}$$

To apply our short cut using cross-multiplication, we multiply the numerator of one fraction by the denominator of the other as follows:

$$4 \times W_L = 78 \times 10$$

$$4W_L = 780$$

Now, we have a familiar equation form to work with and we know that if

$$4W_L = 780, \text{ then}$$

$$W_L = 780 \div 4 = 195$$

Therefore, the weight of the large, bulky piece of cable is 195 lbs.

Another example of the same problem in a slightly different situation might be quite common in your work in electronics. Suppose the longer piece of cable were wound on a reel and you wanted to know how long it was without unreeling it. Since it was wound on the reel, it would be easy to handle and we could weigh it quite easily. Then, by weighing the shorter piece, and setting up the proportion using the two weights and the length of the short piece, we could find the length of the long piece. Suppose the cable on the drum weighed 425 pounds while the short piece was four feet long and weighed ten pounds. First, we would have to subtract the weight of the reel

itself, say 25 pounds, and then we would set up the proportion:

$$\frac{L_L}{L_S} = \frac{W_L}{W_S} \text{ then}$$

$$\frac{L_L}{4} = \frac{(425 - 25)}{10} \text{ or}$$

$$\frac{L_L}{4} = \frac{400}{10}$$

By cross-multiplying, we have:

$$10 \times L_L = 4 \times 400$$

$$10\,L_L = 1600$$

$$L_L = 1600 \div 10$$

and therefore $L_L = 160$ ft.

The steps for solving any direct proportion are always the same. First,

1. Set up the direct proportion

$$\frac{X_1}{X_2} = \frac{Y_1}{Y_2}$$

2. Substitute numbers where possible:

$$\frac{10}{100} = \frac{50}{X}$$

3. Cross-multiply $10 \times X = 50 \times 100$.

4. Simplify $10X = 5000$.

5. Solve for the unknown:

$$X = 5000 \div 10$$

6. Divide. ANS. $X = 500$.

Inverse Proportion. So far in our discussion of proportion, we have considered only what happens when two quantities vary directly. Many times two quantities depend on each other, but instead of varying directly, they do just the opposite. When one increases, the other must decrease an appropriate amount. When this occurs, we say the two quantities vary indirectly or "inversely" and that they are inversely proportional. The current and the resistance in an electrical circuit with a fixed voltage is a good example of an inverse proportion. As the resistance increases, the current decreases.

We can set up inverse proportions mathematically just as we do direct proportions except for one major difference. In an inverse proportion, we always set up the second ratio in the opposite or inverse order. For example, consider the parallel circuit shown in Fig. 2-12

In this circuit we are given the values of the two resistances and the current through one of them. We could find the current I_2 by finding the voltage across R_1, and since the voltage across R_2 would be the same we could find I_2 by using this voltage. However, we can set up and solve a proportion much easier. There is just one thing to remember. The current and the resistance vary inversely and, therefore, we must use an inverse proportion. To do this, we set up the first ratio. It doesn't make any difference which one we use first or how we set

it up as long as we set up the next one in the opposite manner.

For example, in the circuit in Fig. 2-12, let's use the current ratio first as: $\dfrac{I_1}{I_2}$. Then, the resistance ratio in the reverse order $\dfrac{R_2}{R_1}$, and then set them equal to each other as follows:

$$\frac{I_1}{I_2} = \frac{R_2}{R_1}$$

Substituting,

$$\frac{1}{I_2} = \frac{150}{200}$$

$$150 \times I_2 = 200 \times 1$$

$$150 I_2 = 200$$

$$I_2 = 200 \div 150$$

$$I_2 = 1.33 \text{ amps.}$$

As you can see, the solution is obtained in exactly the same manner as in a direct proportion. The only difference is that we reversed the order of the second ratio from that of the first when we set up the ratios.

You will recall that when we first discussed establishing ratios, we mentioned that a ratio could be written as 5:2 as well as $\dfrac{5}{2}$. We can also

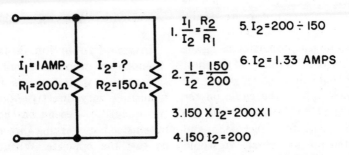

Fig. 2-12. Using an inverse proportion to solve for current.

write proportions in two ways, depending upon which way we indicate our ratios. For example, the proportion $\frac{10}{20} = \frac{50}{100}$ would be written as

$$10 : 20 :: 50 : 100$$

using the two dots as ratio signs and the four dots to indicate proportion. When a ratio is written in this way, there is no cross-multiplication indicated as there is in the fractional form and we use a different way of indicating the solution.

In the form $10 : 20 :: 50 : 100$, we give a name to both parts of the proportion. We call the two outside numbers, 10 and 100, the "extremes" of the proportion. The two inside numbers, 20 and 50, are called the "means" of the proportion. Now, we say that the product of the means is equal to the product of the extremes. In other words, the product of the two outside numbers is equal to the product of the two inside numbers. As you can see, remembering this and using it with this form of the proportion gives us exactly the same thing as cross-multiplying a proportion that is written in the fractional form.

$$\frac{10}{20} = \frac{50}{100}$$

$$20 \times 50 = 10 \times 100$$

or

$$10 : 20 :: 50 : 100$$

$$20 \times 50 = 10 \times 100$$

Using ratios in proportion to solve for unknown quantities is one of the handiest tools in mathematics. It is not only easy to use and work with, but it is also easy to remember the rules. No matter where you go or what you do, you can almost always find some use for ratio and proportion in solving problems. You will be very pleased with the amount of work it can save you. To make sure that you thoroughly understand it, try solving the following problems.

Problems: Find the ratio of (1) 6 V to 18 V, (2) 250 MV to 1 V, (3) 3 hp to 2.25 kw; (4) A is directly proportional to B, and $A_1 = 15$, $A_2 = 6$, $B_1 = 90$; find B_2; (5) A is inversely proportional to B and $A_2 = 4$, $B_1 = 100$, $B_2 = 150$; find A_1. Answers: (1) 1 to 3; (2) 1 to 4; (3) 1 to 1; (4) 36; (5) 6.

2-4. Positive and Negative Numbers

Many of the calculations, graphs, and tables that are used to solve problems in both ac and dc circuits require an understanding of positive and negative numbers. These numbers are commonly called signed numbers and are used to indicate opposite amounts. These opposite amounts might be such things as gain or loss in voltage, an increase or decrease in volume, currents that flow in opposite directions, capacitive or inductive reactance, and many other similar situations.

In our everyday lives we commonly indicate opposite quantities such as these by various pairs of words such as north and south, up and down, and gain or loss. In electronics, we use opposite quantities so often that it is much easier to indicate them by using plus (+) signs and minus (—) signs. For example, 5° above zero is written as +5° and 5° below zero is written as —5°. A current in one direction might be +10 amps, but a current in the opposite direction would be written as —10 amps.

Numbers preceded by a minus sign are called negative numbers and are always indicated by the minus sign in front of them. A positive number is indicated by a plus sign; however, many times a positive number will not have any sign at all. Thus, a number with no sign is always considered to be a positive number and a number is never considered to be negative unless it has a minus sign. Generally, increases and gains, directions to the right and upward, are considered to be positive (+). Losses and decreases, directions to the left and downward are written as negative (—).

Since your work in electronics involves these signed numbers so often, you must be very familiar with them. You will have to be able to add and subtract them from each other as well as be familiar with multiplying and dividing them. In this section of the lesson you will learn how to perform these basic operations with signed numbers.

Addition and Subtraction

Probably the best way to gain an understanding of positive and negative numbers is to represent them on a graph as shown in Fig. 2-13. As you can see, there is a reference point or zero

mark at the center of the scale with the positive numbers extending to the right and the negative numbers to the left. A scale of numbers like this is very handy for showing both addition and subtraction of signed numbers.

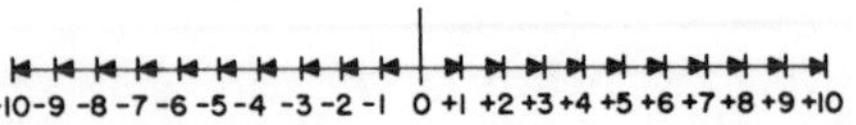

-10 -9 -8 -7 -6 -5 -4 -3 -2 -1 0 +1 +2 +3 +4 +5 +6 +7 +8 +9 +10

Fig. 2-13. Graph showing arrangement of positive and negative numbers.

For example, if we want to add +3 and +5, we start at zero and count three numbers to the right which will bring us to +3. Then, we start at +3 and count five more numbers to the right, which brings us to +8, as shown by the arrows in Fig. 2-14

Thus, adding +3 and +5 gives us +8 and is just the same as the addition which we studied in basic arithmetic. Likewise, suppose we want to add —4 and —3. We can also do this graphically as shown by the arrows in Fig.2-15.Notice that we first count four units to the left of the zero because all negative numbers increase in size as we move toward the left. This brings us to —4 and then we start from —4 and count three more units to the left which brings us to —7. Thus, the sum of —4 and —3 are simply added together to give us —7.

This brings us to the first rule for dealing with signed numbers. When two or more numbers have the same sign (all positive or all negative), they

-10 -9 -8 -7 -6 -5 -4 -3 -2 -1 0 +1 +2 +3 +4 +5 +6 +7 +8 +9 +10

Fig. 2-14. Adding +3 and +5 graphically.

are said to have "like signs." The first rule for addition of signed numbers is: To add two or more numbers with like signs, find the sum of the numbers as you would in ordinary arithmetic and place the sign of the numbers added in front of this sum. Thus, the sum of —3, —5, and —7 would be —15; and the sum of +6, +8, +9, and +2 would be +25.

Now, however, since we are dealing with both positive and negative numbers, it is very unlikely that we will have to add numbers with like signs all the time. We are quite apt to have to find the sum of several numbers that do not have the same signs. For example, suppose we have to find the sum of +2 and —5. We know how to add two and five when both numbers have the same sign, but here each has a different sign. How will we handle it?

To begin with, let's start with a graph as we did for numbers with like signs. First, we start at the zero refer-

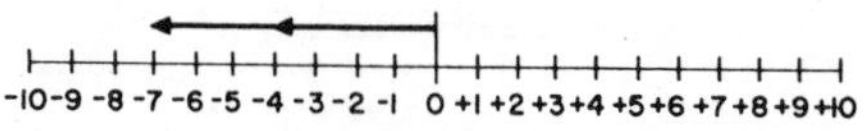

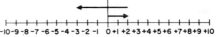

Fig. 2-15. Adding —4 and —3 graphically.

ence point and count two units to the right which brings us to +2, as shown by the short arrow in Fig.2-16.This takes care of the +2 in our addition and now we can consider the —5. We know that in order to arrive at —5 we would normally start at zero and count five units to the left. However, we are at +2 and must start at +2 instead of zero when we begin to add our —5. Therefore, instead of starting at the zero reference and counting five units to the left, we start at +2 and count five units to the left as shown by the long arrow in Fig.2-16.

This brings us to —3 on the graph. Accordingly, since we have added two arrows, one which is +2 units long and

and the other —5 units long and arrived at —3, it follows that the sum of +2 and —5 must be —3. If we look at this addition of two numbers with "unlike" signs closely, we can see that we have actually found the difference between the two numbers (5 — 2 = 3) and then used the sign of

-10-9 -8 -7 -6 -5 -4 -3 -2 -I   0 +I +2 +3+4 +5+6 +7+8+9 +I0

Fig. 2-16. Adding numbers with unlike signs graphically.

the largest number (—5) in front of our answer (—3). This is the rule for the addition of a positive number and a negative number. To state it a little more formally, we say: The sum of two signed numbers with unlike signs is equal to the difference between the two numbers, preceded by the sign of the largest number. Remember, although we find the difference of the two numbers, this is not subtraction. It is the addition of numbers with unlike signs.

Here are a few examples of the addition of signed numbers following the two rules which we have learned. Try them and see if you get the same answers that we do.

—7	—9	+10	—63	+½	—.25
—8	+7	— 6	+46	—¼	+.05
—15	—2	+ 4	—17	+¼	—.20

	+5	6	—20
	+6	—5	+18
	+11	+1	—2

Subtraction of Signed Numbers.
When you studied basic subtraction in the earlier chapter, you asked yourself, "What number must be added to a given number to give another given number?" In other words, in subtracting 5 from 9 you asked, "What number added to 5 will give 9?" The answer is 4, because 4 + 5 is equal to 9. In subtracting signed numbers, you do exactly the same, but you have to be very careful to watch the signs.

For example, consider the problem of subtracting —4 from —9. In order to do this, we ask what number added to —4 will give us —9. Of course, there is only one number and that is —5, because —4 + (—5) is equal to —9. Therefore, —4 from —9 is equal to —5.

We can also illustrate this graphically as shown in Fig.2-17. First, we

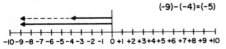

(-9)-(-4)=(-5)

Fig. 2-17. Subtracting signed numbers graphically.

draw an arrow from the zero point to —9 as shown by the long arrow. Then, we draw an arrow from zero to —4 to represent the value (—4) that we are subtracting, as shown by the short arrow. Now, if we count the units between —4 and —9 as shown by the dotted arrow, we can see that we have five units to the left which means that —5 is our answer.

Now that we have seen what happens when we subtract a positive number from a positive number (+9) — (+5) = (+4) and also what happens when a negative number is

subtracted from a negative number (—9) — (—4) = (—5), let's consider the subtraction of numbers with unlike signs. Suppose that we want to subtract —3 from +6. First, we ask ourselves, "What number added to —3 will give us +6?" If we look at this closely, we will see that +9 is the only number that can be added to —3 to give us +6 because

$$(+9) + (—3) = +6.$$

Therefore, (+6) — (—3) must be equal to +9.

Fig.2-18 shows this graphically. First, we draw an arrow from zero to +6 to represent +6. Then, we draw an arrow from zero to —3 to represent the —3. Now, we start at the —3 and count towards the right to see how many units would have to be added to —3 to give us +6. If we count off

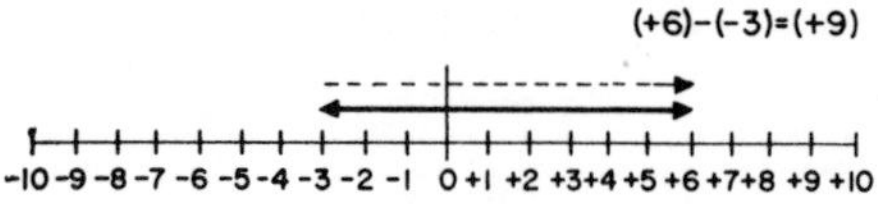

(+6)-(-3)=(+9)

Fig. 2-18. Subtracting numbers with unlike signs.

these units, we will find that there are nine of them. Since we move from left to right, the nine must be +9. Thus, we can prove that

$$(+6) — (—3) = +9.$$

Suppose, however, that we have the same numbers with the signs reversed. What is (—6) — (+3) equal to? Once again, we ask ourselves, "What number added to +3 will give —6?" Of course +3 plus —9 is the only answer. Therefore, (—6) — (+3) must be equal to —9. Graphically, we can show this as in Fig.2-19. We draw an arrow from zero to —6. Then we draw an arrow from zero to +3. Now, we can see that —6 is nine units to the left of +3, as shown by the dotted arrow. Since we go to the left, this 9 must be —9.

Now, look carefully at the examples that we have just discussed:

$$
\begin{array}{cccc}
+9 & -9 & +6 & -6 \\
-(+5) & -(-4) & -(-3) & -(+3) \\
\hline
+4 & -5 & +9 & -9
\end{array}
$$

Notice that they all have one thing in common. That is: If we change the sign in the subtrahend (the number subtracted), and then add the two numbers, we will get the proper answer. For example, consider the problem of:

$$
\begin{array}{r}
-9 \\
-(-4) \\
\hline
-5
\end{array}
$$

If we set this up and change the —4 to a +4 as

$$
\begin{array}{r}
-9 \\
+4 \\
\hline
\end{array}
$$

and then add, we will get —5 for an answer if we follow the rules for addition of signed numbers.

For this reason, the rule for subtracting signed numbers is: *To subtract signed numbers, change the sign of the number you wish to subtract (subtrahend) and then add the two numbers.* This rule will work for subtracting any two signed numbers no matter how small or large they may be. We have given some examples for you to try. Notice that the numbers and their signs are usually enclosed in

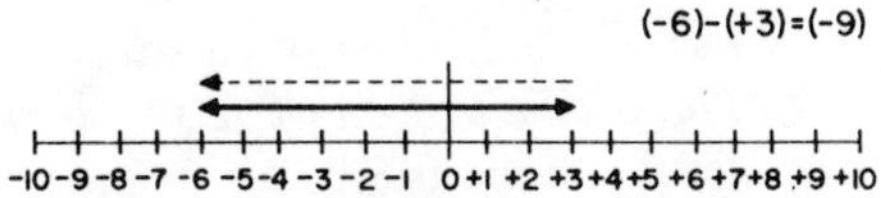

(-6)-(+3)=(-9)

Fig. 2-19. Subtracting +3 from —6 graphically.

parentheses so they will not be confused with the subtraction (—) sign.

1. $(-25) - (-15)$

$\quad = (-25) + (+15) = -10$

2. $(-18) - (+6)$

$\quad = (-18) + (-6) = -24$

3. $(+29) - (+7)$

$\quad = (+29) + (-7) = +22$

4. $\left(-\dfrac{1}{8}\right) - \left(+\dfrac{1}{16}\right)$

$\quad = \left(-\dfrac{2}{16}\right) + \left(-\dfrac{1}{16}\right) = -\dfrac{3}{16}$

5. $(+.36) - (-.05)$

$\quad = (+.36) + (+.05) = +.41$

Multiplication and Division

You learned that multiplication is the addition of a number to itself an indicated number of times. Thus, 5×6 tells us to either add 6 to itself five times or to add 5 to itself six times. The multiplication of positive and negative numbers is just the same, except that we must consider what to do about the signs. In order to do this, let's consider all the possible combinations of signs that we might have in multiplying two numbers.

There are only four possible combinations and they are as follows:

(1) $(+2) \times (+3) = ?$

(2) $(-2) \times (+3) = ?$

(3) $(+2) \times (-3) = ?$

(4) $(-2) \times (-3) = ?$

Now, you already know that the first situation is the same as saying that $+2$ is to be added three times, or:

$$(+2) + (+2) + (+2) = +6$$

Therefore,

$$(+2) \times (+3) = +6.$$

In the same manner, the second situation simply states that -2 is to be added together three times, or:

$$(-2) + (-2) + (-2) = -6$$

Therefore,

$$(-2) \times (+3) = -6.$$

From what we have seen this far, we can easily see that multiplying two positive numbers together gives us the product of the two numbers preceded by a plus sign. Also, in a similar manner, the product of a negative number multiplied by a positive number is the product of the two numbers preceded by a minus sign. Thus, we have taken care of the first two situations.

The third situation says that we must add $(+2)$ to itself -3 times. If we stop to consider this for a minute, we can see that if we add a number to itself a minus number of times, it will be just the same as subtracting the $+2$ from zero three separate times.

Therefore,

$$(+2) \times (-3) \text{ is the same}$$

as:

$$-(+2) - (+2) - (+2)$$

If we change the signs and add as we do in any subtraction of signed numbers, we have

$$(-2) + (-2) + (-2) = -6.$$

Thus, $(+2) \times (-3)$ must be equal to -6. This is the same answer we got for the second situation which was

$$(-2) \times (+3) = -6.$$

This is as it should be, because you learned in an earlier lesson that the order in which the numbers are arranged does not make any difference in multiplication. Thus, we can now say that the product of any two numbers with unlike signs is always negative.

Now, let's look at the fourth situation. Here we have $(-2) \times (-3)$ which is the same as saying -2 added to itself -3 times. Once again, adding a number to itself a minus number of times must be the same as subtraction. Therefore, we can write it as

$$-(-2) - (-2) - (-2)$$

However, once again we are subtracting signed numbers and we must change the signs and add. Consequently, we would rewrite the problem

$$(+2) + (+2) + (+2)$$

which of course equals $+6$. From this, we can say that

$$(-2) \times (-3) = +6$$

and, accordingly, the product of any two negative numbers is always positive.

Reviewing all that we have just discussed, we find that there are two simple rules for the multiplication of two signed numbers:

1. *The product of any two numbers with like signs is always positive.*

2. *The product of any two numbers with unlike signs is always negative.*

With these two rules, you can handle the multiplication of any two signed numbers.

Sometimes, you may have more than two signed numbers to multiply together. In such a case, you simply take the numbers two at a time and then multiply the products by the next number. For example:

$$(-2) \times (+3) \times (-4) = ?$$

First, take $(-2) \times (+3)$ which equals —6, then the product $(-6) \times (-4) = +24$. Therefore, $(-2) \times (+3) \times (-4) = +24$. Likewise:

$$(+2) \times (-5) \times (-7) \times (+11) = ?$$

First, $(+2) \times (-5) = (-10)$

Then, $(-10) \times (-7) \times (+11) = ?$

Now, $(-10) \times (-7) = +70$

Then, $(+70) \times (+11) = +770.$

Dividing Signed Numbers. Because division is just the reverse of multiplication, you should not have any trouble learning to divide signed numbers. Remember, when you divide one number by another, you ask, "What number, when multiplied by the divisor (the number you divide by), will equal the dividend?" In other words, if you wish to divide 30 by 5, you say, "Since five times six is equal to thirty, then $30 \div 5$ must equal 6."

In dividing signed numbers, you do the same thing except that you must be careful to obtain the proper sign for the quotient. Once again, let's consider all the possible combinations of signs that we might have in dividing one number by another. There can be only four combinations as follows:

(1) $(+30) \div (+6) = ?$

(2) $(-30) \div (+6) = ?$

(3) $(+30) \div (-6) = ?$

(4) $(-30) \div (-6) = ?$

Because division is the opposite of multiplication, we must have the following:

(1) $(+30) \div (+6) = +5$ because $(+5) \times (+6) = +30$

(2) $(-30) \div (+6) = -5$ because $(-5) \times (+6) = -30$

(3) $(+30) \div (-6) = -5$ because $(-5) \times (-6) = +30$

(4) $(-30) \div (-6) = +5$ because $(+5) \times (-6) = -30$

Therefore, our two rules for division of signed numbers are as follows:

1. *If both numbers have like signs, the quotient is always positive.*

2. *If the numbers have unlike signs, the quotient is always negative.*

This is all you need to know in order to handle the division of any two signed numbers.

Expansion and Roots

Let's consider the effect of signs on numbers with exponents or roots. You have already learned that the square of a number is the product of a number that is multiplied by itself. You also learned that you can use a small number "2" written above and to the right of a number to indicate that it is to be squared. Thus, 13^2 means 13×13, which is 169 and we call the small "2" above the 13 an exponent.

When we use 2 as an exponent to indicate the operation of squaring a number, we sometimes say that it means raising the number to its second power.

Just as we can raise a number to its second power by multiplying it by itself, we can also raise numbers to other powers. For example, 13^3 means that the number is to be raised to its third power, or $13 \times 13 \times 13$, which equals 169×13 or 2197. In this case, the exponent is a 3 and indicates that the number must be raised to its third power. In the case of the third power of a number, we have a special name for the operation just as we do for the second power (square). For the third power, we call it cubing a number, or finding the cube of a number.

Of course, we can raise a number to any power that we desire, simply by multiplying it by itself the proper number of times. In each case, the exponent indicates the power to which the number must be raised. Thus, 23^4 means $23 \times 23 \times 23 \times 23$, and 17^6 means $17 \times 17 \times 17 \times 17 \times 17 \times 17$. However, beyond the third power (cube) we have no special names because the operation is not common enough. We simply say the "fourth power of the number" or the "sixth power" or whatever power the exponent may indicate.

If a number has a sign in front of it, we proceed just as we would in multiplying any series of signed numbers. For example, $(-3)^2$ would be

$$(-3) \times (-3) = +9.$$

$(-3)^3$ would be

$$(-3) \times (-3) \times (-3)$$
$$= (+9) \times (-3)$$

$$= -27$$

Likewise, $(-2)^4$ would be

$$(-2) \times (-2) \times (-2) \times (-2)$$
$$= (+4) \times (-2) \times (-2)$$
$$= (-8) \times (-2)$$
$$= +16$$

It is interesting to notice that a negative number squared is always a positive product, while a negative number cubed always gives a negative product. This is true because any two negative numbers multiplied always give a positive product and any three negative numbers multiplied always give a negative product. With a negative number, any even-numbered exponent such as 4, 8, 28, or 32 always gives a positive product and any odd-numbered exponent gives a negative product.

Just as a number can be raised to any power, every number has an infinite number of roots. You learned earlier in this lesson what is meant by the square root of a number and that this operation is indicated by the use of the radical sign $\sqrt{}$. Therefore, you know that if $(13)^2 = 13 \times 13$ or 169, that $\sqrt{169}$ is equal to 13. However, you also learned that $-13^2 = (-13) \times (-13)$ which is also 169. Therefore, we must have two possible square roots of 169, either $+13$, or -13. In fact, any positive square has two possible square roots: a positive root or a negative root. If there is ever any question as to the sign of a square root, we write the root and use both signs. Thus, we would indicate the square root of 169 as ± 13. We read this as "plus or minus 13."

The symbol for square root is, of course, the radical sign $\sqrt{}$. However, the same basic sign is used to indicate the root of any number, except that we use an "index" number in the notch of the sign to indicate the particular root. Thus, $\sqrt[3]{27}$ means the cube root of 27 which is 3 because $3 \times 3 \times 3$ equals 27. Likewise, $\sqrt[4]{16}$ means that we are to find the fourth root of 16 which is 2 because $2 \times 2 \times 2 \times 2 = 16$. Of course the square, or second root, of any number really should be indicated with an index of 2 in the radical sign as $\sqrt[2]{4}$. However, in square root it is common practice not to write in the index so we just use the radical sign by itself. Thus, a radical sign with no index always indicates square or second root and any other desired root must be indicated by using the proper index.

Just as the root of any positive square may be either positive or negative, the even-numbered roots of any number raised to a power may also be either positive or negative. In other words, $\sqrt[4]{16}$ may be either $\pm$ because either $(-2)^4$ or $(+2)^4$ is equal to $+16$. Cube roots, however, or any other odd-numbered roots will be positive or negative depending on the sign of the number. Thus, $\sqrt[3]{27}$ must be $+3$ because $(+3) \times (+3) \times (+3)$ equals 27. $(-3) \times (-3) \times (-3)$ can never equal $+27$; it must always equal -27. Therefore, $\sqrt[3]{-27}$ equals -3 and the cube root of any negative number must be equal to a minus number. Other odd-numbered roots follow

the same rule. For example, $\sqrt[5]{32}$ always equals $+2$ because

$$(+2) \times (+2) \times (+2) \times (+2) \times (+2)$$
$$= +32$$

while

$$(-2) \times (-2) \times (-2) \times (-2) \times (-2)$$
$$= -32$$

You will notice that we have not mentioned how to take the square root of a negative number. This is because it seems impossible to obtain the square root of a negative number; as far as we know now, there is no number multiplied by itself which can give a negative square. A negative number squared is always positive, and a positive number squared is also always positive. $+2 \times (-2)$ is not a square because we are not multiplying the same number by itself if we consider the signs. We will learn more about this later in the book . For now we have all we need to know about signed numbers and their exponents and roots.

Before you leave this section, try the following examples to make sure that you have learned to handle signed numbers correctly.

Problems:

(1) Add $-72, +13, -12, +57, +17, -6$.

(2) Subtract -42 from -69.

(3) Subtract $+42$ from -69.

(4) Multiply $-3, +7, -12, -7, +4$.

(5) Divide $+50.778$ by -23.4.

Answers: (1) -3. (2) -27.
(3) -111. (4) -7056. (5) -2.17.

2-5. Vectors

You know that an ac voltage actually consists of a series of different instantaneous values of voltage and that these different voltages all occur at specified times in the ac cycle. Also, the current forced through a complete electrical circuit by an ac voltage was likewise made up of a series of instantaneous values of current that occurred at specified time in the cycle. However, one of the most important factors that we must consider in dealing with ac circuits is that these peak ac voltages and peak ac currents do not necessarily occur at the same instants of time.

In your study of coils, you found that the current actually lags the voltage by 90° in a purely inductive circuit. Conversely, you discovered that in a purely capacitive circuit, the current leads the voltage by 90°. In fact, the only time that the instantaneous values of the current and voltage can be in phase with each other throughout the entire circuit is in a purely resistive circuit. Actually, most practical circuits contain some combination of resistance, inductance, and capacitance and the phase relationship between the ac current and voltage is a result of the combined action of these effects.

Because of this difference in phase between the voltage and current in ac circuits, we cannot use ordinary arithmetic in our circuit calculations. In ordinary arithmetic, we have only simple numbers or "scalors," as they are sometimes called, which we can use. The numbers or scalors can only indicate the size or the magnitude of the voltage or current quantities. They cannot in any way that we know of indicate the time difference or phase angle which we must also consider. However, through the use of what we call "vectors" and vector arithmetic, we can indicate both the size of the quantities and the times at which they occur. Actually, the vectors used in ac circuit calculations are not vectors at all but are phasors. However, they are similar to vectors and are usually called vectors so we will use the name also. By using these so-called vectors, we are able to perform any ac circuit calculation quite simply and accurately.

In this section of the chapter, you will learn about vectors and how they can

Fig. 2-20. Vectors showing magnitude and direction.

be used in ac circuit calculations. You will apply many of the rules of ordinary arithmetic, square root, signed numbers, and even some ratio and proportion in working with vectors. Vectors are extremely important in work with ac, because without vectors, any of the methods for solving ac circuit calculations would be useless. They are all based on vector principles and you will discover later in the course that many of the explanations for circuit characteristics are made easier to understand through the use of simple vectors.

Definition of a Vector

A vector is simply a straight line having a definite length and direction. Fig.2-20 shows several different vectors, each with a certain length and direction. Although these vectors do not represent any particular values or functions, they are all true vectors and could be used for any number of purposes. Notice that each vector starts at a certain point and ends a certain distance away in a specific direction. The starting point of any vector is usually represented by a dot and is called the "tail" of the vector. The ending point of the vector is represented by an arrowhead and is called the "head" of the vector.

Remember, the distance between the head and tail of the vector is used to indicate or designate the magnitude of a quantity. The direction of the vector from a common reference point or line represents the second factor which we must consider. This second factor may be either "direction" or "time." For example, the vectors in Fig.2-21 represent the flight of an airplane. They are drawn so that vector A represents a 125-mile flight to the south, while vector B represents a 150-mile flight to the east. The tail of Vector A shows where the airplane started, and the head of Vector B shows where the flight ended. The fact that the tail of Vector B starts from the head of Vector A tells us that the airplane flew south first and then east. The arrow in the diagram shows us where north is and becomes the reference line from which the direction of the vectors may

be determined. The notation "Scale: $\frac{1}{4}'' = 25$ mi." tells how far the airplane traveled in each direction because each quarter-inch of vector length is equal to 25 miles of travel. Thus, the vector diagram gives an accurate and descriptive picture of where the airplane went. As you can

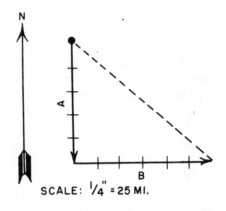

SCALE: $\frac{1}{4}'' = 25$ MI.

Fig. 2-21. Use of vectors to show results of motion.

see, this is much more valuable than simply saying that the airplane flew 275 miles.

Another thing about a vector diagram is that it can show how far the airplane actually went from the starting point. Notice in Fig.2-21 that, even though the airplane actually flew 275 miles, it did not end its flight 275 miles from the starting point. The head of Vector B is not 275 miles away from the tail of Vector A. Since the diagram is drawn to scale, you can measure this distance with a ruler as shown by the dotted line in Fig.2-21. If you do this carefully, you will find that it is just under 2 inches from the tail of A to

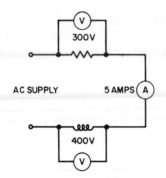

Fig. 2-22. Ac circuit containing resistance and inductance.

the head of B. Since each quarter-inch on the diagram equals 25 miles, you know that the airplane ended its flight less than 200 miles from the starting point even though it flew 275 miles to get there.

Further, by comparing the direction of this dotted line with the reference arrow, you can determine the direction of the end of its flight from the starting point. If you do this, you can see that the flight ended approximately southeast of the starting point. Therefore, the vector diagram gives a complete picture of the airplane's flight as well as giving its progress away from the starting point.

Vectors in Electronics. In electronics work, we do not use vectors often to indicate motion. Instead, we use the direction of vectors to indicate the time of an occurrence. For example, suppose that we have a series circuit containing a coil and a resistor as shown in Fig. 2-22. The ammeter in the circuit shows that there is an ac current of 5 amps flowing through the circuit and we know that the current in a series circuit is the same through any part of the circuit. Therefore, there is a current of 5 amps through the coil.

Now, the voltmeter across the re-

sistor indicates 300 volts and the one across the coil indicates 400 volts. You know from your studies of ac circuits that these voltages across the coil and resistor do not occur at exactly the same instant of time. For example, if we were to draw a sine-wave diagram of the ac current through the circuit, we might have a wave shape like the solid line in Fig. 2-23A. This sine wave rises from zero to a maximum of such a value that the effective value of the alternating current is 5 amperes. Using this ac current sine wave as a reference point

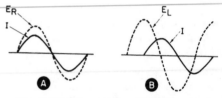

Fig. 2-23. Sine waves of voltage and current in (A) resistor, (B) coil.

for time and comparing the rise and fall of the voltage sine waves with it, we can actually see that the two voltages do not occur at the same instant.

We know that in a purely resistive circuit the current and voltage actually rise and fall together. We say that they are in phase. Therefore, the voltage across the resistor, E_R, must rise and fall in such a way that it will be maximum when the current is maximum. Further, the maximum value of this ac voltage must be large enough so that its effective value will be 300 volts as measured by the voltmeter. Accordingly, if we were to draw a voltage sine wave for the voltage E_R using the current sine wave as a time reference, we would have a wave shape like that shown by the dotted line in Fig.

2-23A.

On the other hand, the current and the voltage do not rise and fall together as far as the coil is concerned. The coil current actually lags the coil voltage by 90°. Therefore, we would draw their respective sine waves 90° out of phase, as shown in Fig. 2-23B where the solid line, I, represents the coil current and the dotted line, E_L, represents the coil voltage. The current sine wave is the same sine wave that we used in Fig. 2-23A and occurs at exactly the same instant. The current is common throughout the circuit. The voltage wave, E_L, has a maximum value necessary to produce the effective value of 400 volts, as indicated by the voltmeter in Fig. 2-22.

Since the current sine waves in Fig. 2-23A and 2-23B represent the same current at the same instant of time, we can combine the two drawings as shown in Fig. 2-24. Here the one current sine wave, I, represents the common circuit current through both the coil and the resistor. The voltage wave, E_R, represents the sine-wave voltage that gives the effective value of 300 volts across the resistor and the voltage wave, E_L, represents the sine wave that produces the effective value of 400 volts across the coil. It is easy to see from this drawing that the two voltages do not rise and fall together. They are 90° out of phase.

Through the use of vectors, we are able to represent this difference in "time" between the two voltages and between the current and the coil voltage much more simply than by using sine waves. We do this by means of a rotating vector. As the vector rotates through 360°, the projection from the end of the vector traces out a sine

curve. Looking at the current waveform in Fig. 2-23A, we see that the current is zero at the start of the cycle. This is represented by the vector shown in Fig. 2-25A. One-quarter of a cycle later the current has reached its peak positive value. This is represented by rotating the vector 90° (one-quarter of a turn) to the position shown in Fig. 2-25B. At the end of another quarter-cycle, the current waveform will have gone through one-half cycle, and will be back to zero. This is represented by the vector shown in Fig. 2-25C. Here the vector has rotated through 180° (one-half turn).

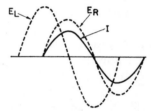

Fig. 2-24. Sine waves showing E_R lagging E_L.

The vector in Fig. 2-25D represents the current waveform one-quarter cycle later when the current is at its peak negative value and the vector in Fig. 2-25E represents the current at the end of one complete cycle. Here the vector has rotated through 360° (one complete turn) and is back at the starting point.

Notice that we rotated the vector in Fig. 2-25 in a counterclockwise direction. Be sure to remember the direction of rotation; you'll need to know this to understand the vector diagrams in the rest of this lesson and in later lessons.

Now that you've seen how we use a rotating vector to show the current phase throughout a cycle, let's see how

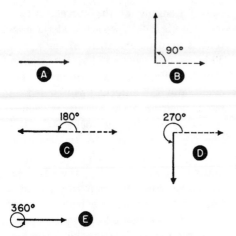

Fig. 2-25. A rotating vector showing one complete ac cycle.

tween the voltage across the coil and the current through it. Let's start with the current vector at zero representing the start of the current cycle as shown in Fig. 2-27A. This vector is the same as the current vector in Fig. 2-25A. Now, to draw the vector representing the voltage across the coil, we must consider the phase relationship. You will remember that the voltage across a coil leads the current by 90°. This is shown in Fig. 2-23B. Thus if the current vector is drawn at zero, we must

vectors can be used to show the phase relationship between the voltage and current across the resistor in Fig. 2-22 throughout a cycle.

At the start of the cycle at 0°, E_R and I are in phase. We show the phase relationship by drawing the two vectors E_R and I as shown in Fig. 2-26A. Notice that the vectors are drawn superimposed on each other which is as it should be because at the start of the cycle both the voltage and current are zero. One-quarter cycle later the voltage and current have reached their maximum positive values. This is shown by the vectors in Fig. 2-26B Again the vectors are superimposed because the voltage and current are in phase—they are both at their maximum values at the same instant, one-quarter cycle or 90° after they were both zero. In Fig. 2-26C we have shown the vectors at the end of one-half cycle, in Fig. 2-26D at the end of three-quarters of a cycle and in Fig. 2-26E at the end of a complete cycle.

Now, let's see how vectors can be used to show the phase relation be-

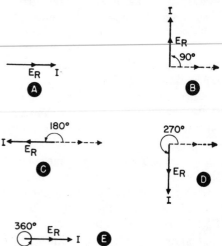

Fig. 2-26. Vector diagrams showing phase relationship between voltage across and current through resistor without a complete cycle.

advance the voltage vector 90° (rotate it counterclockwise) as shown in Fig. 2-27B. Thus, the vectors in Fig. 2-27B show the phase of the voltage and current at the start of the current cycle.

One-quarter of a cycle later, both vectors will have rotated through 90° shown in Fig. 2-27C. At that point the current is at its peak positive value and the voltage has dropped to zero as shown in Fig. 2-23. The vector diagram indicates this condition. A quarter cycle later, when the current has gone through one-half cycle, the current will be zero again and the voltage will be at its peak negative value. This is shown in Fig. 2-23 and by means of vectors in Fig. 2-27D. Fig. 2-27E shows the phases one-quarter cycle later when the voltage is back to zero and the current is at its peak negative value. Fig.2-27F shows the voltage and current vectors at the end of a complete cycle.

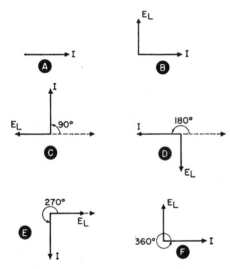

Fig. 2-27. Vector diagrams showing phasing relationship between voltage across and current through coil throughout a complete cycle.

Notice that throughout the illustrations in both Figs.2-26 and 2-27, the phase relations remain constant. Fig. 2-26 shows the resistor voltage and current in phase through the entire cycle. Fig. 2-27 shows the coil voltage leading the current by 90° through the entire cycle.

In Fig.2-24, we have shown the current, coil voltage, and resistor voltage on the same diagram. It does not matter whether we start working with the current, coil voltage, or resistor voltage in constructing our diagram as long as we show the correct phase relationship. However, in circuits of this type, the usual practice is to start by drawing the current vector I, as shown in Fig.2-28A. Let's draw the vector to represent zero current at the start of the current cycle. We can draw the current vector any convenient length because we are not going to use it for anything other than a reference vector.

Now, let's draw a vector to represent the voltage across the resistor. In Fig. 2-22 we see that the voltage is 300 volts. Let's draw the vector to scale so the length of the vector represents 300 volts. If we use a scale of $\frac{1}{2}'' =$ 100 volts then the vector should be $1\frac{1}{2}''$ long. Since the voltage across the resistor is in phase with the current the voltage vector is drawn superimposed on the current vector, as shown in Fig. 2-28B.

To draw the vector representing the coil voltage first we note from Fig.2-22 that the voltage is 400 volts. Therefore, using the scale of $\frac{1}{2}'' = 100$ volts, the vector should be 2″ long. Since the coil voltage leads the current by 90°, we draw this vector as shown in Fig.2-28C. Now we have a vector diagram showing the phase relationship between the current and the two voltages at the start of the current cycle. As a matter of fact, this diagram shows the phase differences between the coil voltage, the resistor voltage, and the current throughout the entire cycle because, as we saw from Figs.2-26 and 2-27, these relation-

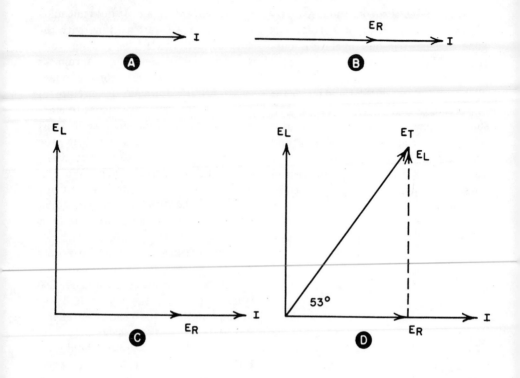

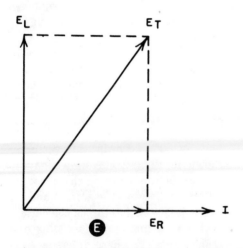

Fig. 2-28. Vector addition of resistor and coil voltages.

ships did not change. The coil voltage always leads the resistor voltage and the current by 90°.

We can use the vector diagram of Fig. 2-28C to determine the total voltage across the coil and the resistor. This is equal to the source voltage in Fig. 2-22. We do this by adding the vector representing the coil voltage to the vector representing the resistor voltage. Since we have drawn these vectors to scale, we should be able to scale the resulting vector to get the total voltage.

There are two ways of making this addition. The first way is to place the coil voltage vector at the end of the resistor voltage vector like we did to determine how far the plane traveled in Fig. 2-21. This addition is shown in Fig. 2-28D. Notice the resultant vector, E_T, which represents the total voltage leads the current by a value somewhat less than 90°. This is what we might expect. In a circuit with pure resistance, the voltage and current will be in phase—in other words the phase difference is 0°. In a circuit with pure inductance, the voltage leads the current by 90°. Thus, in a circuit with both resistance and inductance, we would expect both to influence the phase relation between the voltage and current so that the phase difference will be somewhere between 0° and 90°. If you construct the diagram carefully and measure the angle between E_T and I, you will find that it is about 53°.

To determine the amplitude of E_T, measure the length of the vector and you will find it is 2½" long. Since the scale used in constructing the diagram is ½" = 100 volts, the amplitude of E_T must be 500 volts.

The other method of adding the two vectors is shown in Fig. 2-28E. Here a dotted line is drawn from the end of vector E_R parallel to vector E_L. A second dotted line is drawn from the end of vector E_L parallel to E_R. The point where the two dotted lines meet locates the end of vector E_T and the angle between it and vector I will be the same when the vector is obtained with this method as it is using the previously discussed method.

To really see the advantage of the vector method of representing these voltages, look at Fig. 2-29. Fig. 2-29A shows the two voltages and the current and Fig. 2-29B shows how these sine waves can be added to get the total voltage. To do this, many instantaneous values must be added to enable you to plot the curve of E_T. This is tedious and, in addition, is not nearly as easy to evaluate as Fig. 2-28D or Fig. 2-28E.

You might wonder why we started our construction of Fig. 2-28 by putting I in the 0° position. We did this simply because it was convenient to do so. We could actually put I in any position and, as long as we keep the correct position between I, E_R, and E_L, the value of E_T, and the phase angle between it and I will be the same.

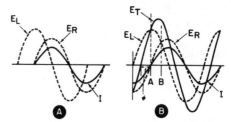

Fig. 2-29. Adding sine waves to obtain voltage total, E_T.

Vector Arithmetic

Now that we have seen what vectors are and how they can be used in electronics to represent size and phase or time for ac circuit calculations, let's learn more about handling them.

Actually, the rules for working with vectors are quite simple and are similar to any arithmetic that involves

Fig. 2-30. Adding in phase vectors.

signed numbers. The most important differences are in learning to deal with the angles and establishing the qualifications for lead and lag.

To begin with, we have seen that any vector diagram must have a reference line so that the directions of the individual vectors can be established in accordance with a common reference for comparison. The reference we used in the preceding example was the current. The best type of reference to use when learning about vectors is a scale similar to one we used when learning to deal with positive and negative numbers. In Fig. 2-30, we have drawn such a scale with a center reference point. All positive values extend to the right of the center and all negative values extend to the left.

Now suppose that we have two quantities representing the same direction or instant of time: one +5 units long and the other +3 units long. In order to add them vectorially, we simply lay them out along the reference line to scale and in the same direction with the head of one starting at the tail of the other, as shown in Fig. 2-30. Vector A starts at the reference point, 0, and continues for five units. Vector B starts at the head of Vector A and continues along the reference for three units. To add the two vectors, we simply draw a new

vector, C, from the tail of A to the head of B. Since A and B both point in the same direction, this new vector lies along the same line as A and B and is +8 units long. Therefore, the sum of two vectors extending in the same direction is a new vector equal to the combined length of the two vectors and pointing in the same direction.

In Fig. 2-31, we have added two vectors that point in the same direction, but both of them are negative so their direction is just opposite to those in Fig. 2-30. Therefore, their sum is a new vector that is —6 units long plus —3 units long or —9 units long. Thus, as long as two or more vectors point in the same direction, regardless of what that direction is, their sum is a new vector pointing in that direction that is equal to the combined length of the individual vectors.

Another problem in working with vectors is one where the vectors point in exactly opposite directions. This will often come up when two voltages or other circuit quantities are exactly 180° out of phase. For example, suppose we have two opposing voltages working against each other in an ac circuit. One of these has a peak value of 90 volts and the other a peak of 40 volts. The two are exactly out of phase at all times, so we can lay them out vectorially, as shown in Fig. 2-32, by

Fig. 2-31. Adding in phase vectors.

using a scale of 1 unit equals 10 volts. Notice that since the two are 180° out of phase, one vector points from the reference point 0, along the reference line in one direction while the other starts at the reference point and extends in the opposite direction.

It does not make any difference which vector we use for which direction in this particular case. We know that each one changes sign during every cycle and we are just stopping the action at a particular time. No matter what we get for an answer, its sign will automatically change during the next alternation because we are working with ac. The thing that really does matter is that both vectors represent the same instant of time so that the 180° phase difference is represented by the vector directions.

To add these two vectors, we must do the same thing that we do in the other vector additions. We place the tail of one vector against the head of the other vector, being careful not to change the direction or length of the vector that we relocate. In this problem, we have drawn a dotted line from the head of the 90-volt vector B that is exactly the same length and that points in the same direction as the 40-volt vector A. Notice· that we have drawn the dotted line (B) slightly above the reference line so that we can see it better. Now, we complete our addition by drawing a new vector, C, from the tail of the 90-volt vector. This new vector is 5 units or 50 volts

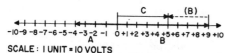

SCALE : I UNIT = IO VOLTS

Fig. 2-32. Adding vectors 180° out of phase.

long and points in the direction of the longest vector. Thus, we can see that

the vector sum of the two out-of-phase voltages is a new vector extending from the tail of one vector to the head of the other after they have been properly joined head to tail for addition.

Representing Lead or Lag. As you can see, all the vector addition that we have considered so far follows the same basic pattern. We lay the vectors out to their proper scale length and orient them in their proper direction. Then, we lay them head to tail, being careful not to alter either their length or direction in the process, and draw a resultant vector between the tail of the first vector and the head of the last to represent their sum. The length of this resultant represents the magnitude of the vector sum, and its direction in relation to the reference line indicates the phase or time of the resultant quantity.

All vector computation follows these same basic rules. However, the problems that we have considered so far have dealt with vectors that are exactly in phase or exactly 180° out of phase. As you know, many of our problems in electronics deal with reactance calculations where the phase shift will be only 90°. Also, this reactance phase shift may be either 90° lagging, in the case of capacitance, or it may be 90° leading in problems dealing with inductance. Accordingly, we must now consider what to do about laying out and computing vectors that are affected by reactance.

To do this, let's go back to our basic idea of a phasor. A phasor is a rotating vector. We have shown that this vector rotates counterclockwise. Thus, if we start a vector at 0°, as in Fig. 2-33A, and rotate it 90° to represent

one-quarter of a cycle, it will move to
the position shown in Fig.2-33B The
vector at B has passed through ¼
cycle more than the one at A. Thus,
vector B is leading vector A by 90°.
The vector diagram in Fig.2-33C shows
how the voltage leads the current by
90° in a coil.

In Fig.2-34 we have shown an example of a lagging voltage. We started
with our current vector at A and then
drew a second vector 90° behind it at
B. Vector B is following vector A by
90°. A complete vector diagram showing how the voltage lags the current
in a capacitor is shown in Fig.2-34C.

You might think that, since the two
vectors are rotating counterclockwise,
the voltage vector is leading the current by 270°. Since the voltage is lagging one current cycle by 90°, it will
indeed be leading the following current cycle by 270°. However, it is the
90° phase difference we are interested
in.

Now it is fairly easy to see that, if
we consider our discussions of vectors
up to this point, we can call the right-
hand end of the scale the "in phase
reference line." Likewise, the end of
the horizontal line extending to the
left of center towards 180° can be
called the "180° out of phase reference
line." If we do this, all vectors parallel
to the horizontal reference and pointing right will be in-phase vectors, and
those pointing toward the left will be
180° out of phase. Thus, our horizontal
line divided in the center in this way
can represent a phase shift or time
lag of 180° depending on whether we
point our vectors from the center to
the right towards zero or towards the
left to 180°.

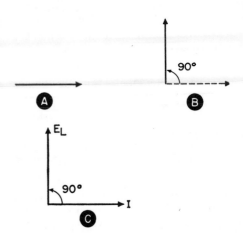

Fig. 2-33. Vector diagrams showing a 90°
phase shift where the voltage leads the
current.

The vertical line represents a phase
shift of 90°. Since our vector rotates
counterclockwise, the vector representing the voltage in Fig.2-33C is leading the current vector by 90°. It's not
always necessary or even advisable to
place the current vector at 0°. However, regardless of how we start the
diagram and what we place on the 0°
axis, all voltages or current leading
the reference value are shown rotated
in a counterclockwise direction and

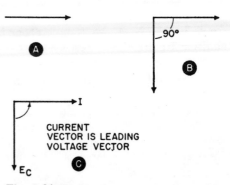

CURRENT
VECTOR IS LEADING
VOLTAGE VECTOR

Fig. 2-34. Vector diagrams showing a 90°
phase shift where the voltage lags the
current.

voltages or current lagging the reference value in a clockwise direction. Any voltage.or current can be taken as our reference value, but in most series circuits it is easiest to use the current as a reference.

Sometimes we may want to construct an impedance diagram of resistance and inductive or capacitive reactance. You might wonder if one of these reactive elements should be drawn above or below the reference line. The rule is to draw inductive reactance above and capacitive reactance below. Inductive reactance is considered positive and capacitive reactance negative. You'll see later when you study the J-operator that this is necessary so that the currents have the correct phase. Thus, if we consider our reference line extending from the center right toward 0° as our current reference line in ac circuit problems, our inductive reactance (voltage leading current) values will go above the reference and our capacitive reactance (voltage lagging current) values will go below the reference. Another thing that will help you to remember this rule is to notice that vectors are always considered to rotate counterclockwise from zero.

Also notice that the 90° lead point from 0° can also be considered to lag the 0° reference by 270°. It doesn't make any particular difference which way you think of it. Either way, it amounts to the same thing. The important thing is to make sure that when you construct a scale like this for a series circuit and use the current as the reference vector, you should remember:

1. Right from center: in phase, I, R,

or E_R.

2. Left from center: 180° out of phase.

3. Straight up from center: 90° lead, X_L or E_L.

4. Straight down from center: 90° lag, X_C or E_C.

Vector Calculations

Now that we have discussed some of the basic rules and principles for laying out vectors and computing with them, we need to gain a little practice to become thoroughly familiar with this type of computation. We considered a problem dealing with a coil and a resistor a little earlier. Now, let's consider a circuit containing a resistor and capacitor in series like the one shown in Fig. 2-35A. In this circuit we are told the capacitor voltage and the resistor voltage and asked to find the supply voltage, E_T, and the phase angle, θ. (θ is the Greek letter theta. It and ϕ, the Greek letter phi, pronounced "fee," are often used to represent a phase angle.)

In order to do this, we first lay out the current vector as the reference vector because the current in the circuit, I, is the same in all parts of the circuit. Using the horizontal line extending to the right toward 0° to represent the current as we have learned to do completes our preliminary setup for the problem as shown in Fig. 2-35B. Notice that we do not have the value of this current. You see, we don't need it to work the problem. We are only using I as a reference line from which to indicate our voltage-phase relationships. Its value is not important, only its position as the common reference concerns us here.

Using the scale of $\frac{1}{2}'' = 100$V, we can lay out the voltage vector E_R to scale along the reference line to show that the voltage across the resistor is in phase with the current through it. We call this voltage the in-phase component of the total volt-age. The vector diagram at this stage is shown in Fig. 2-35C. Then, we can lay out the voltage vector, E_c, to scale $90°$ behind the reference current because I will be leading it by $90°$. The diagram at this point is shown in Fig. 2-35D. To add these two vectors, we

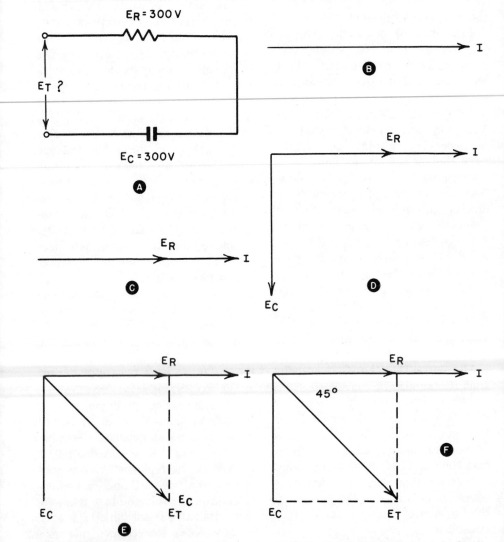

Fig. 2-35. Vector addition of the voltage E_R and E_C in the circuit at A shown in detail.

can move one of them so that the two are head to tail as shown by the dotted vector (E_C) in Fig. 2-35E and then draw in E_T, the total voltage. Notice that we are careful to construct the dotted vector (E_C) so that its length and direction are not changed. We can also get E_T by drawing a line parallel to E_R from the end of E_C and a second line parallel to E_C from the end of E_R. Where the two lines meet locates the end of E_T as shown in Fig. 2-35F.

Now, we can draw the resultant vector, E_T, that represents the vector sum of the two quantities. If we measure E_T carefully and our other vectors are to scale, we will find that E_T is $2\frac{1}{8}''$ long. From our scale, we know that each $\frac{1}{2}''$ of E_T is equal to 100V. Therefore, we can quickly compute that $1''$ must equal 200 volts, and therefore $2''$ must be equal to 400 volts. Now, $\frac{1}{8}''$ is equal to $\frac{1}{4}$ of 100 or 25 volts. Accordingly, our E_T vector must equal 400 + 25 or 425 volts.

We are also asked to find the phase angle, θ, for our supply voltage. We will have to do this by measurement with a protractor which will measure angles. If we do this, we will find that the angle between E_T and the reference, I, is 45°. As a matter of fact, we can see by estimating that E_T lies about halfway between E_C and I which are 90° apart, so E_T must be approximately 45° out of phase with the current. Thus, through the use of vectors, we have determined that E_T is 425 volts and is 45° out of phase with the current. Since E_T is below the reference I, the current must *lead* the voltage (or the voltage lags the current, whichever you prefer) by this 45°.

Before we leave this circuit, let's consider one other thing. In converting our length of E_T of $2\frac{1}{8}''$ to 425 volts,

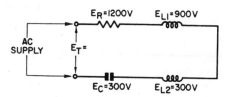

Fig. 2-36. Finding E_T in a simple series ac circuit containing R, L, and C.

we went through a series of steps. Ratio and proportion would have saved us a lot of time. For example, we could have set up two ratios as follows:

$$\frac{\frac{1}{2}''}{2\frac{1}{8}''} \quad \text{and} \quad \frac{100V}{E_T}$$

Now our proportion:

$$\frac{\frac{1}{2}''}{2\frac{1}{8}''} = \frac{100V}{E_T} \quad \text{or}$$

$$\frac{\frac{1}{2}''}{\frac{17}{8}''} = \frac{100V}{E_T}$$

Now cross-multiplying, we have:

$$\frac{17}{8} \times 100 = \frac{1}{2} \times E_T$$

$$\frac{1700}{8} = \frac{E_T}{2}$$

and then.

$$8 \times E_T = 1700 \times 2$$

$$8E_T = 3400$$

$$E_T = \frac{3400}{8} = 425 \text{ volts}$$

This is just another example of a good use for ratio and proportion.

In Fig. 2-36, we have shown a more difficult problem. Here we have a resistor, two coils, and a capacitor in series with each other. Let's see how we would handle the problem of finding the total voltage for this circuit vectorially.

First, we lay out our vector reference scale and call the horizontal line from center to 0° the current reference as before. This is shown in Fig. 2-37. Then, we can draw in the voltage vector E_R superimposed on I to show the two in phase. Since E_R is 1200 volts, we used a scale of $\frac{1}{4}'' = 100$, instead of $\frac{1}{2}'' = 100$ volts as before, in order to keep the diagram a reasonable size in the book. If you try drawing this diagram you can use a scale of $\frac{1}{2}'' = 100$ volts if you wish. Then E_R would be twice as long. Next, we draw vector E_{L1} leading I by 90°. This vector represents 900 volts so, using the scale of $\frac{1}{4}'' = 100$ volts, we make it $9 \times \frac{1}{4}'' = \frac{9}{4} = 2\frac{1}{4}''$ long.

The next step is to add the vector E_{L2} to the diagram. Since this voltage

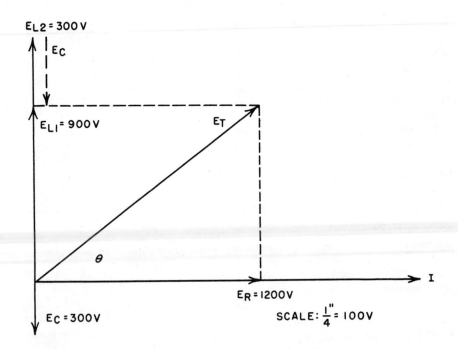

Fig. 2-37. Vector solution of multiple reactance circuit.

also leads I by 90°, we draw E_{L2} starting at the head of E_{L1} to add these two in-phase voltages. E_{L2} is made ¾″ long to represent 300 volts.

The next vector we draw is E_C. Since this represents 300 volts we know it should be ¾″ long. Also, since it represents a voltage across a capacitor, we know it will lag I by 90°. The position of this vector is shown on the diagram. Notice that it is 180° out of phase with E_{L1} and E_{L2}. We now add this vector to the sum of E_{L1} and E_{L2} following the same procedure as shown in Fig. 2-32. We move vector E_C to the head of E_{L2} as shown by the dotted line and then the head of E_C represents the total reactive voltage. We have shown E_C dotted and slightly to one side of E_{L2} so you can see it; actually it should be superimposed on E_{L2}.

To complete the vector diagram and get E_T, we draw a line parallel to vector E_R from the end of the vector representing the sum of $E_{L1} + E_{L2} + E_C$. Then we draw a second line parallel to the E_{L1} vector from the end of E_R. The point where these two lines intersect locates the end of E_T. Now we can draw vector E_T to represent the sum of our reactance and resistance vectors and carefully measure it. We find that it is exactly 3¾″ long. Now, by setting the ratios and proportion between our scale values and our measurements, we can convert our vector measurements to volts as follows:

$$\frac{\frac{1}{4}''}{3\frac{3}{4}''} = \frac{100}{E_T}$$

$$\frac{1}{4} \times E_T = 3\frac{3}{4} \times 100$$

$$\frac{E_T}{4} = \frac{15}{4} \times 100$$

$$\frac{E_T}{4} = \frac{1500}{4}$$

$$4E_T = 4 \times 1500$$

$$E_T = 1500 \text{ volts}$$

We can then determine the value of θ by measuring it: $\theta = 36\frac{1}{2}°$.

So far, in working with vectors, we have considered only the addition of vectors to find a total. We can also break down a given resultant vector to find some of its components. In other words, if we have E_T, we can find E_R and the total circuit reactance voltage. This process is important when working with parallel ac circuits, so let's see how it is done.

Suppose we are given a statement regarding the voltage of a circuit as follows: "The voltage applied to a series circuit is equal to 140 volts and it leads the current by a phase angle of 45°. What is the value of the resistance in the circuit if the current is 5 amperes?" Although this might seem difficult at first glance, it is really quite easy to solve. First, let's see what we know about the voltage.

We can see that it leads the current (or that the current lags the voltage) and, therefore, the total reactance in the circuit must be inductive. We know the phase angle is 45° and that the voltage value is 140 volts. With this information we can lay out our standard reference diagram for vector solutions and construct a vector that represents the total voltage applied. Using a scale of ¼″ = 20 volts, our total voltage vector E_T can be laid out to scale as shown in Fig. 2-38. We have drawn this vector above the reference line I at the phase angle of 45° to show that it is inductive and leads the current. Now this vector, E_T, is a resultant vector and must be made up of at least two component vectors; one resistive, the other reactive. Any vector that is not out of phase with the reference by some multiple of 90° can always be broken down into at least two components that are at right angles to each other. Because of this rule, we can separate the vector E_T into two component vectors, E_X and E_R as shown.

Doing this, we find that the reactive component of voltage in the circuit E_X is equal to 100 volts and the resistive component, E_R, is also equal to 100 volts. Now that we have the resistive voltage drop of 100 volts, it is easy to find the resistance. We know that it is a series circuit and, therefore, the current is common. Accordingly,

$$R = \frac{E_R}{I} = \frac{100}{5} = 20 \text{ ohms}$$

Thus, by breaking the vector value of applied voltage down into its two components, we are able to determine quite a lot about the circuit. You will find that this is a very valuable process in your work in electronics.

Up until now, we have been working primarily with the voltages in a circuit. We can use our vector diagrams and computation methods just as well to find the impedance of a circuit. For example, suppose we wanted to find the total impedance of the circuit shown in Fig. 2-39A. We would simply lay out our vector diagram and add

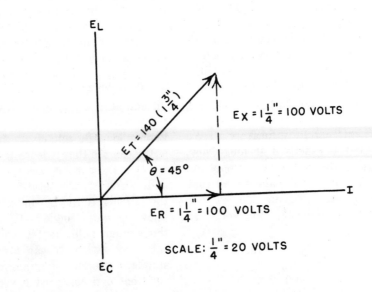

Fig. 2-38. Breaking a vector down into two components.

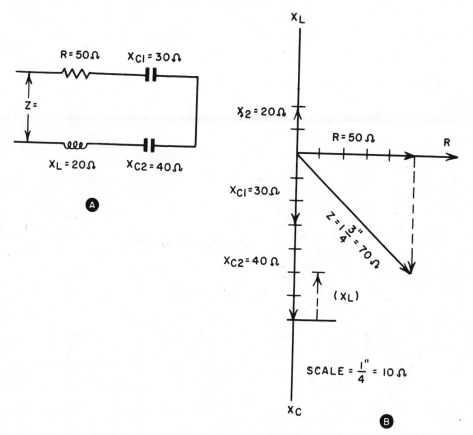

Fig. 2-39. Solving for impedance with vectors.

the component vectors just as we did when we were working with voltage as shown in Fig. 2-39B. Notice that we use R as the reference line because it represents the in-phase component of the impedance Z. You should have no trouble following the solution of this simple vectorial computation.

Pythagorean Theorem for Vector Solutions

You will remember that earlier in the chapter we said we could use formulas instead of vectors for ac circuit solutions. One of the most familiar is the formula for impedance which is

$$Z = \sqrt{R^2 + X^2}$$

This formula is really just a mathematical solution of a vector diagram. By using it, we involve ourselves in the problem of finding square root, but it is often much more desirable and usually more accurate than solving vectors by measurement. In measuring vectors for the solution of vector diagrams, we need to take care in laying

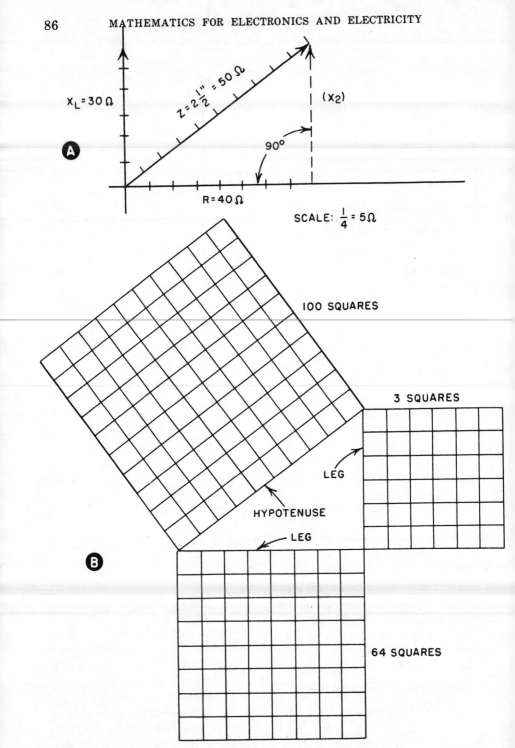

Fig. 2-40. The derivation of the Pythagorean Theorem.

out the diagrams, and measuring the angles and lengths of the vectors.

In working with the formulas, we are given a method of solving for the lengths of the vectors, but not the angles. Since the formula allows us to use a mathematical solution for the length of the vectors in vector diagrams, it eliminates the need for the accuracy of layout and measurement. Let's look at a typical vector diagram and see how it is possible to consider the formula $Z = \sqrt{R^2 + X^2}$ as the mathematical solution.

In Fig. 2-40A, we have laid out the solution of a typical vector diagram for finding the impedance of an ac circuit. The vector representing R, the dotted vector representing X_L, and the resultant vector Z representing the impedance of the circuit form a three-sided, completely enclosed figure. Such a three-sided figure, as you probably know, is called a triangle. However, this is a special type of triangle, called a right triangle. Any triangle that contains one angle that is equal to $90°$, such as the angle between vectors X_2 and R, is a right triangle, no matter what the other two angles or the lengths of the sides may be. Any triangles involved in vector solutions for ac circuits will also be right triangles because two of the sides must be $90°$ displaced from each other.

It is important that you realize this and understand it, since many of the laws for ac circuit solutions depend on this fact. In Fig. 2-40B, we have drawn the triangle of Fig. 2-40A, leaving out the arrowheads and values so that we can show you a very important fact about all right triangles. First of all, notice that we have given names to the

sides of our right triangle in Fig. 2-40B. The longest side, or the side opposite the right angle is always called the hypotenuse. The other two sides are simply known as legs or sides.

Many years ago, a mathematician named Pythagorus discovered a very interesting fact about right triangles. He discovered that if you squared each side of the right triangle and filled in all the squares in between as we have shown, the sum of all the squares created by squaring the two legs was exactly equal to the number of squares created by squaring the hypotenuse. You can actually prove this to yourself by counting all the squares in the two legs. You will find that there are 64 in the bottom leg square and 36 in the. vertical leg square. The sum of 64 and 36 is, of course, 100. Now, if you count all the squares made by squaring the hypotenuse, you will find that there are also exactly 100. Thus, we have the theorem which Pythagorus discovered:

The square on the hypotenuse of any right triangle is equal to the sum of the squares on the other two sides.

If we apply this theorem to our vector diagram in Fig. 2-40A, we have:

$$Z^2 = R^2 + (X_L)^2$$

Then, by substituting our values, we have:

$$Z^2 = 40^2 + 30^2$$

$$= 1600 + 900 = 2500$$

Then, if $Z^2 = 2500$, $Z = \sqrt{2500} = 50$. You will notice that this is the same answer we obtained by measurement. You will also notice that our statement: $Z^2 = R^2 + X_L^2$ is the same as one of our formulas: $Z = \sqrt{R^2 + X_L^2}$. We usually use the general formula $Z = \sqrt{R^2 + (X_L - X_C)^2}$ because we always find our total reactive compo-

nent, X, before we find our squares. In this way, we can solve for any right angle vector diagram without using a measurement solution.

2-6. Solving Circuit Problems

In this chapter you have studied some of the mathematical procedures that can be used in ac circuit calculations. Although you may feel at the present time that you have mastered all the procedures, it is quite possible that you will forget many of the details of what you have learned. One of the best ways to prevent forgetting this information and to insure that you really do understand it thoroughly is to get some practice in using it.

Therefore, in this section of the chapter, we will present several typical circuit problems and ask you to find the solutions. As you will see, we have given the answers to the problems, but not the methods used to obtain them. It will be up to you to determine how to solve these problems and then see if you can get the given answers. Remember, in solving these problems, it may be necessary many times to solve for intermediate values in order to obtain the necessary factors for use in finding the answers. However, you should be able to obtain all the answers without too much difficulty.

To help refresh your memory and prevent your having to look up too much information regarding these problems, we have listed some of the more important formulas. If you find that you do not thoroughly remember and understand these useful and com-

mon formulas it will be a good idea to review them before you start working the problems.

Inductance of Coils in Series:

$$L_T = L_1 + L_2 + L_3 \pm L_M$$

Inductance of Coils in Parallel:

$$L_T = \frac{L_1 \times L_2}{L_1 + L_2}$$

Inductive Reactance:

$$X_L = 2\pi f L$$

(f = cycles; L = henries)

Q of a Coil: $Q = \dfrac{X_L}{R}$

Capacitance of Capacitors in Series:

$$C = \frac{C_1 \times C_2}{C_1 + C_2}$$

Capacitance of Capacitors in Parallel:

$$C = C_1 + C_2 + C_3$$

Capacitive Reactance (C in mfd.):

$$X_C = \frac{1}{2\pi f C}$$

Time Constant of RC Circuits:

R (in megohms) $\times$ C (in mfds)

Ohm's Law for AC Circuits:

$$E = I \times Z$$

Impedance in AC Circuits:

$$Z = \sqrt{R^2 + X^2}$$

Total Voltage in AC Circuits:

$$E_T = \sqrt{E_R^2 + E_X^2}$$

Resonant Frequency:

$$f_0 = \frac{1}{2\pi \sqrt{L \times C}}$$

Turns Ratio of Transformers:

$$\frac{N_1}{N_2} = \frac{E_1}{E_2}$$

$$\frac{N_1}{N_2} = \frac{I_1}{I_2}$$

$$\frac{N_1}{N_2} = \sqrt{\frac{Z_1}{Z_2}}$$

Problems

The following problems are difficult. We made them difficult on purpose to give you real practice. So don't be discouraged if you find you can't work all of them.

The first step in solving these problems is to draw a schematic diagram. Mark all known voltages and currents on the diagram. Show values beside each part.

Be sure you have all quantities in the correct units. For example, if you are asked to find power in a circuit and are given the voltage in volts and the current in milliamps, you must convert the current to amperes by moving the decimal point three places to the left. When you need to find either inductance or capacitive reactance, be sure that you have frequency in cycles and inductance in henries or capacitance in farads. To convert microhenries to henries or microfarads to farads, move the decimal point six places to the left.

The following examples should help you:

Example 1. Find the current in a series circuit consisting of a 150-ohm resistor, a 292 millihenry coil, and a 7.0 microfarad capacitor if the line voltage is 120 volts and line frequency is 150 cycles/sec.

Solution: To find the current in an ac circuit, you divide the voltage by the impedance of the circuit. This is Ohm's Law for ac circuits.

$$I = \frac{E}{Z}$$

We know E, but we do not know Z so we must find Z.

$$Z = \sqrt{R^2 + (X_L - X_C)^2}$$

We know R, but we do not know X_C or X_L so we must find these values.

$$X_L = 2\pi fL$$

and $$X_C = \frac{1}{2\pi fC}$$

Since we know f, L, and C we can find X_L and X_C, then we can get Z and with this get I so our first steps in the problem are to find X_L and X_C. Let's do that now:

$$X_L = 2\pi fL$$

$2\pi = 6.28$, f = 150 cycles/sec and L = 292 millihenries.

To use our formula, f must be in cycles/sec which it is and L must be in henries. So we must convert 292 millihenries to henries by moving the decimal three places to the left.

Thus 292 millihenries = .292 henries.

Now $X_L = 6.28 \times 150 \times .292$

$$
\begin{array}{r}
6.28 \\
150 \\
\hline
31400 \\
628 \\
\hline
942.00
\end{array}
$$

$$
\begin{array}{r}
942 \\
.292 \\
\hline
1884 \\
8478 \\
1884 \\
\hline
275.064
\end{array}
$$

Thus $X_L = 275.064$ ohms, which we can round off to 275 ohms.

Now let's find X_C using the formula

$$X_C = \frac{1}{2\pi\, fC}$$

Again $2\pi = 6.28$, $f = 150$ cycles/sec and $C = 7.0$ microfarads. C must be in farads so we move the decimal six places to the left.

Thus 7.0 microfarads $= .000007$ farads.

$$X_C = \frac{1}{6.28 \times 150 \times .000007}$$

$6.28 \times 150 = 942$ (we did this when finding X_L)

$$
\begin{array}{r}
942 \\
.000007 \\
\hline
.006594
\end{array}
$$

Now dividing

$$
\begin{array}{r}
.006594)\overline{1} \\[2pt]
151.6 \\
6594)\overline{1000000.} \\
6594 \\
\hline
34060 \\
32970 \\
\hline
10900 \\
6594 \\
\hline
43060
\end{array}
$$

Thus, $X_C = 151.6$ ohms which we round off to 152 ohms.

Now that we know R, X_L, and X_C, we can get Z using

$$Z = \sqrt{R^2 + (X_L - X_C)^2}$$

Subtracting X_C from X_L we get:

$$
\begin{array}{r}
275 \\
-152 \\
\hline
123
\end{array}
$$

Therefore, $X_L - X_C = 123$ ohms.

Now, squaring 123 we get

$$
\begin{array}{r}
123 \\
123 \\
\hline
369 \\
246 \\
123 \\
\hline
15129
\end{array}
$$

And squaring R

$$
\begin{array}{r}
150 \\
150 \\
\hline
7500 \\
15 \\
\hline
22500
\end{array}
$$

Now adding $R^2 + (X_L - X_C)^2$

$$
\begin{array}{r}
22500 \\
15129 \\
\hline
37629
\end{array}
$$

Now to get Z we must take the square root of 37629.

$$
\begin{array}{r}
1\ 9\ 3.\ 9 \\
\sqrt{37629.00} \\
1 \\
\hline
29)\,\overline{276} \\
261 \\
\hline
383)\ \overline{1529} \\
1149 \\
\hline
3869)\ \ \overline{38000} \\
34821 \\
\hline
\end{array}
$$

Thus, Z is 193.9 ohms which we can round off to 194 ohms.

Now, to find I we use

$$I = \frac{E}{Z}$$

$$I = \frac{120}{194}$$

$$\begin{array}{r} .618 \\ 194\overline{)120.0} \\ \underline{1164} \\ 360 \\ \underline{194} \\ 1660 \\ \underline{1552} \\ 108 \end{array}$$

Thus the line current is .618 amps. Notice how we solved this problem. We worked backwards to find what we had to determine in order to get the required answer and then began by evaluating the terms needed to get the final solution.

Example 2: Find the voltage across the inductance in a series circuit having an inductive reactance of 4 ohms, a capacitive reactance of 12 ohms and a resistance of 6 ohms if the voltage applied to the circuit is 50 volts at 60 cycles/sec.

Solution: To find the voltage across the coil, we need to know the current flowing in the circuit, then we can use the formula

$$E_L = I \times X_L$$

To get I, we need the impedance and then we can use

$$I = \frac{E}{Z}$$

So we start by getting Z.

$$Z = \sqrt{R^2 + (X_L - X_C)^2}$$

$X_L = 4$ and $X_C = 12$ so we have

$$\begin{array}{r} 4 \\ -12 \\ \hline -8 \end{array}$$

Thus $\quad Z = \sqrt{6^2 + (-8)^2}$

Remember the $(-8)^2$ is $(-8) \times (-8)$ and your rules for multiplying signed numbers tell you that $(-8) \times (-8) = 64$

Therefore, $\quad Z = \sqrt{36 + 64}$

$$= \sqrt{100}$$

$$= 10 \text{ ohms}$$

Thus, $\quad I = \frac{50}{10} = 5$ amps

and the voltage across the coil is

$$E_L = I \times X_L$$

$$= 5 \times 4 = 20 \text{ volts}$$

You might wonder about the 60 cycles/sec — we didn't use this. We didn't have to, we had the reactance of the coil and capacitor so we could get the impedance directly. Often in problems and in actual practice you'll find you have more data than you need. You have to learn to take what information is needed and use it and ignore unneeded information.

Now try your hand at the following problems.

1. If a 500-ft. roll of copper hookup wire has a resistance of 30 ohms, how much resistance will an 850-ft.

roll of the same wire have?

ANS: 51 ohms.

2. What ac voltage will be needed to force a current of .02 amps through an 8K ohm resistor?

ANS. 160 volts.

3. What value of ac current will flow through a 10-henry coil with negligible resistance if the voltage supplied is 120-volt, 60-cycle ac?

ANS.: .0318 amps.

4. Find the current sent through a .03-henry choke coil by an ac voltage of 188.4 volts at 1 kc.

ANS: 1 amp.

5. In the circuit shown below, find the resistance of R_1.

ANS: $R_1 = 100$ ohms.

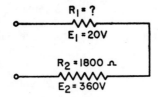

Fig. 2-41. Circuit for Problem 5.

6. A 10 mf capacitor draws 300 ma of current at a frequency of .4 kc. What is the voltage dropped across the capacitor?

ANS: 12 volts.

7. What turns ratio should we have for a transformer that we wish to use to match a source impedance of 490 ohms to a load of 10 ohms?

ANS: 7 to 1.

8. What is the total inductance of two coils connected in series if the inductance of one is .2 henrys and the other is .8 henrys and their mutual inductance is zero?

ANS: 1 henry.

9. What is the impedance of a series ac circuit having an inductive reactance of 14 ohms, a resistance of 6 ohms, and a capacitive reactance of 6 ohms?

ANS: 10 ohms.

10. What is the resonant frequency of a series circuit containing a 500 micromicrofarad capacitor, a 150 microhenry choke and a 10-ohm resistor?

ANS: 581 kc.

11. What is the impedance of an ac circuit containing a 3-ohm resistor in series with an inductive reactance of 7 ohms?

ANS: 7.6 ohms.

12. If three capacitors of 1, 3, and 5 microfarads are connected in parallel, what will the total capacitance be?

ANS: 9 microfarads.

13: If we assume that a coil has a negligible resistance and that 215 ma of current are forced through it by a supply voltage of 110 volts at 25 cycles, what is the inductance of the coil?

ANS: 3.26 henrys.

14. If we supply 240 volts at 60 cycles to a capacitor and obtain a current of 452 ma, what is the capacitance?

ANS: 5 microfarads.

15. If a circuit containing a 175-ohm resistor is connected in series with a 5-microfarad capacitor across a source of 150 volts at 120 cycles, what current will flow in the circuit?

ANS: .472 amps.

16. If a potential of 110 volts is applied to a series circuit containing a capacitive reactance of 10 ohms, an inductive reactance of 25 ohms, and a resistance of 15 ohms, what will the phase angle be?

ANS.: 45°.

17. If a transformer has a primary voltage of 4400 volts and a secondary voltage of 220 volts, and its efficiency is 98% when it is furnishing 23 amperes of secondary current, what will the primary current be?

ANS: 1.173 amperes.

18. What is the capacitive reactance of a capacitor at a frequency of 1200 kc if its reactance is 300 ohms at 680 kc?

ANS: 170 ohms.

19. If the capacitive reactance, inductive reactance, and resistance of an ac series circuit are each equal to 10 ohms, and the frequency of the circuit is reduced to 40% of its resonant value, what will the impedance of the circuit be at the new frequency?

ANS: 23.3 ohms.

20. If a series circuit has a resistance of 4 ohms, an inductive reactance of 4 ohms, and a capacitive reactance of 1 ohm, and it is supplied with an ac voltage of 50 volts, what will the voltage drop across the inductance be?

ANS: 40 volts.

2-7. Review Problems

1. Find the square root of:
   (a) 576   (b) 4489   (c) 16,384

2. Find the square root of:
   (a) 41,616   (b) 73,652   (c) .0625

3. Find the value of X in each of the following:
   (a) 4 : 5 :: X : 20   (b) 47 : 329 :: 7 : X

4. Find the value of X in each of the following:
   (a) $\dfrac{62}{124} = \dfrac{3}{X}$ (b) $\dfrac{X}{72} = \dfrac{1}{12}$

5. Solve the following:
   (a) $(-47) \times (51)$ (c) $(37) \times (-62)$
   (b) $(-23) \times (-17)$ (d) $(-11) \times (-7) \times (-6)$

6. Solve the following:
   (a) $72 \div (-8)$ (c) $(-64) \div (-8) \times (-7)$
   (b) $(-144) \div (-12)$ (d) $(-48) \div (12) \times (-4)$

7. Find the value of E_T in the circuit at the right by means of a vector diagram. (Show your diagram.)

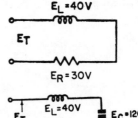

8. Find the value of E_T in the circuit at the right by means of a vector diagram. (Show your work.)

9. What is the total impedance of a coil that has an inductive reactance of 124 ohms in series with a 95 ohm resistance?

10. Find the current in a series circuit made up of a coil with an inductance of 325 millihenries, a capacitor of 4 microfarads, and a resistor of 120 ohms if the source voltage is 120 volts at 100 cycles.

CHAPTER THREE

Simple Circuit Algebra

3-1. Introduction

FOR THE MOST PART, the basic arithmetic and operations with signed numbers and vectors that you studied for use with ac and dc circuits calculations can be applied in the calculations for tube and transistor circuits. However, as the equipment and circuits become more involved, it will become increasingly difficult to keep up with their operation and maintenance if you rely only on mathematical processes that you have already learned. You will need many new short cuts and some new mathematical tools to keep your studies and work in electronics simple and straightforward.

In previous chapters you saw how important vectors are in analysis and calculations dealing with ac circuits. As you continue with your studies, these simple vectors will become even more important. However, the simple measurement solutions that you have been using to solve vector problems will become very awkward to use as the circuits become more complex. In addition to requiring careful construction and measurement, they require a lot of space and can become very involved, especially in parallel circuits. Although we can overcome these problems to some extent by using the Pythagorean Theorem, it also has its limits.

However, there is a handy method for working with ac circuit vectors so that they can be solved mathematically. It involves using a special tool known as the J-operator. This simple operator allows us to easily add, subtract, multiply, and divide vectors, regardless of their complexity.

In order to use the J-operator successfully, you should have at least a basic understanding of essentials of another mathematical process known as "algebra." As many of you already know, algebra is simply a form of mathematics that simplifies complex operations in arithmetic by using letters. Through these letter solutions of practical problems, we are able to speed up and simplify operations that would take a long time and involve a lot of tedious work if we used numbers alone. For this reason alone, a little time spent learning the fundamentals of algebra will be well worthwhile.

Therefore, in this chapter on circuit calculations, you will learn to use and apply the fundamentals of algebra and the "J" operator in electronic circuit calculations. If you have never studied these subjects, you may be a little uneasy about tackling them. However, you have already seen that math makes a lot more sense and becomes much easier when you have a practical use for it, such as your work in electronics.

As you study this chapter, remember these subjects are like all the others. All you have to do is learn a few rules and get some practice using them. Once you have done this, you have accomplished your goal of learning new processes that will help make your work much easier and more efficient. If you have already studied these subjects, you will find that this chapter will give you a good review and some valuable pointers on circuit applications.

3-2. Basic Algebra

Anyone who can add and subtract, multiply and divide, and perform the other operations of basic arithmetic should find algebra easy to understand. The only difference between algebra and arithmetic is that in algebra you work with letters as well as with numbers. Therefore, we can consider that algebra is simply arithmetic with letters. Consequently, all we have to do is get used to applying the rules of arithmetic to combinations of letters.

You are probably wondering just how we can use letters to compute with, because letters have no indicated values such as numbers have. We merely select the letters that are appropriate to the problems, and then let these letters represent the values that we wish to work with. For ex-

ample, you are already familiar with working with formulas such as Ohm's Law which states that $E = I \times R$. Here we have simply used certain letters to indicate various quantities in our circuit and have used these letters in a mathematical equation that represents their relationship in an electrical circuit. This is algebra.

In ordinary arithmetic, our next step would be to substitute the actual number values in place of the letters and solve our problem. In algebra, we may also do this, but many times we will find that it is easier to work with the letters awhile before we substitute the numbers. In order to do this, we will have to learn certain rules and how to apply them. In this section of the chapter, we will start at the very beginning and learn just what algebra is and what it is all about.

The Language of Letters

In the earlier chapters you learned how to substitute numbers for letters in certain formulas. As you continue in your work in electronics, it will be handy to know more about the process of computing with both numbers and letters. You are already familiar with this sort of reasoning: "If I have one resistor and you give me another resistor, I will have two resistors." Or, "If you give me four capacitors and then someone else gives me five more capacitors, I will have nine capacitors." This is simply addition as applied to physical things.

Addition, as you know, can only be performed with like things. We can add resistors to resistors, or capacitors to capacitors, but we can never add a number of resistors to a number of capacitors and get a sensible answer. Thus, the result of any addition is the sum of the number of things added followed by their name. Now, we know that it is possible to represent various quantities by letters. For example, suppose that we receive three orders of parts as follows:

(1) 5 choke coils, 7 resistors, 4 capacitors.

(2) 3 choke coils, 2 resistors, 3 capacitors.

(3) 7 choke coils, 4 resistors, 5 capacitors.

If we want to know the total number of parts received in these orders we can simply add the number of like parts in each order together to give us a total of 15 choke coils, 13 resistors, and 12 capacitors.

However, in doing this we must be very careful to keep the numbers associated with the coils separated from the numbers associated with the resistors, the resistors separated from the capacitors, etc. Otherwise, there is a possibility that we might get the numbers confused and start adding the coils to one of the other parts. To keep them separated, we can list them carefully in separate columns and write down the names of the parts as we just did. While this will work very well, you can easily see that it would require a lot of tedious writing if we needed to add a number of different things.

A much simpler way would be to choose abbreviations for the parts. For example, we could decide to let the letter "c" stand for the coils, the letter "r" stand for the resistors, and then let another letter such as "a" stand for the capacitors to be sure that the coils and capacitors are kept separate, since they both begin with "c." Now our additions and notations would look something like this:

(1) 5c, 7r, 4a Where: c = choke coils

(2) 3c, 2r, 3a r = resistors

(3) 7c, 4r, 5a a = capacitors
———————
15c, 13r, 12a

By doing this we could save ourselves a lot of work and still perform the addition in such a way that it would make sense and eliminate the chance of getting the different parts confused with each other.

In this way, it is possible to represent any number of different things or quantities with letters. Once we have chosen letters to indicate quantities, we can add or subtract them, or multiply and divide them by simply performing the operations with the letters instead of using the quantities themselves.

For example, let's say that we

choose the letter "a" to represent a quantity. This means that the letter "a" written by itself will always mean "1 a," the term "2a" will mean "2 a's," "3a" will mean "3 a's," etc. Thus, a term such as "5a" means that the quantity represented by the letter "a" is to be multiplied by 5. When we get ready to substitute and actually find the value or the meaning of the term "5a," we will need to know what the letter "a" stands for. In the meantime, we can go along and work with the term itself without worrying about what it means.

Another example of a term that we are likely to meet is one such as "6ab." This simply means that a quantity represented by "a" is to be multiplied by a quantity represented by "b." Then the product of quantity "a" times quantity "b" is to be multiplied by 6. Thus, 6ab means "6" times "a" times "b" or $6 \times a \times b$. In working with algebra we usually do not use the letter "x" as a "times" sign because it can also be used to represent a quantity, just as any other letter can. If we were to use $\times$ as a times sign and $\times$ as a quantity too, we could become quite confused. Sometimes dots are used between letters to indicate multiplication, as "$6 \cdot a \cdot b$," but generally the letters are simply written close together without any sign between them.

Before we go on to learn the rules of using letters, there are some special names given letter combinations that we should be familiar with. A letter by itself is called a "term." Thus, "a" is a term, "b" is a term, "x" is a term, etc. The indicated product of a group of letters such as "6ab" is also called a term. In this term, the 6, the a, and the b, are all factors of the indicated product, just as 6 and 8 are factors of 48.

We may have "like" terms or "unlike" terms in algebra. For example, 6ab, 3ab, and 5ab are all "like" terms because their letter factors are all the same. Terms such as 6xy, 10xa, 7ab, are "unlike" terms because their letter factors are not all the same.

The written number that indicates how many times the letter term is to be multiplied is called the "numerical coefficient" of the term or, more simply, just the "coefficient." Thus, a term may be a single letter, or it may consist of an indicated product between two or more letters, or between one or more letters and a numerical coefficient. Remember, a term may consist of one or more letters and numbers, but if more than one letter appears, it is a term only if multiplication is indicated. The expression, "a + b", is two separate terms because addition is indicated between the two letters. Likewise, an expression such as 6ab − cd is also made up of two terms.

An algebraic expression made up of one term such as "7xyz" is called a "monomial" term. An expression made up of two or more terms, such as 6ir + 7abc, or 8xy + 7cd − ab is called a "polynomial." If a polynomial has only two terms, it is usually called a "binomial" and one with three terms is often called a "trinomial." Thus, ab + ac is a binomial, and ab + ac + ad would be called a trinomial. We have no special names for polynomials that consist of more than three terms. For example, an expression such as xy + ab − ac − yb would simply be called a four-term polynomial.

Now, with the names given to these various expressions firmly in mind, let's see how to perform simple arithmetic with letters.

Arithmetic with Letters

The rules for performing arithmetic with letters are the same as those with numbers. We can add like terms to each other, but we cannot add unlike terms. The rules for working with signed numbers also apply to working with letters. Likewise, the rules of order for performing a series of indicated operations apply to letter arithmetic, or algebra, just as they do to numbers. The only real difference is that many times we will have to be satisfied with simply indicating the operations to be performed.

A term consisting of a letter with a coefficient, such as 5a, means that "a" is to be taken five times, or $a+a+a+a+a$. A term such as 6a means $a+a+a+a+a+a$. Therefore, to add 5a and 6a together really means $(a+a+a+a+a) + (a+a+a+a+a+a)$, or a total of 11 a's which we would write as 11a. Accordingly, we can say that $5a + 6a = 11a$. We can perform the indicated addition because the letter factors are the same and we can add like things together. Notice that in adding these like terms, we simply added their numerical coefficients (6 and 5) and used this sum as the new coefficient for the common letter. Thus, the sum of like terms is the sum of the coefficients of the terms followed by the common term. For example,

$$6ab + 3ab = 9ab$$

$$4abc + 3abc + 5abc = 12abc$$

$$xy + 3xy + 8xy = 12xy$$

When working with unlike terms, however, we can only indicate the addition to be performed. Thus $a + b$ can only be written as $a + b$. Likewise, $6a + 5b$ must remain as $6a + 5b$ as far as the addition is concerned. Thus, addition of unlike terms always results in a polynomial term. Consequently, when we have addition indicated in a problem such as

$$6a + 7b + 9ab + 4a + 3b + b,$$

we would proceed as follows:

First, we would arrange the terms so that all the like terms were grouped together. Thus, we would have $6a + 4a + 7b + 3b + b + 9ab$. Now, adding the like terms gives us

$$6a + 4a = 10a,$$

and $7b + 3b + b = 11b$. Since we now have $10a + 11b + 9ab$, which are all unlike terms and cannot be added any further, our answer to our problem of

$$6a + 7b + 9ab + 4a + 3b + b,$$

is simply $10a + 11b + 9ab$. Thus, to add a group of terms in algebra: arrange the like terms so that they are together, then add all the like terms by adding their coefficients and then use these sums in an indicated addition of the unlike terms. The process of rearranging and adding the like terms is often called "collecting" terms.

In working with letters, we will often run into terms with negative signs just as in working with numbers. We handle these signed algebraic terms like signed numbers. For example, to add two terms with like signs, we add the coefficients and use the common sign in front of the sum. Thus, $(-6ab) + (-4ab)$ would be equal to $-10ab$, just as $+3ab$ plus $+4ab$ would equal $+7ab$.

If we have to add terms with unlike signs, we simply find the difference between the coefficients and use the sign of the largest coefficient. Thus,

$$+5c + (-3c) = +2c$$

and

$$-7cd + 4cd = -3cd$$

In a more complicated problem that consists of like and unlike terms as well as like and unlike signs, we would simplify the problem by collecting all like terms with like signs and then perform the addition. Thus, for a problem such as

$$4c + (-9d) + 6e + (-3e) + 12d$$

$$+ (-4x) + 2c + (-c)$$

$$+ 3d + 4e + (-3c) + (-3d),$$

we would first collect all our like terms and like signs as follows:

$$4c + 2c + 6e + 4e + 12d + 3d$$

$$+ (-c) + (-3c) + (-3e)$$

$$+ (-9d) + (-3d) + (-4x).$$

Then,

$$6c + 10e + 15d + (-4c)$$

$$+ (-3e) + (-12d) + (-4x).$$

Now, $6c + (-4c) = 2c$

$$10e + (-3e) = 7e$$

$$15d + (-12d) = 3d$$

$$-4x + 0 = -4x$$

And our answer would be

$$2c + 7e + 3d + (-4x)$$

or simply $2c + 7e + 3d - 4x$.

We will also find terms like this to add:

$$(6ab - 7xy) + (5ab - xy)$$

$$+ (-3ab + 4xy).$$

Here we have to add three binomials but the terms in each binomial are alike, so we can add them quite easily like this:

$$\begin{array}{r} 6ab - 7xy \\ 5ab - xy \\ -3ab + 4xy \\ \hline \end{array}$$

Answer: $8ab - 4xy$

Or, collecting terms like this:

$$6ab + 5ab + 4xy - 3ab - 7xy - xy$$

then:

$$11ab + 4xy - 3ab - 8xy$$

and:

$$11ab - 3ab + 4xy - 8xy = 8ab - 4xy$$

Now suppose we had a problem like this:

$$(4x - 3y + 6c) + (-3x + 2y - 3d)$$

$$+ (2x - 7c + 2d).$$

Here we have three trinomials with terms that are not all alike. In a case like this we can set up our problem as follows:

$$\begin{array}{l} 4x - 3y + 6c \\ -3x + 2y - 3d \\ 2x - 7c + 2d \\ \hline \end{array}$$

Answer: $3x - y - c - d$

Since we cannot add unlike terms, this is as far as we can go with our answer. Notice that we could also have proceeded like this:

$$(4x - 3y + 6c) + (-3x + 2y - 3d)$$

$$+ (2x - 7c + 2d).$$

Collecting like terms and like signs:

$$4x + 2x - 3x + 2y - 3y$$

$$+ 6c - 7c + 2d - 3d$$

Then: $3x-y-c-d$ which is the same answer we got before.

Now you should be able to add the following terms without any trouble:

(1) $3x-2y+4z+2x+8y-2z+12x$
$+y+z =$

(2) $5ab-6xy-3ab+12xy+3ax$
$-5xb+ab-3xy-2xb =$

(3) $(12a+6c-3d)$
$+ (-20a+8c-5d)$
$+ (10a-2c+d) =$

Answers: (1) $17x+7y+3z$

(2) $3ab+3xy+3ax-7xb$

(3) $2a+12c-7d$

Subtraction of Letters. When you learned to subtract signed numbers, you found by experimenting with numbers of various signs that a simple rule would apply to all subtraction with signed numbers. This rule stated that: *To subtract signed numbers, change the sign of the number in the subtrahend (the number you are subtracting) and then proceed as in adding signed numbers.* Following this rule, $+7$ minus -6 would be handled this way:

$$+7 \qquad +7$$
$$= $$
$$-(-6) \qquad +6$$
$$\overline{ \quad +13}$$

Thus, $+7-(-6) = 13$.

To prove this, add the subtrahend, -6, and the answer, $+13$, which gives $-6+13 = +7$, which is the minuend. Likewise, $-7-(-6) =$

$$-7 \qquad -7$$
$$= $$
$$-(-6) \qquad +6$$
$$\overline{ \quad -1}$$

The proof is that $-1+(-6) = -7$.

Subtracting terms in algebra is just like subtracting signed numbers in arithmetic. Thus, if we want to subtract 6a from 8a we would have: $+8a$ minus $+6a$, which is written $(+8a) - (+6a)$. Now, changing both signs in front of 6a, we get

$$(+8a) + (-6a).$$

Adding: $+8a$
$\qquad\quad -6a$
$\qquad\quad \overline{+2a}$

To prove this, we add $+6a$ (the subtrahend) and $+2a$ which gives us the $+8a$ that we started with. As with addition in algebra, we can subtract only like terms. Thus, we can state a rule for subtraction in algebra which is: *To subtract in algebra, change the sign of the terms in the subtrahend and then add the coefficients of the like terms.*

This rule for subtraction in algebra holds true for either single terms or for polynomials. For example, to subtract $(2a-2b-3c)$ from $(3a-4b+5c)$ we would first change the sign of the subtrahend. $2a-2b-3c$ then becomes $-2a+2b+3c$. Now, we proceed to add:

$$(3a-4b+5c) + (-2a+2b+3c)$$
$$= \text{(collecting terms)} \ 3a-2a$$
$$-4b+2b+5c+3c = a-2b+8c.$$

Or, we could set it up like this:

$$3a-4b+5c$$
$$+ \quad -2a+2b+3c$$
$$\overline{\quad a-2b+8c}$$

In either case, the difference is equal to $a-2b+8c$, which is the correct answer. To prove it, add the difference of $a-2b+8c$ to the subtrahend $2a-2b-3c$ which, by collecting terms, gives the sum:

$$a+2a-2b-2b+8c-3c$$
$$= 3a-4b+5c$$

Thus, the important thing to remember in subtracting letters is to change the sign of the subtrahend and then add.

Now that we have seen how to add and subtract with letters, let's prove that what we are doing with the letters is correct by substituting numbers in place of the letters. Suppose that we want to add $5a+3b$ to $-2a-6b$. Collecting terms, this gives us

$$5a-2a+3b-6b = 3a-3b.$$

Now, let's substitute some numbers in this same problem. For example, suppose that we have chosen the letter "a" to represent "115" and the letter "b" to represent "95." We would set up the problems side by side, one using the letters, and the other using the number values of the letters, as shown in Fig. 3-1.

LETTERS	NUMBER SUBSTITUTES
$(5a+3b)+(-2a-6b)$	$[5(115)+3(95)]+[-2(115)-6(95)]$
$=5a-2a+3b-6b$	$= (575+285)+(-230-570)$
$=3a-3b$	$= 860-800=60$

Fig. 3-1. Substituting numbers in place of letters in addition.

In this way, we find that the letter answer is $3a-3b$, while the answer we got by substituting numbers is 60. If this is true then $3a-3b$ must be equal to 60. To prove that it is, we can now substitute for the letter values in our answer $3a-3b$. Doing this, we have:

$$3a-3b$$
$$= 3(115) - 3(95)$$
$$= 345-285$$
$$= 60$$

Thus, if we substitute the numbers in place of the letters in the beginning, we get an answer of 60. If we wish to work with the letters as long as we can, we get an answer $3a-3b$. However, we find that this is also equal to 60 when we substitute at the end of the problem. Since we get an answer of 60 either way, our process of adding letters must be correct.

Now, let's check a problem in subtraction the same way. Again, let $a = 115$ and $b = 95$. This time the problem is to subtract $3a-2b$ from $5a-7b$ as shown in Fig. 3-2. As you can see, the answer with the letters is $2a-5b$ and the answer with the number substitutes is -245. Now let's substitute in our letter answer to see if we also get -245 for our final solution. Doing this, we have: $2a-5b = 2(115)-5(95) = 230-475 = -245$. Consequently, our method of handling subtraction with letters must also be correct, since in either case we get -245 for the final solution.

Next, let's take a look at multiplying and dividing with letters.

Multiplication of Letters. Multiplication with letters such as 3 times "a" may be indicated simply as 3a, which means "a" taken three times, or $a+a+a$. Likewise, $2 \times b$ is written 2b, which means "b" taken two times, or $b+b$. In multiplying two letters together such as "a" $\times$ "b" we write "ab", which means "a" taken "b" times, or "b" taken "a" times. For multiplication of two terms with coefficients, such as 3a times 2b, we actually perform the multiplication of the coefficients and then indicate the letter multiplication. We can do this because $3a \times 2b$ really means

$$3 \times a \times 2 \times b = 6 \times a \times b$$
$$= 6 \times ab = 6ab$$

Following this method,

$$3a \times 4b \times 2c$$

would equal

$$3 \times 4 \times 2 \times a \times b \times c = 24abc.$$

Now suppose that we want to multiply two like terms such as 2a × 3a.

This can be rewritten as

$$2 \times 3 \times a \times a$$

or 6 × a × a = 6aa. However, in arithmetic when we wanted to multiply a number by itself such as 5 × 5, we found that we would simply say, 5^2. The small "2" indicated the 5 was to be raised to the second power (multiplied by itself) or squared, and we called the "2" an exponent. We can also use exponents in algebra to indicate that a letter is to be multiplied by itself. Thus, 2a × 3a = 6aa or $6a^2$. A multiplication such as a × a × a is aaa or a^3 (read a cubed), and a × a × a × a × a is aaaaa or a^5 (read a to the fifth).

Using exponents in this way saves time. For example, 4a times 3ab becomes 4 × 3 × a × a × b or $12a^2b$. Now, there is an interesting thing about exponents that we should know. When we write the letter "a" alone, we really mean "a" taken once or a^1. However, just as we never indicate a coefficient of one, we never indicate an exponent of one. We say that the one is understood. For right now though, let's use the exponent "1" for a moment in order to examine the exponents as we multiply.

When we multiply a × a, we can say that we have $a^1 \times a^1$. We know that this is equal to aa or a^1a^1 or a^2.

Now, notice that the exponent "2" in a^2 is the sum of the exponents in the indicated multiplication.

$$a^1a^1 = a^{1+1} = a^2$$

Likewise,

$$a \times a \times a$$
$$= a^1 \times a^1 \times a^1$$
$$= a^{1+1+1}$$
$$= a^3$$

Thus, we have a rule for exponents in multiplication which states that: *To find the product of two or more powers of the same base, add the exponents.* According to this rule, $a^2 \times a^3 = a^{2+3}$ or a^5. If we do it the long way, we find that $a^2 = a \times a$ and

$$a^3 = a \times a \times a.$$

Therefore, (a × a) × (a × a × a) = a taken five times, which is:

$$a \times a \times a \times a \times a = a^5.$$

Therefore, the rule for adding exponents must be correct.

Accordingly, a multiplication such as 5ab × $3a^2b$ must equal

$$5 \times 3 \times a^{1+2} \times b^{1+1}$$
$$= 15 \times a^3 \times b^2 = 15a^3b^2.$$

Likewise,

$$(3a^2b^3c^4) \times (25ab^2c^3)$$
$$= 3 \times 25 \times a^{2+1} \times b^{3+2} \times c^{4+3}$$
$$= 75a^3b^5c^7$$

LETTERS	NUMBER SUBSTITUTES
FROM 5a -7b TAKE 3a-2b	5(115)-7(95) TAKE 3(115)-2(95)
5a-7b - (3a-2b)	5(115)-7(95) - [3(115)-2(95)]
CHANGING SIGNS:	
= 5a-7b + (-3a+2b)	= 575 - 665 + [-3(115)+2(95)]
= 5a-7b - 3a+2b	= 575 - 665 - 345 +190
= 5a-3a - 7b+2b	= 575 - 345 - 665+190
= 2a-5b	= 230 - 475 = -245

Fig. 3-2. Substituting numbers in place of letters in subtraction.

Can you multiply $6a^3b^4$ by $5a^2b^3c$? The answer is $30a^5b^7c$.

These few simple steps cover the process of multiplying one single term (monomial) by another. However, in algebra, we must not only consider multiplying one monomial by another monomial, but we must also consider multiplying one polynomial by a monomial, and a polynomial by another polynomial. In considering the multiplication of a polynomial by a monomial, let's go back to our work with numbers for a moment.

For example, consider a number problem such as: $7 \times (3 + 2 + 5)$. We can write this down and solve it in a number of different ways. We can do the addition separately first, which gives us $7 \times (3+2+5) = 7 \times 10 = 70$, or we can multiply each number by seven and then add. This would give:

$$(7 \times 3) + (7 \times 2) + (7 \times 5)$$
$$= 21 + 14 + 35$$

which also equals 70. Since this is true with numbers, it must also be true with letters.

Let's multiply the polynomial

$$b+c+d$$

by the monomial a. We would set it up like this:

$$a \times (b+c+d)$$
$$= a(b+c+d)$$
$$= ab+ac+ad$$

Thus, we can say that the product of a monomial and a polynomial is the sum of the products of the monomial and each term of the polynomial. Accordingly,

$$a(b-c+d-e) = ab-ac+ad-ae.$$

Notice that, as with signed numbers,

multiplication of unlike signs in algebra always gives a negative product, while the product of two terms with like signs is always positive. Or,

$$-b(a-c+d-e)$$
$$= -ab+cb-db+eb.$$

With this in mind, we are ready to do a multiplication problem such as $3a^2b(2a+3b-7c)$. This equals

$$(3a^2b \times 2a)+(3a^2b \times 3b)$$
$$+[(3a^2b)\times(-7c)]$$
$$= 6a^3b+9a^2b^2-21a^2bc$$

Or, we can set up the problem a different way. Let's try it with this problem: $4I^2R(3IR+5I+6R)$. Now, multiplying each term of the polynomial by the monomial gives us:

$$4I^2R \times 3IR = 12I^3R^2$$
$$4I^2R \times 5I = 20I^3R$$
$$4I^2R \times 6R = 24I^2R^2$$

Now, we take the sum of the products, which is $12I^3R^2+20I^3R+24I^2R^2$, and the answer to the problem.

Multiplying one polynomial by a binomial or by another polynomial is much the same. For example, multiplying the polynomial $(a+b-c)$ by the binomial $(a-b)$, we can think of $(a-b)$ as being a single multiplier. Thus, multiplying $(a-b)$ by each of the terms in the polynomial, we would have $(a-b)a$, then $(a-b)b$, and then $(a-b)(-c)$. Putting them together, we have

$$(a-b)a + (a-b)b + (a-b)(-c).$$

Now, the partial products would be:

$$(a-b)a = a^2-ab$$
$$(a-b)b = ab-b^2$$
$$(a-b)(-c) = -ac+bc$$

Then, adding these products gives us $a^2-ab+ab-b^2-ac+bc$. Collecting terms, we get $a^2-b^2-ac+bc$ as the answer. Notice that the $-ab$ and the $+ab$ cancel each other out just as $+2+(-2)$ would do.

In this way, we can say that the product of

$$(a-b)(a+b-c) = a^2-b^2-ac+bc.$$

We can prove that the solution to this problem is correct by substituting any numbers we want in place of the letters. For example, let's have $a = 5, b = 3$, and $c = 2$. If we do this and substitute these values for the letters we have:

$$(a-b)(a+b-c) = a^2-b^2-ac+bc$$

Then,

$$(5-3)(5+3-2)$$
$$= 5^2-3^2-(5 \times 2)+(3 \times 2)$$

and

$$2 \times 6 = 25-9-10+6$$
$$12 = 25-19+6 = 6+6 = 12$$

Since the problem works out so that $12 = 12$, our multiplication of the letters must be correct.

We can also perform the multiplication by setting it down as in Fig.3-3.

As you can see, we simply multiply all the terms in the polynomial by each term of the binomial. We do this by multiplying $a+b-c$ first by a, then by $-b$, and then adding the two partial products.

$$
\begin{array}{l}
 a + b - c \\
\times\ \underline{a - b} \\
\text{MULTIPLYING BY } a:\quad a^2 + ab - ac \\
\text{MULTIPLYING BY } -b:\quad \underline{-ab-b^2+bc} \\
\text{ANSWER:}\quad a^2-ac-b^2+bc
\end{array}
$$

Fig. 3-3. Multiplying a polynomial by a binomial.

There are three polynomial products that we will find quite often in our work with algebra. They are:

(1) $(a+b)(a-b) = a^2-b^2$

(2) $(a+b)(a+b)$ or $(a+b)^2$
$$= a^2+2ab+b^2$$

(3) $(a-b)(a-b)$ or $(a-b)^2$
$$= a^2-2ab+b^2$$

If we work each one of these out, we will find that the listed products are correct. Thus:

$$
(1)\quad
\begin{array}{l}
a + b \\
\underline{a - b} \\
a^2 + ab \\
\underline{- ab - b^2} \\
a^2 \ - b^2
\end{array}
$$

$$
(2)\quad
\begin{array}{l}
a + b \\
\underline{a + b} \\
a^2 + ab \\
\underline{+ ab + b^2} \\
a^2 + 2ab + b^2
\end{array}
$$

$$
(3)\quad
\begin{array}{l}
a - b \\
\underline{a - b} \\
a^2 - ab \\
\underline{- ab + b^2} \\
a^2 - 2ab + b^2
\end{array}
$$

Sometimes these products are stated in words and used as rules:

1. The product of the sum of two terms $(a+b)$ and the difference of the same two terms $(a-b)$ is equal to the square of the first term minus the square of the second term (a^2-b^2).

This is a handy rule, because any time that we have to multiply the sum of two terms by the difference of the same two terms, we can just set down the answer without working it out. For example,

$$(4abc+6xyz)(4abc-6xyz)$$

must equal $(4abc)^2 - (6xyz)^2$. Likewise,

$(4a^2b^3c^5+7x^2yz^3)$ $(4a^2b^3c^5-7x^2yz^3)$

must equal $(4a^2b^3c^5)^2 - (7x^2yz^3)^2$.

The second example stated in words is:

2. The square of the sum of two terms $(a+b)^2$ is equal to the square of the first term plus the square of the second term plus twice the product of the terms $(a^2+2ab+b^2)$.

By using this rule, we automatically know that a binomial such as

$$(5xy+3ab)^2$$

is equal to $(5xy)^2+2(15xyab)+(3ab)^2$.

The third example covers the square of the difference of two terms:

3. The square of the difference of two terms $(a-b)^2$ is equal to the square of the first term plus the square of the second term minus twice the product of the terms.

Thus, $(16cd-5x^2y)^2$ is equal to

$$(16cd)^2-2(80cdx^2y)+(5x^2y)^2.$$

Since we often have to work with either the square of the sum or the square of the difference of two terms, we will use these rules quite a lot.

Can you find the products for the following problems?

(1) $(2x-3)(3x+7)$ (2) $(2x+3)^2$

(3) $(5x^2-4y^2)(5x^2+4y^2)$

(4) $(6ab-c^2)^2$

Answers:

(1) $6x^2+5x-21$

(2) $4x^2+12x+9$

(3) $(5x^2)^2-(4y^2)^2$ or $25x^4-16y^4$

(4) $(6ab)^2-2(6abc^2)+(c^2)^2$ or
$36a^2b^2-12abc^2+c^4$.

Division with Letters. Division in algebra is just the reverse of multiplication. In division, we are given a product and one of the factors of the product and are asked to find the other factor. Remember, there are special names for the quantities in a division problem. The dividend is the product that is to be divided. The divisor is the factor by which the dividend is to be divided. The quotient is the result of the division, or the factor which we are to find. Thus: dividend ÷ divisor = quotient.

Also, multiplication is the proof of a division problem. Thus, $24 \div 6 = 4$ because $4 \times 6 = 24$; likewise,

$$24 \div 4 = 6$$

because $4 \times 6 = 24$. Accordingly, we can say that $ab \div a = b$ because $a \times b = ab$. The rules for the division of signed numbers also apply to the division of signed terms in algebra. Thus:

$+24 \div +6 = +4$ because
         $+4 \times (+6) = +24$

$-24 \div +6 = -4$ because
         $-4 \times (+6) = -24$

$+24 \div -6 = -4$ because
         $-4 \times (-6) = +24$

$-24 \div -6 = +4$ because
         $+4 \times (-6) = -24$

Accordingly, our rules for division of signed numbers and signed terms are:

If the dividend and the divisor have like signs, the quotient is positive.

If the dividend and the divisor have unlike signs, the quotient is negative.

Thus:

    $ab \div b = a$ because $a \times b = ab$

    $-ab \div b = -a$ because
            $-a \times b = -ab$

$ab \div -b = -a$ because

$$-a \times -b = ab$$

$-ab \div -b = a$ because

$$a \times -b = -ab$$

With this review and application of the general rules for division to letter problems, we are ready to look at the rules for handling exponents in division. You are already familiar with the fact that a^4 means

$$a \times a \times a \times a$$

and a^2 means $a \times a$. With this in mind, let's divide a^4 by a^2 and see what we get for an answer.

$$a^4 \div a^2 = \frac{\cancel{a} \times \cancel{a} \times a \times a}{\cancel{a} \times \cancel{a}} = \frac{a \times a}{1}$$
$$= a \times a = a^2$$

Likewise:

$$b^6 \div b^4 = \frac{b^6}{b^4}$$
$$= \frac{\cancel{b} \times \cancel{b} \times \cancel{b} \times \cancel{b} \times b \times b}{\cancel{b} \times \cancel{b} \times \cancel{b} \times \cancel{b}}$$
$$= \frac{b \times b}{1} = b^2$$

And:

$$c^3 \div c^2 = \frac{c^3}{c^2} = \frac{\cancel{c} \times \cancel{c} \times c}{\cancel{c} \times \cancel{c}} = \frac{c}{1} = c$$

If you look at these examples closely, you will see that we could have obtained the same results by subtracting exponents.

$$a^4 \div a^2 = a^{4-(+2)} = a^2$$
$$b^6 \div b^4 = b^{6-(+4)} = b^2$$
$$c^3 \div c^2 = c^{3-(+2)} = c$$

Thus, just as we can multiply powers

with the same base by adding exponents, we can divide two powers with the same base by subtracting exponents. Consequently,

$$a^6b^3 \div a^5b^2 = ab$$

and

$$x^3y^2 \div xy = x^2y$$

We can prove these answers by multiplying the quotients by the divisors to see if we get the original dividends. Doing this, we would have

$$ab \times a^5b^2 = a^{1+5}b^{1+2} = a^6b^3$$

and

$$(xy)(x^2y) = x^{1+2}y^{1+1} = x^3y^2$$

As we start working with division, we will find a few new situations regarding exponents. We know that any number divided by itself is equal to one. Thus,

$$\frac{6}{6} = 1, \quad \frac{a}{a} = 1, \quad \frac{3}{3} = 1$$

Now, if we follow our rules of dividing by subtracting exponents, we can see that if $\frac{a^3}{a^3} = 1$, that $a^3 \div a^3 = a^{3-(+3)} = a^0$ · which must also equal one. Likewise,

$$\frac{a}{a} = 1$$
$$a \div a = a^{1-(+1)}$$
$$= a^0 = 1$$

and

$$\frac{a^6}{a^6} = 1$$
$$a^6 \div a^6 = a^{6-(+6)}$$
$$= a^0 = 1$$

Thus, we have a new situation brought on by division which gives us an exponent of zero, and any factor with a zero exponent must equal 1. Remember, a factor by itself, such as "x", is considered to have an exponent of one, or x^1, and is equal to itself; but, a factor with an exponent of zero, such as b^0, can only be equal to the number 1.

If we look further into this problem of dividing by subtracting exponents, we will find that we can not only have positive exponents, such as 1, 2, 5, etc., and zero exponents, but we can also have negative exponents. This would occur if we had a division problem, such as $a^2 \div a^5$. This would be written either as

$$\frac{a^2}{a^5} = \frac{\cancel{a} \times \cancel{a}}{\cancel{a} \times \cancel{a} \times a \times a \times a}$$

$$= \frac{1}{a \times a \times a}$$

$$= \frac{1}{a^3}$$

or it could be written as

$$a^2 \div a^5 = a^{2-(+5)} = a^{-3}$$

If our answer can be either $\frac{1}{a^3}$ or a^{-3}, then a^{-3} must equal $\frac{1}{a^3}$. Thus, we can say that any factor with a negative exponent is equal to one divided by the factor with the exponent positive.

Accordingly, $x^{-5} = \frac{1}{x^5}$ and $c^{-3} = \frac{1}{c^3}$.

Once again, we can prove that the reasoning behind negative exponents is correct by multiplying. For example, $x^4 \div x^7 = x^{4-(+7)} = x^{-3}$ because $x^{-3} \times x^7 = x^{-3+7} = x^4$ or $\frac{x^4}{x^7} = \frac{1}{x^3}$ because

$$\frac{1}{x^3} \times x^7$$

$$= \frac{x^7}{x^3} = x^4$$

The problems of division in algebra can be broken down into three general considerations the same as multiplication. First, we have the division of one monomial by another. Second, we have the division of a polynomial by a monomial. Third, we have the division of a polynomial by another polynomial.

In our review of division in general and our studies of handling exponents in division, we have covered the problem of dividing one monomial by another monomial. There is only one more thing that we must learn and that is what to do with the coefficients of terms. For example, suppose we want to divide $-12a^3x^4y$ by $4a^2x^2y$. We can set this up as

$$\frac{-12a^3x^4y}{4a^2x^2y},$$

and then break it up into

$$\left(\frac{-12}{4}\right)\left(\frac{a^3}{a^2}\right)\left(\frac{x^4}{x^2}\right)\left(\frac{y}{y}\right).$$

We can see that this will equal:

$$\frac{-12}{4} = -3, \frac{a^3}{a^2} = a, \frac{x^4}{x^2} = x^2 \text{ and } \frac{y}{y} = 1.$$

Now, putting the quotients together we have $-3ax^21$ or just $-3ax^2$, since any quantity times one equals itself.

By breaking up our division problems in this way and following the rules for division of signed numbers and exponents, we can see how division is accomplished. As a general rule, we will not need to do this, because the division of most monomials by another monomial can be worked out mentally. For example, see if you can follow the following monomial divisions:

$$(1) \quad \frac{-14a^2b^4c}{-7ab^2c^3} = \frac{2ab^2}{c^2}$$

(2) $\dfrac{4x^3y^5}{8x^5y^2} = \dfrac{y^3}{2x^2}$

(3) $\dfrac{28a^2b^4c^3}{-7b^3c^3} = -4a^2b$

(4) $\dfrac{-16e^3i^2r^5}{-4e^2i^2r^3} = 4er^2$

In order to divide a polynomial by a monomial, let's consider numbers for a moment. $16 \div 2 = 8$ because $2 \times 8 = 16$. Thus, if $3(a+4) = 3a+12$, then $(3a+12) \div 3$ must equal

$$\dfrac{3a+12}{3} = a+4.$$

Similarly, if

$$3x(2x+3y) = 6x^2+9xy,$$

then $\dfrac{6x^2+9xy}{3x}$ must equal $2x+3y$.

Thus, we have a very simple rule for dividing a polynomial by a monomial. It is: Divide each term in the polynomial dividend by the divisor, and then collect the terms in the quotient with the proper signs.

For example,

$$8a^2b^3c - 12a^3b^2c^2 + 4a^2b^2c$$

divided by $4a^2b^2c$ can be set up as follows:

$$\dfrac{8a^2b^3c - 12a^3b^2c^2 + 4a^2b^2c}{4a^2b^2c} =$$

$$\dfrac{8a^2b^3c}{4a^2b^2c} = 2b \quad \text{and}$$

$$\dfrac{-12a^3b^2c^2}{4a^2b^2c} = -3ac \quad \text{and}$$

$$\dfrac{4a^2b^2c}{4a^2b^2c} = 1$$

Now, collecting terms we have

$$2b - 3ac + 1$$

for our answer.

Another example:

$$-27x^3y^2z^5 + 3x^4y^2z^4 - 9x^4y^3z^5$$

divided by $-3x^3y^2z^4$ is equal to:

$$\dfrac{-27x^3y^2z^5}{-3x^3y^2z^4} = 9z \quad \text{and}$$

$$\dfrac{3x^4y^2z^4}{-3x^3y^2z^4} = -x \quad \text{and}$$

$$\dfrac{-9x^4y^3z^5}{-3x^3y^2z^4} = 3xyz$$

Now, collecting our quotient terms, we have our answer: $9z - x + 3xyz$. Any polynomial can be divided by any monomial in this way.

In order to divide one polynomial by another polynomial, we must arrange the terms in a certain order before we actually divide. To do this, we simply make sure that all the terms in the dividend are arranged in the same order as those of the divisor. In doing this, we always place the term with the largest exponent first. Thus, in the problem $3x^2 + 4 - 8x$ divided by $3x - 2$, the divisor is correctly arranged, but the dividend isn't. Therefore, we must arrange it properly before we can proceed. Properly arranged, it should be written

$$3x^2 - 8x + 4.$$

Now that we have our terms arranged properly, we can set up our problem exactly as we did with long division of numbers shown in Fig. 3-4.

$$3X - 2\overline{)3X^2 - 8X + 4}$$

Fig. 3-4. Setting up a polynomial for division by another polynomial.

Notice that we have the dividend set up under the division sign and the divisor at the left. Our process now is really just plain long division, as shown in Fig. 3-5. First, we see how many times the first term of our divisor will go into the first term of our polynomial dividend. For example,

$$\begin{array}{r} x \\ 3X-2\overline{)\ 3x^2-8X+4} \\ 3x^2-2X \\ \hline -6X \end{array}$$

X(3X)=3X² SO,

X(3X-2)=3X²-2X

Fig. 3-5. First steps in polynomial division.

3x will go into $3x^2$, x times, because 3x times x is equal to $3x^2$. Thus, x becomes our first term in our quotient as shown. Now we multiply our entire divisor, $3x - 2$, by x to give us our first trial product of $3x^2-2x$. We place this trial product under the proper terms of the dividend and subtract.

Our remainder from this subtraction, plus the other term which we bring down from the dividend, can be considered to be a new dividend, as shown in Fig. 3-6. Notice the sign

$$\begin{array}{r} x-2 \\ 3X-2\overline{)\ 3x^2-8X+4} \\ 3x^2-2X \\ \hline -6X+4 \\ -6X+4 \end{array}$$

-2(3X)=-6X SO,

-2(3X-2)=-6X+4.

Fig. 3-6. Next step in polynomial division.

of the first term. Signs are very important in algebra. Now, we see how many times the first term in our divisor will go into the first term in this new dividend. Since -2 times 3x equals $-6x$, we will try the number 2 as the second term in our quotient. To do this, we place the -2 beside the x in our quotient, as shown, and then multiply our entire divisor by -2. As you can see, this gives us $-6x + 4$ as a trial product to sub-

tract from the dividend. Since $-6x + 4$ from $-6x + 4$ leaves no remainder, our division is complete.

In this way, we find that $3x^2 - 8x +4$ divided by $3x - 2$ is equal to $x - 2$. To check our answer, we simply multiply the divisor by the

$$\begin{array}{r} 3X-2 \\ X-2 \\ \hline 3X^2-2X \\ -6X+4 \\ \hline 3X^2-8X+4 \end{array}$$

Fig. 3-7. Checking the answer in polynomial division.

quotient to see if we can get our dividend, as shown in Fig. 3-7. Since our answer checks, our problem is correct.

To make sure that we understand this, let's do another problem following the rules. Divide

$$5x - 42 + 2x^3 - 3x^2$$

by $x - 3$. Our first step is to rearrange the dividend in the proper order, which would give us

$$2x^3 - 3x^2 + 5x - 42$$

Now, we set up the problem for division, as shown in Fig. 3-8. Then, we see how many times x will go into $2x^3$. Since $2x^2$ times x is equal to $2x^3$,

$$\begin{array}{r} 2X^2+3X+14 \\ X-3\overline{)\ 2X^3-3X^2+5X-42} \\ 2X^3-6X^2 \\ \hline +3X^2+5X \\ 3X^2-9X \\ \hline +14X-42 \\ 14X-42 \end{array}$$

X(2X²)=2X³ SO,

2X²(X-3)=2X³-6X²

X(3X)=3X² SO,

3X(X-3)=3X²-9X

X(14)=14X SO,

14(X-3)=14X-42

Fig. 3-8. Another problem in polynomial division.

we place $2x^2$ in our quotient and multiply the entire divisor by it. Since $2x^2(x-3) = 2x^3-6x^2$, we use this as our first trial product and subtract it from the proper terms in the dividend.

Our remainder from this subtraction, plus the next term of our dividend, gives us a new dividend of $3x^2 + 5x$ to work with. x will go into $3x^2$, 3x times, so 3x becomes our next quotient term.

$$3x(x-3) = 3x^2-9x,$$

which is the term we subtract from our new dividend. This makes our next dividend $14x-42$, as shown, and $x-3$ will go into it exactly 14 times. Thus, our answer is $2x^2+3x+14$. We can check this in the usual way, by multiplying the quotient and the divisor.

Some problems in division may not come out exactly even. It is possible to have a remainder in algebraic division, just as we do when working with numbers. An example of such a problem is shown in Fig. 3-9. Notice that we proceed to work it out just as we would any other problem until

Fig. 3-9. A polynomial division with a remainder.

we get to a point where the first term of the divisor will not go into the

dividend. When we come to this point, we simply stop and carry the remainder as a fraction in our answer, just as we do in ordinary arithmetic.

DIVIDE $a^2b^2+a^4+b^4$ BY a^2-ab+b^2

REARRANGED $a^4 + a^2b^2 + b^4$

NO a^3b OR ab^3 TERMS IN DIVIDEND SO ZEROS ARE PUT IN THEIR PLACE

Fig. 3-10. A polynomial divided by a trinomial.

In Fig. 3-10, we have worked a problem where the divisor is a trinomial. As you can see, this is really no different from the problems we have been working, where the divisor is a binomial. You shouldn't have any trouble following this example. Can you work the two following problems and get the answers that we have indicated?

(1) Divide $6x^3 + 12 - 7x - x^2$ by $2x + 3$.

(2) Divide $26x^2 + 15x^3 + 10-39x$ by $3x-2$.

Answers: (1) $3x^2 - 5x + 4$

(2) $5x^2 + 12x - 5$

3-3. Equations

You have now learned how to do arithmetic with letters. Since many of these fundamental operations of algebra were new to you, you had a lot to learn so we did not take the time to see how they could be put to practical use in your work in electronics. Now, however, we have covered most of the elementary processes in algebra and it is time to see how to put these new mathematical tools to work in the solution of circuit problems. This can be done through the use of equations.

An equation is simply a mathematical statement that two quantities are equal to each other. The two equal quantities in an equation are called the "members" of the equation and they are always separated by an equal sign ($=$). Thus, the mathematical statements that $12 = 12$, $6 \times 2 = 6 \times 2$, $6 \times 2 = 12$, or $6 \times 2 = 3 \times 4$ are all equations, because the quantities on each side of the equal sign are equal to each other. Sometimes, when we want to be specific, we call the quantities on the left of the equal sign the "left member" of the equation and the ones on the right, the "right member."

Although you may already be somewhat familiar with equations and their use, it will be a good idea to review some of the more common facts that you will use in working with them. Of course, the most important thing to remember is that an equation is always a statement of equality between the two members, and that in order to use it, we must never upset this equality or balance between the members. Thus, in an equation such as $24 = 24$, if we make any changes in one member, we must be very careful not to upset the balance of the whole equation. For example, we can change $24 = 24$ to $24 \times 1 = 24$, $12 \times 2 = 24$, $6 \times 4 = 24$,

$$6 \times 4 = 12 \times 2,$$

$3 \times 2 \times 4 = 6 \times 2 \times 2$, etc., because our changes do not upset the equality of the two members. Likewise, an equation such as $4Ir + 4IR = 4Ir + 4IR$ may be written as

$$4(Ir + IR) = 4Ir + 4IR,$$

$$4I(r + R) = 4Ir + 4IR, \text{ or}$$

$$4I(r + R) = 4(Ir + IR)$$

because in any of these cases the equations remain balanced.

We can also do other things to equations without disturbing their equality. For example, we can add or subtract a quantity from one member of an equation as long as we perform the same operation to the other member with the same quantity. Thus, if we have an equation such as $x = x$, we can add the same number to each side without destroying the equation. For example, let's add 2 to each side of the equation $x = x$. This would give:

$$x + 2 = x + 2$$

We can see that this is still an equation, because if we let $x = 4$, and substitute for x, we have:

$$4 + 2 = 4 + 2, \text{ or } 6 = 6,$$

which is still an equation because both members are equal. Likewise, if $x = x$, we can subtract a number from either side, as:

$$x - 3 = x - 3$$

and if $x = 4$, then $x - 3 = x - 3$ becomes

$$4 - 3 = 4 - 3 \text{ or } 1 = 1$$

We can also multiply or divide both members by the same quantity. For example, if ab = ab and we multiply both members by 2, we have: 2ab = 2ab. Or, dividing by 2, we have $\frac{ab}{2} = \frac{ab}{2}$. In either case, our equality can be proved by substitution. Thus, if a = 3 and b = 4, substituting in the equation ab = ab, 3 × 4 = 3 × 4 or 12 = 12. And, 2ab = 2ab, or 2 × 3 × 4 = 2 × 3 × 4, which is 24 = 24. Likewise,

$$\frac{ab}{2} = \frac{ab}{2}, \quad \text{or}$$

$$\frac{3 \times 4}{2} = \frac{3 \times 4}{2}, \text{ or } \frac{12}{2} = \frac{12}{2}, \text{ or } 6 = 6.$$

In all of these cases our equations remain balanced, because one member always equals the other.

From this, we can make the general statement that we can do anything to one side of an equation as long as we do exactly the same thing to the other side. There is only one exception to this rule, and that is that we can never multiply or divide either member by zero. We will show you why we cannot divide by zero a little later, after you have become familiar with working with equations.

These rules for working with equations are very valuable in working with formulas. Formulas are, of course, equations, but they are a special kind of equation. A formula is a rule or a law that is stated as an equation. Thus, both the equations ab = ab, and E = I × R are equations, but only E = I × R is a formula, because there is a law that makes it a true equation. In other words, ab = ab, or I × R = I × R are equations because they meet the requirements of any equation auto-matically. Both members are exactly the same, and therefore equal. However, the fact that E = I × R is an equation is not apparent, and it wouldn't be recognized as an equation unless we knew that it was a statement of Ohm's Law. Here, both members are equal only by definition.

Since formulas are equations, we can use the rules for equations when working with formulas. Let's see how this can help us with a simple formula such as P = E × I. Suppose we want to use this formula to find the power in a circuit, but we don't know the voltage, E. Instead of knowing the values of E and I, we have the values of I and R. Since, according to Ohm's Law, E = I × R, we can substitute I × R in place of E in the power formula. Then, instead of P = E × I, we would have P = I × R × I, or P = I²R. By doing this, we have arranged our formula so that it contains the quantities that we know the values of, but we have not destroyed its equality. We have simply replaced one value, E, with an equal quantity, I × R.

The rules for equations also help us to rearrange formulas so that they indicate directly the quantities we want to find. For example, the formula $Z = \sqrt{R^2 + (X_C)^2}$ tells us how to find the impedance, Z, of a circuit. Suppose, however, we want to find X_C, but do not know the value of C or the frequency of the circuit. However, we have been given the impedance and can measure the resistance. In this case, we can apply the rules for working with equations to rearrange $Z = \sqrt{R^2 + (X_C)^2}$ so that it indicates X_C from Z and R.

We do it like this: $Z = \sqrt{R^2 + (X_C)^2}$. Then, squaring both members, we have

$$(Z)^2 = \left(\sqrt{R^2 + (X_C)^2} \right)^2$$

which equals

$$Z \times Z = \sqrt{R^2 + (X_C)^2} \\ \times \sqrt{R^2 + (X_C)^2}$$

or $\quad Z^2 = R^2 + (X_C)^2$

Now, subtracting R^2 from both members, we have

$$Z^2 - R^2 = R^2 - R^2 + (X_C^2) \text{ or}$$

$$Z^2 - R^2 = (X_C)^2$$

This indicates the value of $(X_C)^2$. But we want only X_C itself, so we take the square root of both members:

$$\sqrt{Z^2 - R^2} = \sqrt{(X_C)^2} \text{ or}$$

$$\sqrt{Z^2 - R^2} = X_C \text{ or}$$

$$X_C = \sqrt{Z^2 - R^2}$$

Now our one basic formula is rearranged to give us X_C directly when Z and R are known.

Likewise, C may be found with the formula $X_C = \dfrac{1}{2\pi f C}$ by rearrangement as follows:

If $\quad X_C = \dfrac{1}{2\pi f C}$, then

$$X_C \times C = \frac{1}{2\pi f C} \times C \text{ or}$$

$$X_C \times C = \frac{C}{2\pi f C} \text{ or}$$

$$X_C \times C = \frac{1}{2\pi f}.$$

Then,

$$X_C \times C \div X_C = \frac{1}{2\pi f} \div X_C \text{ or}$$

$$\frac{X_C \times C}{X_C} = \frac{1}{2\pi f X_C} \text{ or}$$

$$C = \frac{1}{2\pi f X_C}$$

Many of our formulas themselves are the result of the use of algebra and the rules for equations. They are found or derived from the knowledge of other facts.

For example, we often have the inductance of a circuit in microhenries and the capacity in microfarads and want to find the resonant frequency of the circuit. We can do this using the formula

$$f = \frac{159}{\sqrt{LC}}$$

where L is in microhenries, C is in microfarads, and f is in kilocycles. This formula is developed through the knowledge of other facts. For instance, at resonance we know that:

$$X_L = X_C$$

also $\quad X_L = 2\pi f L$

and $\quad X_C = \dfrac{1}{2\pi f C}$

In the formula $X_L = 2\pi f L$, f is in cycles per second and L is in henries; and in $X_C = \dfrac{1}{2\pi f C}$, f is in cycles per second and C is in farads.

Since $\quad X_L = X_C,$

we can substitute for X_L and X_C and get

$$2\pi f L = \frac{1}{2\pi f C}$$

Now, multiplying both sides by $2\pi f C$ we get

$$2\pi f L \times 2\pi f C = \frac{2\pi f C}{2\pi f C}$$

or $\quad 4\pi^2 f^2 L C = 1$

Now, dividing both sides by $4\pi^2 L C$ we get

$$\frac{4\pi^2 f^2 L C}{4\pi^2 L C} = \frac{1}{4\pi^2 L C}$$

or
$$f^2 = \frac{1}{4\pi^2 LC}$$

and taking the square root of both sides

$$\sqrt{f^2} = \sqrt{\frac{1}{4\pi^2 LC}}$$

or

$$f = \frac{\sqrt{1}}{\sqrt{4} \times \sqrt{\pi^2} \times \sqrt{LC}} = \frac{1}{2\pi\sqrt{LC}}$$

$2\pi = 6.28$ and dividing 1 by 6.28 gives .159 so we can rewrite the equation as

$$f = \frac{.159}{\sqrt{LC}}$$

where f is in cycles, L is in henries and C is in farads.

If we substitute L in microhenries and C in microfarads in this equation, we must divide each value by 1,000,000 to convert them to henries and farads. Let's do this in the equation:

$$f = \frac{.159}{\sqrt{\dfrac{L}{1,000,000} \times \dfrac{C}{1,000,000}}}$$

which can be written

$$f = \frac{\dfrac{.159}{\sqrt{LC}}}{\sqrt{1,000,000^2}}$$

which is

$$f = \frac{\dfrac{.159}{\sqrt{LC}}}{1,000,000}$$

This is the same as

$$f = \frac{.159}{1} \div \frac{\sqrt{LC}}{1,000,000}$$

Now to divide by fractions, we invert the divisor and multiply. For example,

$$\frac{1}{3} \div \frac{1}{4} = \frac{1}{3} \times \frac{4}{1} = \frac{4}{3}$$

Similarly,

$$\frac{6}{14} \div \frac{1}{2} = \frac{6}{14} \times \frac{2}{1} = \frac{12}{14}$$

and

$$\frac{.159}{1} \div \frac{\sqrt{LC}}{1,000,000} = \frac{.159}{1} \times \frac{1,000,000}{\sqrt{LC}}$$

Therefore, $f = \dfrac{159,000}{\sqrt{LC}}$

where f is in cycles per second, L is in microhenries and C is in microfarads.

To convert cycles per second to kilocycles per second, we divide by 1000. Therefore,

$$f = \frac{159,000}{\sqrt{LC}} \div 1000$$

$$f = \frac{159,000}{\sqrt{LC}} \times \frac{1}{1000}$$

$$f = \frac{159}{\sqrt{LC}}$$

where f is in kilocycles, L in microhenries, and C in microfarads. Thus, through algebraic manipulation of letters and using the rules for equations, we derive a simple, easy-to-remember formula for finding the resonant frequency.

Short Cuts For Equations

Although we can work with any equations with the rules and information that we have already studied, there are some short cuts which will let us work much faster and more efficiently. They are all derived from the basic rules, so we won't have to learn anything new. We will simply study the rules closely so we can see what the end results of the operations are and learn to apply them directly.

Moving a term from one member of an equation to the other member is an operation that is quite common and is called "transposing." The rule for transposing is:

A term may be transposed from one member of an equation to the other member by changing the sign of the term.

Thus, in an equation such as

$$Z^2 = R^2 + X^2$$

we can transpose the X^2 by simply changing the sign to give

$$Z^2 - X^2 = R^2$$

or transpose the R^2 to give

$$Z^2 - R^2 = X^2$$

or both, to get

$$Z^2 - R^2 - X^2 = 0$$

Using an equation with numbers shows that doing this does not destroy the equality. For example:

If $4 + 2 = 6$, then $4 = 6 - 2$, or $2 = 6 - 4$ or $0 = 6 - 4 - 2$. Likewise, if $10 - 4 - 2 = 4$, then

$$10 - 4 = 4 + 2$$

or $10 - 2 = 4 + 4$ or

$$10 = 4 + 2 + 4.$$

The basic rule of equations that states that we can add or subtract the same quantity from both members of the equation allows us to transpose. For example, in the equation $Z^2 = R^2 + X^2$, if we subtract X^2 from both members, we have:

$$Z^2 - X^2 = R^2 + X^2 - X^2$$
$$= Z^2 - X^2 = R^2$$

Or, in the equation $10 - 4 - 2 = 4$, adding 4 to both members, we have

$10 - 4 - 2 + 4 = 4 + 4$ which is equal to $10 - 2 = 4 + 4$. Thus, transposing terms by changing the sign is simply a short cut for adding or subtracting quantities to both members.

Using the same basic rule, we can also make the statement that:

We can cancel out like terms from the members of an equation, if the same term appears in each member, and is preceded by the same sign.

Thus, if we have an equation like $x + y = z + y$, we can cancel the y's out to give $x = z$. Or, an equation with numbers, like $4 \times 3 + 2 = 12 + 2$ can be reduced to $4 \times 3 = 12$ by canceling the 2's. As you can see, all we are doing when we cancel is to subtract the same term from both members. Thus, $x + y = z + y$ becomes $x + y - y = z + y - y$ or $x = z$. Likewise, $4 \times 3 + 2 = 12 + 2$ becomes $4 \times 3 + 2 - 2 = 12 + 2 - 2$ or simply,

$$4 \times 3 = 12.$$

Another common rule is one that involves the signs of the terms in the equations. Stated simply, it is:

The signs of all the terms of an equation may be changed without changing the equality.

Thus, an equation such as $-x + y = -4 + 3$ may be rewritten as $x - y = 4 - 3$. In doing this, we are simply multiplying both sides of the equation by the same number, -1. In our example,

$$(-x + y)(-1) = (-4 + 3)(-1)$$

or $x - y = 4 - 3$.

When you studied ratio and proportion, you learned to cross-multiply. Thus, $\dfrac{x}{y} = \dfrac{a}{b}$ could be rewritten as xb = ya. Cross multiplication is also made possible through the rules for working with equations. When we do this, we are really multiplying both members by one term and then multiplying both members again by another term. Thus, $\dfrac{x}{y} = \dfrac{a}{b}$ becomes xb = ya, because: If $\dfrac{x}{y} = \dfrac{a}{b}$, then

$$b\left(\frac{x}{y}\right) = \left(\frac{a}{\cancel{b}}\right)\cancel{b}$$

or $\dfrac{xb}{y} = a.$ Again, $\left(\dfrac{xb}{\cancel{y}}\right)\cancel{y} = (a)y$

and xb = ya. Thus, cross multiplication is just a quick way of following the basic rules.

Then, of course, we have the many operations with multiplication and division which help us so much with rearranging our formulas. For example: $I = \dfrac{E}{R}$ because $E = I \times R$ and

$$\frac{E}{R} = \frac{I \times \cancel{R}}{\cancel{R}} \text{ or } \frac{E}{R} = I \text{ or } I = \frac{E}{R}.$$

Likewise, $R = \dfrac{E}{I}$ because $E = I \times R$

and $\dfrac{E}{I} = \dfrac{\cancel{I}R}{\cancel{I}} = \dfrac{E}{I} = R.$ With these

rules and short cuts in mind, and our knowledge of basic algebra, we are ready to practice solving equations.

Solving Equations

The purpose of learning to work with letters and equations is to make it easier to solve the problems in working in electronics. While many of the problems will be straightforward and can be solved by applying basic formulas, some of them will require sound thinking and reasoning before the answer is found. The use of algebra and a good working knowledge of equations will be very helpful in these more difficult solutions. As you have seen, working with letters is not difficult and the rules for operating with equations are both simple and logical. However, to become really proficient with algebra and equations requires a lot of practice.

One of the biggest difficulties in arriving at circuit solutions is not in solving the equations themselves, but in setting up the equations in the first place. This also takes a lot of practice. While it is difficult, if not impossible, to operate by a strict set of rules for solving problems, there are a few general procedures that are worth following.

First, you should read the problem so carefully that everything about it is thoroughly understood. Then, you should determine exactly what you want to know and represent it with a letter. If there are two or more unknown quantities, you should represent them in terms of the first one. Next, you should try to apply the formulas that will allow you to find the unknown quantity from the known facts. If this is not possible, you should try to set up letter equations that will allow you to state the problem in terms of the unknown quantity. Finally, you should solve the equations for the unknown value by substituting letter and number equivalents that are available. Remember, you will often save yourself a lot of time and effort by working with letters as long as possible before substituting numbers.

Now let's solve some simple equations, and later some problems, to see how we can apply these rules.

In the problem

$$3i+14+2i = i+26$$

solve for i. The first thing to do is to get all like terms together. We can do this by transposing the "i" terms to one side and the numbers to the other side. Thus,

$$3i+14+2i = i+26$$

becomes

$$3i+2i-i = 26-14$$

Then, collecting terms, we have: $4i = 12$ and then dividing both members by 4 to solve for i gives us $\dfrac{\cancel{4}i}{\cancel{4}} = \dfrac{12}{4}$

or i = 3.

We can always check this answer by substituting this value of i = 3 back into our original equation. Doing this:

given $3i+14+2i = i+26$

then $3\times3+14+2\times3 = 3+26$

and $9+14+6 = 29$ or $29 = 29$

Thus, our answer of i = 3 must be correct because our equation is balanced if this value is used to check it.

Solve for y in the equation:

$$3(y-2)-10(y-6) = 5.$$

Here, we follow the rules of order and get rid of the values within the parentheses first. This gives us:

$$3y-6-10y+60 = 5$$

Transposing: $3y-10y = 5+6-60$

Then: $-7y = -49$

Changing signs: $7y = 49$

Solving for y: $\dfrac{\cancel{7}y}{\cancel{7}} = \dfrac{49}{7}$ or

$$49 \div 7 = 7$$

Now let's try solving for E in the equation:

$$19-5E(4E+1) = 40-10E(2E-1)$$

Remove parentheses:

$$19-\cancel{20E^2}-5E = 40-\cancel{20E^2}+10E$$

Transposing: $-5E-10E = 40-19$

Then: $-15E = 21$

Solving for E:

$$\dfrac{-\cancel{15}E}{-\cancel{15}} = \dfrac{21}{-15} \text{ or } E = \dfrac{21}{-15} = -1.4$$

Notice the cancellation of equal terms in the second step.

Earlier in our discussion of equations, we mentioned that we could never multiply or divide an equation by zero. This is easy enough to remember, but it is not always so easy to realize that we are in danger of doing it. Now that you are more familiar with working with equations, let's examine this important rule more thoroughly by working the following equation.

First, let:

$$a = b$$

Multiply by a:

$$a^2 = ab$$

Subtract b^2:

$$a^2-b^2 = ab-b^2$$

Now

$$a^2-b^2 = (a+b)(a-b)$$

Therefore:

$$(a+b)(a-b) = b(a-b)$$

Divide by (a−b):

$$\dfrac{(a+b)\cancel{(a-b)}}{\cancel{(a-b)}} = \dfrac{b\cancel{(a-b)}}{\cancel{(a-b)}}$$

Then:
$$a+b = b$$
But,
$$a = b$$
Therefore:
$$2b = b$$
Divide by b:

and:
$$\frac{2\cancel{b}}{\cancel{b}} = \frac{\cancel{b}}{\cancel{b}}$$

$$2 = 1$$

Obviously, 2 cannot equal 1, and somewhere in our manipulation of the equation, we have made a mistake that has destroyed its equality. Although all of our steps seem justified, because we never did anything to one member that we didn't do to the other, we actually have divided by zero at one point. Can you find it? If a = b, then (a−b) must equal zero. Therefore, when we divided both sides of our equation by (a−b), we were dividing by zero, which we can never do.

Setting up Equations. Now let's see what sort of reasoning we have to do to set up an equation for solving a simple problem. For example, consider the following problem: "What value of inductance will produce resonance to 50 cycles if it is placed in series with a 20 μf capacitor"? Looking at the problem carefully, we see that it deals with resonance and that a resonant frequency and a value of capacitance are given. We are asked for the inductance. Thus, we have:

Given:

$$C = 20\ \mu f \qquad f = 50\ \text{cycles}$$

Find: L

Since our problem deals with resonance, we naturally think of our formula for resonance: $f = \dfrac{159}{\sqrt{LC}}$. Com-

paring this with what is given and with what we want to find, we can see that we have the necessary information to use this formula and that L can be found with it, if it is rearranged. Accordingly, we would first rearrange our formula to indicate the value of L.

Doing this:

$$f = \frac{159}{\sqrt{LC}} \quad \text{or } f^2 = \frac{159^2}{LC},$$

then
$$Lf^2 = \frac{159^2}{C}$$

$$L = \frac{159^2}{f^2C}$$

Now, we can substitute our values in the formula and solve for L. However, before we do this, we must check our units of measurement to see if the given values can be substituted directly. In this particular problem, we cannot substitute them directly because the formula $f = \dfrac{159}{\sqrt{LC}}$ is in kilocycles per second when L is in microhenries and C is in microfarads. Therefore, we must convert 50 cycles per second to kilocycles per second by moving the decimal three places to the left. Thus,

$$50\ \text{cycles/sec} = .05\ \text{kc/sec}$$

Now, using the formula

$$L = \frac{159^2}{f^2C}$$

$$= \frac{25,281}{.05 \times .05 \times 20}$$

$$= \frac{25,281}{.0025 \times 20}$$

$$= \frac{25,281}{.05}$$

$$= 505{,}620 \text{ microhenries}$$

$$= .51 \text{ henries (approx)}$$

While this is a simple problem, it does show the basic reasoning behind the handling of any problem. First, examine the problem. Find a formula, if possible. Arrange the formula to indicate the unknown. Check for proper units of measurement. Substitute and solve for the unknown. Now, let's try the procedure again on a more complex situation.

In the circuit shown in Fig. 3-11 suppose we are asked to find the resistance of R_4 from the values given. First of all, examination of the problem shows that we are given all the

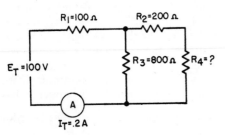

Fig. 3-11. Circuit used for solving for the resistance of R_4.

resistances except R_4 and we are also given the supply voltage and the current. Listing these values, we have:

Given: $E_T = 100V$

$$I_T = .2A$$

$$R_1 = 100\Omega$$

$$R_2 = 200\Omega$$

$$R_3 = 800\Omega$$

Find: R_4

If we had the total resistance of the circuit, we could set up an equation because we know the total resistance must be equal to R_1 plus the resistance of the parallel branch made

up of R_3 in parallel with R_2 and R_4. The resistance of this branch can be expressed using the formula for parallel resistors and treating R_2 and R_4 in series like a single resistance. The resistance of the parallel branch is

$$R_p = \frac{R_3(R_2 + R_4)}{R_3 + R_2 + R_4}$$

Thus, the total resistance of the circuit R_T is

$$R_T = R_1 + \frac{R_3(R_2 + R_4)}{R_3 + R_2 + R_4}$$

Now in this equation we do not know the value of R_T or R_4. But we do know the total voltage E_T and the total current I_T so we can find R_T.

$$R_T = \frac{E_T}{I_T}$$

Thus, it looks like we can use the equation expressing R_T in terms of R_1, R_2, R_3, and R_4 to solve for R_4. Indeed we can do this, but look at the term for the resistance of the parallel branch. Notice we have R_4 in both the top and bottom of this expression. We will have to do a great deal of manipulation before we can solve for R_4. Before we start on this task, let's look at the circuit again to see if any easier solution is available.

First, notice that the total current is .2 amp. This means that the current through R_1 is .2 amp so we can easily find the voltage drop across the resistor using:

$$E = I_T R_1$$

$$= .2 \times 100 = 20 \text{ volts}$$

If we have a source voltage of 100 volts and a voltage drop of 20 volts across R_1, we must have $100 - 20 = 80$ volts across the parallel branch. Now let's find the current through

R_3, which we can do using

$$I = \frac{E}{R}$$

$$= \frac{80}{800} = .1 \text{ amp}$$

If the total current is .2 amp and .1 amp flows through one branch of the parallel circuit, the current in the other branch must also be .1 amp. Therefore we have .1 amp flowing through R_2 and R_4.

We know the voltage across R_2 and R_4 in series is 80 volts. Let's find the voltage across R_2 using:

$$E = IR_2$$

$$= .1 \times 200 = 20 \text{ volts}$$

This means the voltage across R_4 must be $80 - 20 = 60$ volts. Now we know the voltage across R_4, 60 volts, and the current through it, .1 amp, so we can find R_4 using:

$$R = \frac{E}{I}$$

$$= \frac{60}{.1} = 600 \text{ ohms}$$

Thus we have solved the problem, using a series of simple steps and avoided some complicated work by taking a second look at the problem.

In a similar fashion, we could solve for E_T if we had the following values given for the circuit in Fig. 11:

Given: $R_1 = 350\Omega$

$R_2 = 300\Omega$

$R_3 = 500\Omega$

$R_4 = 600\Omega$

Find E_T if the voltage drop across R_4 is 60V.

First, since you know the voltage across R_4 and the resistance of R_4, find the current through R_4. Once you have this current you can find the voltage across R_2 because the same current flows through R_2 and R_4. When you get the voltage across R_2, you can find the current through R_3 because the voltage across R_3 will be equal to the voltage across R_2 plus the voltage across R_4.

Now you can determine the total current flow in the circuit and then find the voltage across R_1. Once you have this voltage you should be able to find the total voltage. Work out this problem using the values given. The answer is 188 volts.

Thus, by applying the simplest formula or equation that we can, and working through the problem a step at a time, we can find the solutions to many different types of problems. As you can see, one of the greatest difficulties is in choosing a basic equation that can be made to use our known quantities. We want to be sure to choose the equation that will lead to the simplest solution. This takes sound reasoning and a lot of practice. Once you learn to do this, your knowledge of algebra and equations will let you solve the problems readily. You will get some more practice in this type of work as you study the "J" operator in the next section.

3-4. The "J" Operator

The "J" operator, or J multiplier as it is sometimes called, is simply a device that allows us to represent a vector mathematically. Through the use of this operator "J" (which may also be written j), we are able to simplify a great deal of work in ac circuits. Instead of having to lay out a vector accurately for each separate value of resistance or reactance, we can simply state them all mathematically and then compute their final value algebraically. This is a great advantage in dealing with the complex arrangements found in tube and transistor circuits as well as any other complex ac circuit.

Being able to compute vectors mathematically means that we can multiply and divide vectors as easily as we can add or subtract them. This in itself is something that we have never been able to do before. In this section of the lesson, we will see exactly what we mean by the term "J" and how it can be used as an operator in ac circuits. We will learn how to do "J" arithmetic, and then we will apply these new principles to ac circuit calculations.

Numerical Representation of a Vector

When you studied vectors you learned that they could be used in electronics to represent the time or phase as well as the magnitude of ac circuit quantities. In constructing vector diagrams, we used two scales at right angles to each other, like those shown in Fig. 3-12. Our reference vectors were laid out from the center of the scale to the right towards 0° and were used to represent zero time or in-phase components. Those that

represented quantities that occurred 90° before the reference vectors were laid out vertically from the center towards 90°. Those that were exactly 180° out of phase were laid out on the horizontal scale, pointing from the center towards the left, or 180°. Those that represented quantities occurring 90° after the reference vector were drawn down the vertical scale from the center towards 270°.

Thus, any vector that was laid out so that it pointed towards 90° was considered to occur before 0° and after 180°. Similarly, a vector pointing down towards 270° was considered to occur after 0° but before 180°. Because of this, we arrived at the statement that vectors could be rotated about a common point to indicate the time of an occurrence. Furthermore, if 90° represents before zero, but after 180°, the vectors represent the relative time of occurrences by rotating counterclockwise. In this way, vector A in Fig. 3-12 occurs before 0°, but after 90°; vector B before 90°,

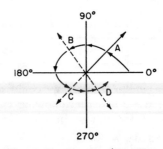

Fig. 3-12. Rotation of vectors.

but after 180°; vector C before 180°, but after 270°, and vector D before 270° and after 0°.

In your study of algebra, you learned that you could represent any quantity or value by a letter. Therefore, let's consider that a force acts upon vectors to cause them to rotate in this way, and that this force can be represented by a letter value. Further, let's assume that the amount of this force necessary to rotate a vector 90° is represented by the letter "J."

Now, let's draw a vector, A, ten units in length, along the reference line from the center towards 0° as shown in Fig. 3-13. In this position the vector is in phase with the reference and occurs at time zero. If we now multiply the vector by "J", which represents a rotating force of 90°, we must consider that the vector will rotate 90° counterclockwise and point towards 90° as shown by vector "J"A in Fig. 3-13. Thus, multiplying the base vector A by J has resulted in its being rotated through 90° until it becomes the new vector "J"A.

Likewise, if we multiply our new vector "J"A by J, it will rotate another 90° and become vector $J \cdot JA$ or J^2A and will point toward 180° as shown. Multiplying by J again will make our vector rotate another 90° to become $J \cdot J^2A$ or J^3A pointing towards 270°. One more multiplica-

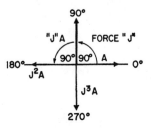

Fig. 3-13. Using J to rotate a vector.

tion by J or $J \cdot J^3A$ gives us J^4A and brings the vector back to its starting point.

When we studied signed numbers, we used a horizontal scale similar to the one we use in our reference dia-

gram for vectors. We represented positive numbers as starting from the center at 0 and working toward the right, as shown in Fig. 3-14. Our negative numbers started at the center and

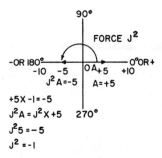

Fig. 3-14. Diagram of $J^2 = -1$.

progressed towards the left. In Fig. 3-14, we have shown the same basic vector reference diagram as we used in Figs. 3-12 and 3-13, but we have also included the positive and negative scales along the horizontal line as shown.

Along our reference line, we have drawn vector A to represent an in-phase vector +5 units long. If we multiply this vector A by J^2, it will rotate 180° and point towards 180° as shown. Now, according to our scale of positive and negative numbers, this new vector J^2A will equal −5. This is as it should be because anything 180° out of phase with +5 must be equal to −5 because it is exactly opposite. Just what is minus 5? One explanation is that minus five is plus five times minus one, because $+5 \times (-1) = -5$. If this is the case, then J^2 must be equal to −1, because $J^2 \times (+5) = -5$, just as

$$-1 \times (+5) = -5.$$

Thus, any time that J^2 is used to represent a force for rotating vectors, J^2 will always be equal to −1, and −1 is substituted immediately for

J^2. If $J^2 = -1$, then J must be equal to $\sqrt{-1}$. Thus, the value of J is often referred to as being imaginary because there is no number equal to $\sqrt{-1}$ because $1 \times 1 = 1$ and $-1 \times (-1)$ also $= 1$. There is no number you can multiply by itself to get -1! Whenever a J^2 term appears in a problem solution, we eliminate it by substituting -1, but where a J term appears we simply leave the J in the term because there is nothing we can substitute for it. Thus, in the term $6 + J8$, the 6 is called the real or in-phase component and the J8, the imaginary or quadrature component.

Now let's go a step further. If $J^2 = -1$, then $J \cdot J^2$ or J^3 must be equal to $-1 \cdot J$ or $-J$. We have already represented vectors drawn down the vertical line towards 270° as being a reference vector times J^3, so either J^3 or $-J$ times a vector must rotate it so that it points downward towards 270°. If $J \cdot J = J^2$ or -1 and $J \cdot J^2$ or $J^3 = J \cdot -1$ or $-J$, then J^4 representing a full 360° rotation of a vector is equal to $J^3 \cdot J$, or $J^2 \cdot J^2$ or $-1 \times (-1) = +1$. Once again this is as it should be, because any vector rotated completely around the diagram will be back where it started and represents a positive or in-phase value.

Once we understand this use of the letter "J" as an operator for determining the final position of a vector, we can use it in our work in electronics. Any time that we have a quantity multiplied by J, we will immediately know that it is a vector quantity pointing towards 90°. Similarly, if we have a $-J$ or J^3 quantity, we will know that it represents a vector drawn down towards 270°. Any positive quantity without a J or one with a J^4 multiplier can be treated as an in-phase component drawn towards 0°, and any minus quantity or one with a J^2 multiplier will represent a vector drawn out of phase towards 180°.

Thus, if we have a series circuit consisting of a resistor and a coil, we can represent the impedance vector with a binomial term. For example, suppose the resistor has a resistance of 6Ω and the coil has an inductive reactance of 8Ω. We can say that the impedance of the circuit is equal to (6Ω + J8Ω). As soon as we see the J in the impedance notation, we can visualize a vector diagram like the one shown in Fig. 3-15. Here the 6Ω has no multiplier so it is drawn along

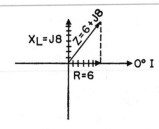

Fig. 3-15.   Diagram of Z = 6+J8.

the reference line I and represents the in-phase component. The J in the +J8Ω tells us that this quantity is drawn upward at right angles to the in-phase component, as shown.

Similarly, if we see a notation such as: E = (-100 - J60), we can visualize a resultant voltage vector that has an E_R of -100 volts for one component and an E_{X_C} of 60 volts as another component, as shown in Fig. 3-16. Another vector such as

$$Z = 50 + J^3 30$$

would be immediately recognized, as shown in Fig. 3-17. In this way, we can represent any vector as a simple binomial term. All we have to do is remember the position values of our various J multipliers.

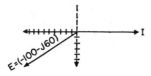

Fig. 3-16. Diagram of E = (−100 − J60).

"J" Arithmetic

Since we are able to represent any vector mathematically as a binomial term through the use of J as a multiplier, we can solve any vector problem through the use of algebra. For example, we learned that the sum of two binomials such as (5a + 66) and (3a − 46) would be

$$5a + 66 + 3a − 46 = 8a + 20.$$

Likewise, the sum of a vector such as (10 + J5) and another equal to

$$(5 − J10)$$

Fig. 3-17.   Diagram of Z = 50 + J³30.

would be

$$(10 + J5) + (5 − J10)$$
$$= 10 + 5 + J5 − J10,$$

or a new vector equal to 15 − J5. To prove that this mathematical solution is correct we can check it against a measurement solution.

First, let's draw our two vectors, (10 + J5) and (5 − J10) as shown in Fig. 3-18A. Now, there are two methods which we can use to add vectors. We can break them both down into their components and add the components as we learned to do in our lesson on vectors, as shown in Fig. 3-18B. Or, we can add the two vectors head to tail on the same diagram by being careful to place them in their proper

position regarding the reference line, and then draw a resultant vector, as shown in Fig. 3-18C . In either case, the components of the resultant vector are the same and equal 15 − J5, which

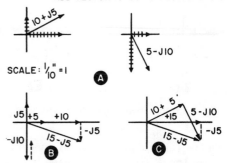

Fig. 3-18. Adding vectors with diagrams to prove mathematical solution.

is exactly what we got mathematically so our mathematical solution must be correct.

To subtract one vector from another, we can also work mathematically with our binomial terms, or we can solve them with diagrams. For example, let's subtract vector B from vector A, as shown in Fig. 3-19. As you can see from the diagram in Fig. 3-19A, vector A can be written as 8 + J10 and vector B can be written as 12 + J6. There are also two ways that we can subtract vectors with a diagram. Let's examine them.

First, there is the resolution method where we break each vector into its two components. Then we take the components of the vector that we are subtracting, reverse their directions and then add them head to tail, as we do in adding vectors. Notice how similar this is to the subtraction of signed numbers. We reverse the direction of the subtrahend (change the signs) and then proceed as in addition.

We have done this in Fig. 3-19B

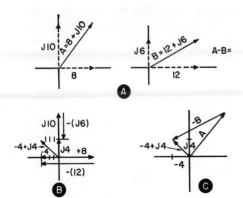

Fig. 3-19. Subtracting vectors with diagrams.

with many vectors at many different angles. For example, consider the vectors A, B, C, and D in Fig. 3-20. Suppose we want to add vector A to vector B and then subtract vectors C and D from this sum. Mathematically this becomes:

$$(15+J3)+(6-J9)-(-8+J4)$$
$$-(+9-J12)$$
$$= 15+J3+6-J9+8-J4-9+J12$$
$$= 15+6+8-9+J3+J12-J9-J4$$
$$= 29-9+J15-J13$$
$$= 20+J2$$

where the J6 and +12 components of vector B have been reversed in direction and then added vectorially to the J10 and +8 components of vector A. As you can see, this gives us a new vector with components of −4 and J4, or simply −4+J4. We can also subtract vectors by subtracting them directly, as shown in Fig. 19C. Here we simply reverse the direction of vector B and add it head to tail to vector A, being careful not to change its position in regard to the reference. Then, the resultant drawn from the tail of A to the head of B is equal to −4+J4, as it was with the other method.

Subtracting vectors mathematically is much simpler. We simply subtract the binomial notations of the vectors just as we would subtract any binomial terms. For example, vector B from vector A will equal:

$$(8+J10)-(12+J6)$$
$$= 8+J10-12-J6$$
$$= -4+J4$$

which is the same as we got with our diagrams. This mathematical method of subtracting vectors is especially valuable in complex problems dealing

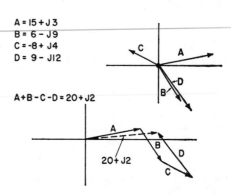

A = 15 + J3
B = 6 − J9
C = −8 + J4
D = 9 − J12

A+B−C−D = 20+J2

Fig. 3-20. Addition and subtraction of vectors by diagram.

The diagram gives us the same thing, but what a lot of work and confusion it is!

Multiplication and Division. In our work in electronics we may want to multiply or divide two or more vectors. The vectors may represent voltages, currents, or impedances of various values at different phase angles. The J operator will be very handy in this case because there is no purely graphical means of multiplying or dividing vectors with different phase angles. However, as we learned in algebra, it is quite simple to multiply or divide binomials.

Since we studied the multiplication and division of binomials earlier in this lesson, we should not have any trouble with the mathematics. Our only job now is to make sure we understand how we represent our vector re-

also increased the angle of this vector from the reference line. If we stop and think a moment, we will have to agree that this should happen because we are multiplying a rotating force by a rotating force when we multiply

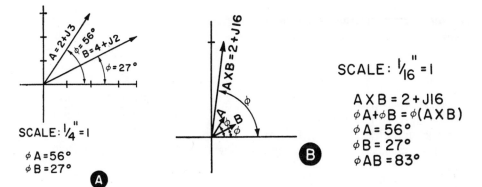

FIG. 21. Multiplying vectors.

sultant. Suppose that we want to multiply vector A by vector B. As shown in Fig. 3-21A, vector A is equal to (2+J3) and vector B is equal to (4+J2). To multiply these two vectors we simply multiply the binomials which gives us:

$$
\begin{array}{r}
2+J3 \\
\times\ 4+J2 \\
\hline
8+J12 \\
+\ J4+J^2 6 \\
\hline
8+J16+J^2 6
\end{array}
$$

But, remember J^2 is equal to -1, so $8+J16+J^2 6$ becomes

$$8+J16+6(-1) = 8+J16-6$$
$$= +2+J16$$

Thus, our resultant vector from this multiplication is equal to a vector of $2+J16$, as shown in Fig. 3-21B.

Notice that we have not only increased the length of the resultant vector by multiplying, but we have

J by J. Further, remember that J alone is enough to rotate a vector 90°, while J^2 rotates it 180°. Looking at this,

$$90°+90° = 180° \text{ and } J \times J = 180°$$

Thus, multiplying J by J is the same as adding the two 90° angles. Now, if you measure the angle that vector A makes with the reference line and add it to the angle that vector B makes with the reference line, the sum of these two angles will equal the angle of the resultant vector.

In our problem: Since $\phi A = 56°$ and $\phi B = 27°$, then

$$\phi A + \phi B = 56°+27° = 83°.$$

If we measure the angle of the resultant vector AB, we will find that its angle is exactly 83°. In addition to this relationship between the angles, there is a relationship between the lengths of vector A and vector B in the resultant vector AB. If we determine the length of vectors A and B through measurement or by using the pythagorean theorem, we will find that A is equal to 3.61 and B is equal to 4.47. Then if we multiply these actual lengths of A and B we find that $A \times B = 3.61 \times 4.47 = 16.13$. Now, either through measurement or by using the pythagorean theorem, we can also determine the length of our resultant vector AB. It is equal to:

$$AB = \sqrt{2^2+16^2} = \sqrt{4+256}$$
$$= \sqrt{260} = 16.13$$

to two decimal places. Thus, our resultant in vector multiplication is a new vector that is equal to the product of the length of all the vectors multiplied and that forms an angle with the reference that is equal to the sum of the angles of all the vectors multiplied. If we stop and think a moment and have understood our previous operations with vectors, we will see that this is what should happen.

In the problem that we just discussed, both of the vectors that we multiplied were made up of positive values. Let's see what happens if we multiply a vector such as $12+J9$ by another vector equal to $7-J6$. Multiplying our binomial, we have:

$$(12+J9) \times (7-J6)$$
$$= 84+J63-J72-J^2 54$$
$$= 84-J9-54(-1)$$
$$= 84+54-J9$$
$$= 138-J9$$

Here, as you can see, we had one vector to the right and above the reference, and another to the right and below the reference. The resultant is a vector that is to the right and below the reference.

Now, suppose we wanted to multiply the following vectors together:

$$(8+J16) \times (5+J2) \times (2+J3)$$

This would give us:

$$
\begin{array}{r}
8+J16 \\
5+J\,2 \\
\hline
40+J\,80 \\
+J\,16+J^2 32 \\
\hline
40+J96+J^2 32
\end{array}
$$

Then:

$$
\begin{array}{r}
40+J96+J^2 32 \\
2+J3 \\
\hline
80+J192+\ J^2 64 \\
+J120+J^2 288+J^3 96 \\
\hline
80+J312+J^2 352+J^3 96
\end{array}
$$

Then:　$80+J312+J^2 352+J^3 96$
$$= 80+J312+(352 \times -1)$$
$$+(96 \times -J)$$
$$= 80-352+J312-J96$$
$$= -272+J216$$

Even though all our multipliers were to the right and above the line, our resultant is to the left and above. Notice that the J^2 term was resolved to its value of -1 and that the J^3 term resolved to its equal value of $-J$.

In order to divide vectors, we simply divide our binomial representations of the vectors involved. The easiest way to do this is to set up the division as a fraction and then clear the J term from the denominator. For example, if we wish to divide a vector such as $2+J16$ by a vector equal to $2+J3$, we would set our division up as a fraction: $\dfrac{2+J16}{2+J3}$.

Then, if we multiply both the numerator and the denominator by $2-J3$, we will not change the value of our fraction, but we will get rid of the J term in our denominator. For example, we will have:

$$\frac{(2+J16)(2-J3)}{(2+J3)(2-J3)}$$

$$= \frac{4+J26-J^2 48}{4-J^2 9}$$

$$= \frac{4+J26+48}{4+9}$$

$$= \frac{52+J26}{13}$$

$$= \frac{13(4+J2)}{13} = 4+J2$$

Thus, $2+16J \div 2+3J = 4+2J$. For proof of this, check Fig. 21 again. As you can see $(4+2J) \times (2+3J)$ are the vectors we previously used in this multiplication problem and our product was $2+J16$. Similarly:

$$138-J9 \div 12+J9$$

$$= \frac{138-J9}{12+J9}$$

$$= \frac{(138-J9)(12-J9)}{(12+J9)(12-J9)}$$

$$= \frac{1656-J1350+J^2 81}{144-J^2 81}$$

$$= \frac{1656-J1350-81}{144+81}$$

$$= \frac{1575-J1350}{225}$$

$$= (7-J6)$$

To prove our answer we simply multiply our quotient $(7-J6)$ by our divisor $(12+J9)$ to get our dividend of $138-J9$. Notice that each time we clear our J term from the denominator by multiplying our numerator and denominator by the same number. This number is always a binomial that is exactly the same as the denominator except that the sign of the

J term is reversed. Such a term is called a "conjugate" term. You'll notice that each time we get a J^2 term or any even power of J, the J term disappears because $J^2 = -1$. Remember, in algebra we pointed out that $(a-b)(a+b) = a^2-b^2$. Thus, if we have $(a-Jb)$, we can multiply it by $(a+Jb)$ to get $a^2-J^2b^2$ and eliminate the J. Similarly, if we have $a+Jb$, we can multiply it by $a-Jb$ to eliminate the J. Thus, we can say that we multiply both the numerator and the denominator by the conjugate of the denominator to clear the J term from the denominator.

When we multiplied two vectors together, we discovered that the product was a new vector equal in length to the product of the vector values at an angle equal to the sum of the angles of the vectors multiplied. In dividing vectors, the opposite relationship exists. If we divide one vector by another and then lay out the dividend vector, the divisor vector, and the quotient vector in a diagram, we will find that:

1. The quotient vector is equal in length to the quotient of the length of the dividend vector divided by the length of the divisor vector.

2. The quotient vector will be at an angle to the reference line that is equal to the difference between the angles of the vectors divided.

Thus, we have two ways that we can multiply or divide vectors. We can multiply or divide the binomial representation of the vectors as we have learned to do in this section, or if we know the vector length we can use it. To multiply, we find the product of the lengths and the sum of the angles. To divide, we find the quotient of the lengths and the difference of the angles.

We mentioned earlier that there was no purely graphical way to multiply and divide vectors. While we can do some of the work graphically, we must always perform some mathematics on the side. Even then, the process of finding the product or quotient in this way is very tedious and involved. Since we already have two methods for finding the products or the quotients mathematically, and since either of these methods is much simpler and faster than the simplest graphical method, it will not be worthwhile for us to study the graphical (plus some math) methods.

In this section of the chapter, you have learned to perform arithmetic operations with vectors. You have learned how to add and subtract vectors, how to multiply and divide by vectors. You will perform all four operations in solving even fairly simple ac circuit problems.

Now, to complete the study of the "J" operator and the binomial representation of vectors, let's apply what you have learned to some circuit problems.

"J" Operator in Circuit Calculations

The best way to make sure that you understand representing vectors with binomials by using the "J" operator is to work with them in circuit calculations. In this way, you will get some practice with "J" arithmetic as well as some more experience in solving circuit problems. We will start with some simple series ac circuits, and then examine some parallel and series parallel combinations. If, after we have done this, you feel that you still need more practice, try applying these methods to some of the ac circuits you have worked with in the other chapters.

In analyzing and working the circuit problems in this section, we will use the mathematical solutions and the J operator. However, we will still use vector diagrams to help visualize the circuit quantities and their relationships. But, since we are not going to use the diagrams for our actual calculations, we will not need to draw them to scale. Thus, for every problem, we will have a simple diagram to use in our analysis and a mathematical solution for the diagram. This is by far the best way to work with any ac circuit problem.

In the circuits shown in Fig. 3-22 we are to find the current. Let's consider the circuit at A first. Since we have an inductance in the circuit along with a resistance, we know that the voltage will lead the current, or another way of saying the same thing is that the current will lag the voltage. Thus, since we are given the value E = 234V, and we draw it at 0°, as in Fig. 3-22C, then the current must lag it as shown. To position the current vector in this position, we must have a −J term in the current.

Now let's look at the circuit in Fig. 3-22B. Here we have a resistance and capacitance in series. We know the current must lead the voltage so we must have a phase relationship like the one shown in Fig. 3-22D. This means we must have a +J term in the current.

We know that capacitive reactance is the opposite of inductive reactance so one must have a +J sign and the other a −J sign. But which should be + and which should be −? The answer is we must use the signs that make the current come out with the correct sign. Let's see what this means. We know that in an ac circuit

$$.I = \frac{E}{Z}$$

In the circuits in Fig. 3-22 the voltage is 234 volts, the resistance 6 ohms, and the reactance 9 ohms. Thus, in one circuit $Z = 6+J9$, and in the other circuit $Z = 6-J9$. Now, let's solve the current in both circuits and then we can see whether a $+J$ term represents inductive or capacitive reactance.

$$I = \frac{E}{Z}$$

$$= \frac{234}{6+J9}$$

$$= \frac{234(6-J9)}{(6+J9)(6-J9)}$$

$$= \frac{1404-J2106}{36-J^2 81}$$

$$= \frac{1404-J2106}{117}$$

$$= 12-J18$$

Now, since we already know that in the circuit with the inductive reactance we need a $-J$ term in the current, this represents the current in Fig. 3-22A, and $6+J9$ must represent the impedance of the circuit in Fig. 3-22A. Therefore, it appears that inductive reactance should be represented by a $+J$ term which means that capacitive reactance will be represented by a $-J$ term. Now let's solve Fig. 3-22B, using $6-J9$ as the impedance, and see if we get a $+J$ in the current term.

$$I = \frac{E}{Z}$$

$$= \frac{234}{6-J9}$$

$$= \frac{234(6+J9)}{(6-J9)(6+J9)}$$

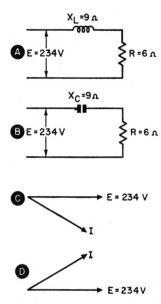

Fig. 3-22. The vector diagrams at C and D show the phase relationships between the voltage and current in the circuits shown at A and B.

$$= \frac{1404+J2106}{36-J^2 81}$$

$$= \frac{1404+J2106}{117}$$

$$= 12+J18$$

Thus we have a $+J$ term in the current. In fact, notice that the only difference in the two current values is in the sign of the J term which is what we might expect since the reactances are equal.

Remember that inductive reactance gets a $+$ sign and capacitive reactance a $-$ sign. Now, let's do another example.

In the circuit shown in Fig. 3-23, we are asked to find the impedance. An examination of the circuit shows that it is a series circuit consisting of resistances, coils, and capacitors. Accordingly, we know that the impedance must be equal to the vector sum of the resistances and reactances. Therefore, in the diagram in Fig. 3-23B, we have made a simple sketch of the vector relationship of all the components. Since it is a series circuit and the current is common, we have used a reference line, I, as a base for the diagram. All the resistance vec-

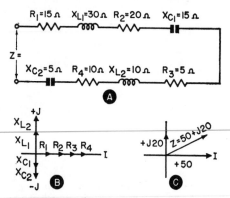

Fig. 3-23. Series ac circuit and vector representation.

tors are indicated along this reference line to show the total effect of the "in phase" components. Voltages across the resistances will all be in phase with I and hence fall along this reference vector.

The voltage across any coil in the circuit will lead the current by 90° if we neglect its resistance, so X_L vectors are drawn so that they lead the resistance vectors by 90°. This conforms with what we just discovered, that inductive reactance terms are $+J$ terms. The voltage across the capacitors, on the other hand, will lag the current, so the X_C vectors are drawn so that they lag the resistance vectors by 90°. Now, notice that the X_C vectors are $-J$ vectors. The resistance vectors, of course, are in phase and are simply represented as the positive number terms.

Now, from our knowledge of circuit laws, vectors, algebra, and the "J"

operator, we can write the following equation for the circuit impedance:

$$Z = R_1 + R_2 + R_3 + R_4 + JX_{L1} + JX_{L2} - JX_{C1} - JX_{C2} \text{ and,}$$

$$Z = 15 + 20 + 5 + 10 + J30 + J10 - J15 - J5$$

$$Z = 50 + J40 - J20 = 50 + J20$$

Thus, we can draw a resultant vector diagram as shown in Fig. 3-23C where $Z = 50 + J20$. Since the J term in our resultant vector is only used to indicate the direction of the final reactive component, or the sign of the resultant phase angle, we can drop it while we compute the impedance with our formula $Z = \sqrt{R^2 + X^2}$. Thus, the impedance is:

$$Z = \sqrt{50^2 + 20^2} = \sqrt{2500 + 400}$$

$$= \sqrt{2900} = 54\Omega \text{ (approximately)}$$

Therefore, we can write the impedance of our circuit in two ways:

As a vector, $Z = 50 + J20$

or from the result of our computation as: $Z = 54\Omega$ (approx).

To show that either of these answers is perfectly correct and acceptable, we can examine the circuit a little further. Suppose that we are told that the current in the circuit is equal to 4 amps and asked to find the voltage. We know that $E = IZ$, so let's substitute both of our answers for Z in this formula and see what we get. First, if $E = I \times Z$, then $E = 4 \times 54$ (approximately) or about 216 volts. Next, if $E = I \times Z$, then

$$E = 4(50 + J20) = (200 + J80)$$

volts. Now, since $E_T = \sqrt{E_R^2 + E_X^2}$ and $200 = E_R$ and $J80 = E_X$, we have, by dropping the J,

$$E_T = \sqrt{200^2 + 80^2}$$

$$= \sqrt{40,000 + 6400}$$

$$= \sqrt{46,400} = 216 \text{ volts (approx.)}$$

Although either the vector representation of the answer or the numerical representation is correct and acceptable, the vector answer is often preferred as it indicates our phase angle and lagging voltage. Thus, we would say that our impedance was $(50 + J20)\Omega$ and our voltage was $(200 + J80)$V.

Now, let's look at the circuit in Fig. 3-24. Here we also have a simple series circuit, and are asked to find the impedance. But, instead of being given all the resistances and the reactances, we are given an assortment of values. However, we still know that Z is equal to the sum of the resistances and the reactances, and we can draw our vector diagram as shown in

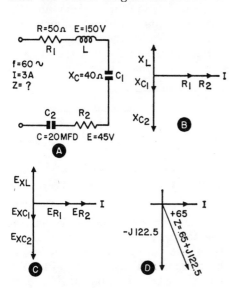

Fig. 3-24. Series ac circuit with vector diagrams.

Fig. 3-24B. Also, Z will be equal to

$E_T \div I$ and E_T will be equal to the sum of the individual voltage vectors, as shown in Fig. 3-24C. Since we are given the total current, the frequency, some of the individual resistances or reactances, some of the voltage drops, and a value of capacitance, we can find the impedance of the circuit either way. The information given is adequate to give us anything we need to know. For example, using $Z = R \pm JX$, we have: $Z = R \pm JX = R_1 + R_2 + JX_L - JX_{C1} - JX_{C2}$ and,

$$Z = R_1 + \frac{E_{R2}}{I} + J\frac{E_L}{I} - JX_{C1} - J\left(\frac{159000}{fC_2}\right)$$

Therefore,

$$Z = 50 + 15 + J50 - J40 - J\left(\frac{159000}{60 \times 20}\right)$$

and

$$\frac{159000}{60 \times 20} = \frac{1590}{12} = 132.5\Omega$$

and

$$Z = 65 + J50 - J40 - J132.5$$

$$= 65 - J122.5$$

as shown in Fig. 3-24D.

Using the other method, we would have:

$$Z = E_T \div I = (E_{R1} + E_{R2} + JE_{XL} - JE_{XC1} - JE_{XC2}) \div I,$$

then

$$Z = [(IR_1) + E_{R2} + JE_{XL} - J(IX_{C1}) - J(IX_{C2})] \div I$$

Now:

$$J(IX_{C2}) = [JI(159000 \div fC_2)]$$

$$= [JI(159000 \div 1200)]$$

$$= J(132.5I)$$

Thus,

$$Z = \frac{IR_1 + E_{R2} + J(E_{XL}) - J(IX_{C1}) - J(132.5I)}{I}$$

Now,

$$Z = R_1 + \frac{E_{R2}}{I} + \frac{J(E_{XL})}{I}$$

$$- J(X_{C1}) - J132.5$$

$$= 50 + \frac{45}{3} + \frac{J(150)}{3} - J40 - J132.5$$

$$= 50 + 15 + J50 - J172.5$$

$= 65 - J122.5$ which is the same answer we got the other way. Of course, by using the pythagorean theorem, we can further find that:

$$Z = \sqrt{65^2 + 122.5^2} = \sqrt{4225 + 15006}$$

$$= \sqrt{19231}$$

$$= 139\Omega \text{ (approximately)}.$$

Notice that we always drop the J when we use the pythagorean theorem, because the J only indicates the position of the impedance vector and there is no way to indicate this in a monomial such as 139. However, we can use the sign of the J operator to indicate the direction by saying "139Ω capacitive."

Parallel Circuits. In our earlier ac circuit calculations, we have worked almost exclusively with series circuits. Although parallel circuits and series parallel circuits can be solved by using vector measurement solutions alone, the vector diagrams generally become quite complex and difficult to work with. However, now that we have a method of solving ac circuits mathematically, we shall be able to handle these more complex circuits.

The major difference in working with parallel circuits is in the choice of a reference. In your study of dc circuits, you learned that the current divides in the branches of a parallel circuit while the voltage across all the branches is common. This is just the opposite from a series circuit where the current is common and the voltage divides. The same is true for ac circuits, so the general rules for dc circuits will apply to ac circuit solutions. Therefore, in our work with ac parallel circuits, we will use the circuit voltage as a reference instead of the current as we did in most of the series circuits. This difference in the choice of the reference value is very important.

Now, let's look at the simple parallel circuit in Fig. 3-25. Here, our circuit contains a coil in one leg and a resistor in the other leg. The voltage applied to the circuit is applied equally to each branch. However, the current as shown by an ammeter in each leg is different in each branch. The total current in the circuit is equal to the sum of the current in the branches. What is this total current?

Since one branch has an inductive current and the other branch has a resistive current, we cannot add the two currents together numerically. We must add them together vectorially just as we would the voltages in a series circuit. If we draw a vector

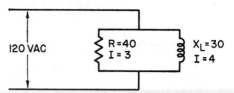

Fig. 3-25. Simple ac parallel circuit.

diagram for this addition, we have to use the voltage as our reference line since the voltage across each branch is the same. Thus, we would lay out our reference line and label it E as shown in Fig. 3-26A. Next, we want to represent our current vectors for each leg. First, we take a vector representing the current in the resistance branch and draw it along the reference line, E, and label it I_R, as shown in Fig. 3-26B. We draw this vector along the reference to show that the current through the resistive branch is in phase with the common voltage.

Next, we want to represent the current through our inductive branch as a vector. Now, we know that neglecting the resistance of the coil, this current will lag the voltage by exactly 90°. Since our E reference is along the horizontal and points to the right, we must draw this current vector downward, as shown in Fig. 3-26C in order to show this lagging effect. Thus, our I_L vector is a $-J$ value. Therefore, our total current vector for the circuit would be indicated mathematically as

$$I_T = I_R - JI_L,$$

as shown in Fig. 3-26C'.

Now, if we substitute the given values for the two currents shown in Fig. 3-25, our total current would equal:

$I_T = I_R - JI_L = I_T = 3 - J4 =$ (dropping the J) $I = \sqrt{3^2 + 4^2}$
$= \sqrt{9 + 16} = \sqrt{25} = 5$ amps.

Our J operator was minus, so our total circuit current is 5 amps (lagging) as shown by the vector $I_T = 3 - J4 = 5$, in Fig. 3-26D.

If we want to find the impedance of this parallel circuit, we can proceed in two ways. The simplest way is to use the total current and the applied voltage in our formula $E = IZ$ and therefore $Z = \dfrac{E}{I}$ or, in our circuit, $Z = \dfrac{120}{5} = 24\Omega$. If we were relying on only vector measurement solutions for parallel circuits, this would be the only way we could find the impedance. The reason for this is that the formula for resistances or impedances in parallel is

$$Z_T = \frac{Z_1 \times Z_2}{Z_1 + Z_2}$$

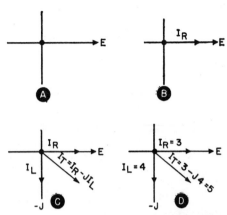

Fig. 3-26. Parallel circuit solution.

and we have no purely graphical way of multiplying or dividing the vectors representing Z_1 and Z_2.

However, since we know how to use the J operator, we can multiply or divide these vectors mathematically. Therefore, we can use this formula to find the total impedance. In the circuit shown in Fig. 3-25, we would have:

$$Z_T = \frac{R(-JX_L)}{R + (-JX_L)}$$

$$= \frac{40(-J30)}{40 - J30}$$

$$= \frac{-J1200(40 + J30)}{(40 - J30)(40 + J30)}$$

$$= \frac{-J48000 - J^2 36000}{1600 - J^2 900}$$

$$= \frac{-J48000 + 36000}{1600 + 900}$$

$$= \frac{-J480 + 360}{25}$$

$$= -J19.2 + 14.4$$

and our impedance total written as a vector would be $(14.4 - J19.2)$. Then, applying the pythagorean theorem to this vector, we would find:

$$Z = \sqrt{(14.4)^2+(19.2)^2}$$
$$= \sqrt{207.36+368.64}$$
$$= \sqrt{576} = 24\Omega.$$

This, of course, is the same answer that we got for the impedance by dividing the total voltage by the total current.

While the impedance of any parallel circuit can be found using either method, you can see that it is much simpler and quicker to use the first method. The current can be found by addition of vectors and then a simple division allows us to find the impedance if we know the voltage. The other way requires both the multiplication and division of vectors which can become quite complex. In fact, in complex circuits, it becomes so involved mathematically that it is almost never used.

Because of this complexity, a method of finding impedance has been worked out that involves the addition of current vectors, even though the voltage is not known. For example, consider the circuit in Fig. 3-27 . Here we have a resistor, a coil, and a capacitor in parallel. We are asked to find the impedance and we have the values of X_C, X_L, and R given. Since we have no values of either current or voltage given, it would seen that we will be forced to use our impedance formulas.

Suppose, however, that we assume a circuit voltage of 120 volts. If we do this, then we can find the current that would flow in each branch with

this assumed voltage applied to the circuit. It would be:

$$I_C = \frac{E}{X_C} = \frac{120}{20} = 6 \text{ amps}$$

$$I_R = \frac{E}{R} = \frac{120}{30} = 4 \text{ amps, and}$$

$$I_L = \frac{E}{X_L} = \frac{120}{40} = 3 \text{ amps.}$$

Now, we can add these currents using the J operator to find the total current that would flow for the value of assumed voltage we have chosen.

Laying out a vector diagram for reference as shown in Fig. 3-28 , we would use our common reference E as a base. Then our I_L vector would be drawn down towards $-J$ to indicate the current lag through the coil. The vector for I_C would be drawn up toward $+J$, indicating the leading current through the capacitor. Finally, the I_R vector would be drawn along the reference to indicate the in-phase current through the resistance. Now, our problem becomes mathematically:

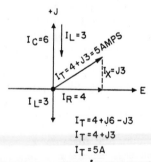

Fig. 3-28. Vector solution of I for circuit in Fig. 27.

$$I_T = I_R + JI_C - JI_L = 4 + J6 - J3$$
$$= 4 + J3$$

Then,

$$I_T = \sqrt{4^2+3^2} = \sqrt{16+9} = \sqrt{25}$$

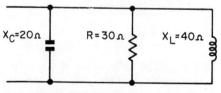

Fig. 3-27. Parallel circuit with X_C, R_1, and X_L. Find Z.

and $I_T = 5$ amps leading (notice the sign of J) with an assumed voltage of 120 volts.

Now, applying our formula $Z = \dfrac{E}{I}$, we have $Z = \dfrac{120}{5} = 24\Omega$. Thus, an assumed voltage forces a total current through the circuit that gives us an impedance of 24Ω. The interesting thing is, that no matter what voltage we assume, the computed current will always be a value such that our impedance for this circuit will work out to 24Ω. Thus, we can assume any voltage for a parallel circuit, compute the total current forced through the circuit by this voltage, and then divide to find the impedance. Naturally, in doing this, we always assume a value of voltage that will be easy to work with to make our problem as simple as possible. Try assuming a couple of different voltages for the circuit in Fig.3-27 yourself, and then compute the current and impedance. You will see that 24Ω is always your answer for this circuit.

Series Parallel Circuits. The next problem is to learn to combine our knowledge of series circuits with our knowledge of parallel circuits for series parallel combinations. Generally, we do this just as we would for dc circuits. We break our circuit down into simple circuits which we solve one at a time, and then combine our answers. For example, let's consider the circuit shown in Fig.3-29.

Here we have a coil in series with a resistor in one branch which is in parallel with another branch containing a resistor and a capacitor. We are given R_1, R_2, L and C, the total voltage, and the frequency. We are asked to find the total current and the total impedance of the circuit. The first thing to do is solve each

of the two branches separately, and then combine them to find the total current; then find the total impedance.

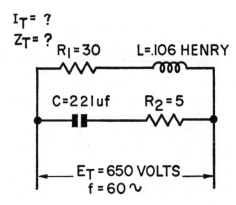

Fig. 3-29. Series parallel ac circuit.

The best way is to proceed as follows: Let's call the branch with the coil, branch A, and the one with the capacitor, branch B. Since we want the total current, we would want to find the current in each leg and then combine them. Starting with branch A, we must first find X_L and then find I_A as follows:

$$
\begin{aligned}
I_A &= E_A \div Z_A \\
&= E_A \div (R_1 + JX_L) \\
&= E_A \div (R_1 + J2\pi fL) \\
&= 650 \div (30 + J6.28 \times 60 \times .106) \\
&= 650 \div (30 + J40) \\
&= \frac{650\,(30 - J40)}{(30 + J40)(30 - J40)} \\
&= \frac{19500 - J26000}{900 - J^2 1600} \\
&= \frac{195 - J260}{9 + 16} \\
&= \frac{195 - J260}{25} \\
&= 7.8 - J10.4
\end{aligned}
$$

Now, notice that I_A is the current through the series circuit of branch A, yet we have it broken up into a J binomial. This probably seems strange since you know that the current is common in a series circuit and the current through the coil is the same as the current through the resistance. While it is true that we have only one current through the series branch, this current is made up of the combined effects of the resistor and the coil. Therefore, this current is a vector that can be considered to consist of two components just the same as any other vector.

The vector diagrams in Fig.3-30 may help you to understand this. In Fig. 3-30A we have shown the impedance vector $30 + J40$ which we found in the first few steps of our equation.

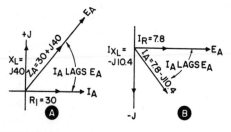

Fig. 3-30. Vector relationships for branch A. (Not to scale).

Since this is a series circuit, we have used the current as a reference for this diagram. Now, if we were to represent the voltage for this series circuit vectorially, it would extend along the same line as the impedance vector, as shown. Thus, the vector diagram in Fig.3-30A shows the relationships of the impedance, the current, and the voltage. Notice that the current lags the voltage.

Now, when we get ready to combine branch A and branch B, we will want to use the voltage as a reference because it is common to both branches. When we do this, we would have to show the current for branch A as a vector lagging the voltage, as shown

in Fig. 3-30B. Thus, either Fig.3-30A or 3-30B shows the proper relationship between the current and the voltage. In order to compute with this current vector using the J operator, we would want to break it up into its components. We can do this in the diagram, shown in Fig.3-30B, because E is the reference. That is why we simply divided the voltage E_A by the binomial of the impedance vector rather than solving for the monomial impedance. In this way, our current is already broken into its binomial term, ready for use in combining with branch B as soon as we divide the voltage by the impedance.

Now, we follow the same general procedure and solve for the current in branch B as follows:

$$I_B = E_B \div Z_B$$

$$= E_B \div (R_2 - JX_C)$$

$$= E_B \div \left(R_2 - J\frac{159000}{fC} \right)$$

$$= 650 \div \left(5 - J\frac{159000}{60 \times 221} \right)$$

$$= 650 \div (5 - J12)$$

$$= \frac{650\,(5 + J12)}{(5 - J12)(5 + J12)}$$

$$= \frac{3250 + J7800}{25 - J^2 144}$$

$$= \frac{3250 + J7800}{25 + 144}$$

$$= \frac{3250 + J7800}{169} = 19.2 + J46.1$$

The vector diagrams for this are shown in Fig.3-31 in the same manner as those in Fig. 3-30. Notice that in the diagram in Fig. 3-30A, the inductive terms are positive or $+J$ to show that the voltage leads the current reference. However, when we use the voltage as a reference, as in Fig. 3-30B, the current term must be negative, or $-J$, in order to show this same lag. Likewise, the sign changes in Figs. 3-31A and B show the same thing except that they are opposite because we are dealing with capacitance or leading current.

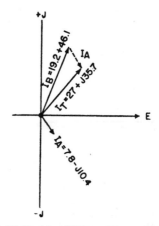

Fig. 3-32. Vector addition of current in Figs. 3-26 and 3-27, (not to scale).

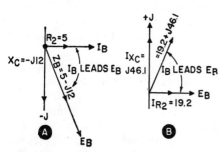

Fig. 3-31. Vector relationships for branch B. (Not to scale).

Now that we have found the current in the two branches, we simply add them as shown by the vector diagram in Fig. 3-32 and the following mathematical solution:

$I_T = I_A + I_B$

$\quad = (7.8 - J10.4) + (19.2 + J46.1)$

$\quad = 7.8 + 19.2 + J46.1 - J10.4$

$\quad = 27 + J35.7$

$\quad = \sqrt{27^2 + 35.7^2} = \sqrt{729 + 1274.5}$

$\quad = \sqrt{2003.5} = 44.7$ amps

Now, the impedance is:

$$Z = \frac{E}{I} = \frac{650}{44.7} = 14.5 \text{ ohms}$$

In solving circuit problems such as this it is wise to set up a complete equation in the beginning. In this you get straight to the heart of the problem and save yourself from doing a lot of work finding things that you do not need. As an example, we found only the binomial expressions for

current and impedance in the circuit we just completed. We did not bother to find the numerical values of the quantities until the last moment. Also, we did not have to find the voltage drops across the individual components. The proper circuit equations will keep you from spending unnecessary time solving for quantities you do not need. Stated as a complete equation, this last circuit would have been:

Given: $E_T = 650\Omega$

$\quad\quad f = 60$ cycles

$\quad\quad R_1 = 30\Omega$

$\quad\quad R_2 = 5\Omega$

$\quad\quad L = .106$h

$\quad\quad C = 22.1\ \mu f$

find I_T, Z_T

Then, $Z_T = \dfrac{E_T}{I_T}$ and $I_T = I_A + I_B$

Therefore:

$\quad Z_T = E_T \div (I_A + I_B)$

But: $I_A = E_A \div Z_A$

$\quad\quad I_B = E_B \div Z_B$

But: $E_B = E_A = E_T$

Then

$$I_A = E_T \div Z_A$$

$$I_B = E_T \div Z_B$$

Therefore:

$$Z_T = \frac{E_T}{[(E_T \div Z_A) + (E_T \div Z_B)]}$$

Now:

$$Z_A = R_1 + JX_L$$

$$Z_B = R_2 - JX_C$$

Therefore:

$$Z_T = E_T \div \{ \, [E_T \div (R_1 + JX_L)]$$
$$+ [E_T \div (R_2 - JX_C)] \}$$

And: $JX_L = J(2\pi fL)$

$$JX_C = J\,(159000 \div fC)$$

Therefore:

$$Z_T = E_T \div \{ [E_T \div (R_1 + J2\pi fL)]$$
$$+ [E_T \div (R_2 - J[159000 \div fC])] \}$$

This is the complete circuit equation and gives us Z_T in terms of our known values. If we go ahead and solve for Z_T, we will get a binominal answer. Then, all we have to do is apply the pythagorean theorem to the binominal term in order to get Z_T as a monomial answer. Once we have Z_T as a monomial, Ohm's Law will give us I_T.

In Fig. 3-33, we have a more complex series parallel circuit. Solving this problem will give you experience in using all of the processes which have been discussed in this chapter. In this problem, the resistances and reactances are given and you are asked to find the total circuit impedance.

Examination of the circuit will show that the total impedance "Z_t"

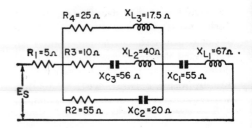

FIND I_T AND Z_T

Fig. 3-33. Series parallel circuit problem.

is equal to the vectorial sum of R_1, X_{L1} and X_{C1} in series with the combined impedance of the three parallel branches. For convenience in discussion, we will refer to the combined impedance of the three parallel branches as "Z_b." We can now write the equation for the total circuit impedance:

$$Z_T = (R_1 + JX_{L1} - JX_{C1} + Z_b)$$

For the moment, we will forget the series components R_1, X_{L1} and X_{C1} and determine the value of Z_b. Later, we can find the total circuit impedance.

As you saw in the previous example, it is easier to solve parallel circuits by using the formula $Z = E/I$. Neither the source voltage E_s, nor the votage drop across any part of the circuit is given. However, we can simplify the work by assuming that a voltage "E_b" exists across the three parallel branches and use this voltage as a reference. Now, we can write the equation:

$$Z_b = \frac{E_b}{I_b}$$

where I_b is the total current flowing in the three parallel branches. Regardless of the assumed voltage E_b, the impedance of the parallel branches will remain the same since the current is proportional to E_b divided by Z_b.

The current I_b is the vectorial sum of the currents flowing through the three individual parallel branches. We will use I_1 to represent the current through R_2 and X_{C2}, I_2 for the current through R_3, X_{C3} and X_{L2}, and I_3 to represent the current through R_4 and X_{L3}. Then, we can write:

$$I_b = I_1 + I_2 + I_3$$

Substituting this in the equation for the impedance of the parallel branches gives us:

$$Z_b = \frac{E_b}{I_1 + I_2 + I_3}$$

The current flowing through each of the parallel branches is equal to the assumed voltage divided by the impedance of the individual branches. The branch currents then are:

$$I_1 = \frac{E_b}{Z_1}$$

$$I_2 = \frac{E_b}{Z_2}$$

$$I_3 = \frac{E_b}{Z_3}$$

The total current flowing between the two points can be expressed as:

$$I_b = \frac{E_b}{Z_1} + \frac{E_b}{Z_2} + \frac{E_b}{Z_3}$$

We can now write the equation for the combined impedance of the parallel branches:

$$Z_b = \frac{E_b}{\dfrac{E_b}{Z_1} + \dfrac{E_b}{Z_2} + \dfrac{E_b}{Z_3}}$$

Substituting individual component value we have:

$$Z_b = E_b \div \left[\frac{E_b}{R_2 - JX_{C2}} + \frac{E_b}{R_3 + JX_{L2} - JX_{C3}} + \frac{E_b}{R_4 + JX_{L3}} \right]$$

and using component values, we write:

$$Z_b = E_b \div \left[\frac{E_b}{55 - J20} + \frac{E_b}{10 + J40 - J56} + \frac{E_b}{25 + J17.5} \right]$$

Let us assume that E_b is equal to 100V (we can assume any value for E_b and still get the same final answer for Z_b) and substitute 100 for E_b in the equation:

$$Z_b = 100 \div \left[\frac{100}{55 - J20} + \frac{100}{10 + J40 - J56} + \frac{100}{25 + J17.5} \right]$$

Combining the J factors gives us:

$$Z_b = 100 \div \left[\frac{100}{55 - J20} + \frac{100}{10 - J16} + \frac{100}{25 + J17.5} \right]$$

To determine the current I_b, we conjugate the denominators of the terms:

$$Z_b = 100 \div$$

$$\left[\left(\frac{100}{55 - J20} \cdot \frac{55 + J20}{55 + J20}\right) + \right.$$

$$\frac{100}{10 - J16} \cdot \frac{10 + J16}{10 + J16} +$$

$$\left.\left(\frac{100}{25 + J17.5} \cdot \frac{25 - J17.5}{25 - J17.5}\right)\right]$$

$$Z_b = 100 \div \left[\frac{5500 + J2000}{3425} + \right.$$

$$\left.\frac{1000 + J1600}{356} + \frac{2500 - J1750}{931}\right]$$

$$Z_b = 100 \div [(1.6 + J.58) + (2.8 + J4.5) + (2.7 - J1.88)]$$

$$Z_b = \frac{100}{7.1 - J3.2}$$

$$Z_b = \frac{100}{7.1 + J3.2} \cdot \frac{7.1 - J3.2}{7.1 - J3.2}$$

$$Z_b = \frac{710 - J320}{60.7}$$

$$Z_b = 11.7 - J5.3\,\Omega$$

We can now substitute the value of Z_b into the series circuit equation along with the values of R_1, X_{L1} and X_{C1} and solve for the total circuit impedance:

$$Z_T = (5 + J67 - J55) + (11.7 - J3.2)\,\Omega$$
$$= (5 + J12) + (11.7 - J3.2)\,\Omega$$
$$Z_T = 16.7 + J8.8\,\Omega$$

Then, we apply the Pythagorean theorem to change the binomial term to a monomial. The total circuit impedance is equal to 18.1 ohms.

3-5. Solving Circuit Problems

In order to learn any subject well, you must get experience applying the information that you study. This is especially true of mathematics and circuit calculations. In this section of the chapter, we will give you some typical circuit problems and their answers. No matter how well you think you may have mastered the information on circuit calculations, you should make sure you understand it by solving these problems to see if you can get the answers we have given.

1. One leg of a parallel circuit contains an impedance equal to $(3+J4)$, the other leg impedance equals $(8-J6)$. What is the total impedance of the circuit?

ANSWER: $(4+J2)$

2. If the impedance vector of a series circuit equals $40-J30$ and the applied .voltage is 100 volts, what is the current in amps?

ANSWER: 2 amps

3. A series circuit consists of R_1, R_2, R_3, C_1, C_2, L_1, and L_2 connected in series. What is the impedance of the circuit if $R_1 = 12$ ohms, $R_2 = 17$ ohms, $R_3 = 11$ ohms, $X_{C1} = 75$ ohms, $X_{C2} = 50$ ohms, $X_{L1} = 40$ ohms, and $X_{L2} = 60$ ohms.

ANSWER: $(40 - J25)$

4. What is the total impedance of a series circuit that contains the following impedances: $1+J6$, $3-J2$, $4-J7$, $3+J14$, $7-J1$.

ANSWER: $(18+J10)$

5. What is the sum of the following polynomials?

$(-9a^3b+6a^2b^2-5ab^3)$

$+ (14a^3b+6a^2b^2-5ab^3)$

$+ (a^3b-3a^2b^2-a^3b)$

ANSWER: $5a^3b+9a^2b^2-10ab^3$

6. What is the value of $(9+J7) \div (3-J2)$?

ANSWER: $(1+J3)$

7. Divide $4a^3-2a^2b + 6ab^2-18b^3$ by $2a-3b$.

ANSWER: $2a^2+2ab+6b^2$

8. If the current through R_2 in the circuit shown in Fig. 3-34 is 2 amps, what is the value of E_T?

ANSWER: 105 volts

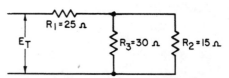

Fig. 3-34. Circuit for Problem 8.

9. In the circuit shown in Fig. 3-35, find the total current, the voltage across the coil, and the voltage across the capacitor. What is the name given to this type of circuit?

ANSWER: $I_T = 25$ amps
  $E_{XL} = 250$ volts
  $E_{XC} = 250$ volts
Series resonant circuit.

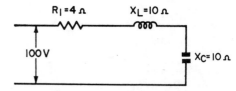

Fig. 3-35. Circuit for Problem 9.

10. Multiply each of the following:

(1) $(a+2b)(a-b)$
(2) $(a^2+2ab+b^2)(a+b)$
(3) $(2a+3b)(2a-3b)$
(4) $(a^2-2a+b^2)(a+b)$
(5) $(a-b)(a+2b^2)$

ANSWERS:

(1) $a^2+ab-2b^2$
(2) $a^3+3a^2b+3ab^2+b^3$
(3) $4a^2-9b^2$
(4) $a^3-2a^2+a^2b-2ab+ab^2+b^3$
(5) $a^2+2ab^2-ab-2b^3$

11. Divide each of the following:

(1) $(a^3-3a^2b+3ab^2-b^3) \div (a-b)$
(2) $(64a^4-81b^6) \div (8a^2+9b^3)$
(3) $(a^5-3a^3+a) \div (a)$
(4) $(2+J46) \div (5+J9)$
(5) $(a^4+2a^2b^2+b^4) \div (a^2+b^2)$

ANSWERS:

(1) $a^2-2ab+b^2$ or $(a-b)^2$
(2) $8a^2-9b^3$
(3) a^4-3a^2+1
(4) $4+J2$
(5) a^2+b^2

12. Perform the following subtractions:

(1) Take $6a-4b+2c$ from $11a+b -2c$
(2) Take $6a^2b+3ab^2-b^3$ from $a^3 -a^2b+4ab^2$
(3) Take $a+b+c+d$ from $3a-4b +c-6d$
(4) Take $4a+7b$ from $2a+6b$
(5) Take $6a^3-a^2b+ab^2-b^3$ from $8a^3+3a^2b-ab^2+b^3$

ANSWERS:

(1) $5a+5b-4c$
(2) $a^3-7a^2b+ab^2+b^3$
(3) $2a-5b-7d$
(4) $-2a-b$ or $-(2a+b)$
(5) $2a^3+4a^2b-2ab^2+2b^3$

13. If an alternating voltage of

117 volts is connected across a parallel circuit made up of three legs, with a 30Ω resistance in one leg, an inductive reactance of 117Ω in one leg, and a capacitive reactance of 39Ω in one leg, what is the total current drawn from the source?

ANSWER: $(3.9+J2)$ amps = 4.4 amps (approx.)

14. A parallel circuit is made up of four branches, three of the four branches being pure resistances of 16, 16, and 8 ohms, respectively. The fourth branch has an inductive reactance of 6Ω. What is the total impedance of the circuit?

ANSWER: $2.78+J1.84$ = 3.33 ohms

15. A series circuit consisting of a 12-ohm resistor, a 20-mfd capacitor, and a .1 henry coil is connected across a 150-volt, 120-cycle ac source. What is the current in the circuit?

ANSWER: $(8.2-J6.02)$ amps = 10.2 amps lagging

16. Find the current through the capacitor in the circuit shown in Fig. 3-36.

ANSWER: $0+J1$ = 1 amp leading

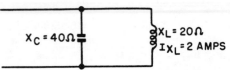

Fig. 3-36. Circuit for Problem 16.

17. Find the source voltage in the circuit shown in Fig. 3-37.

ANSWER: 95 volts

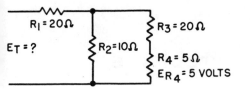

Fig. 3-37. Circuit for Problem 17.

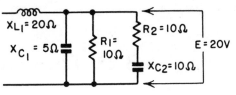

Fig. 3-39.   Circuit for Problem 19.

18. What will the current be in the circuit shown in Fig.3-38, when it is operated at its resonant frequency?

ANSWER: 55 amps

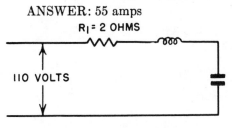

Fig. 3-38. Circuit for Problem 18.

19. Find the source voltage of the circuit shown in Fig.3-39.

ANSWER: 100 volts

20. Find the impedance of the circuit shown in Fig.3-40.

ANSWER: $Z = (500 - J100)$ ohms
= 510Ω

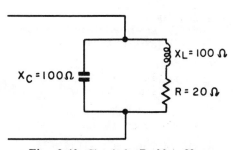

Fig. 3-40. Circuit for Problem 20.

3-6. Review Problems

1. Add the following:
   (1) $(3a^2+2b^2+6c+3d^2)$ plus $(2a^2-b^2+c^2-4d^2)$
   (2) $(ax^3+bx^2y+cxy^2+y^3)$ plus $2ax^3+ax^2y+6cxy^2-4y^3$.

2. Perform the following subtractions:
   (1) From $6a-3b+2c+d$ take $2a-4b-c+3d$
   (2) From $12ax^2-6by^2-4cz^2$ take $6ax^2+2by^2-5cz^2$

3. Multiply:
   (1) (a^2-b^2+3c) times $(a+b)$
   (2) $(3x^2+y)$ times $(3x^2-y)$

4. Divide:
   (1) $(4a^2-8ab+4b^2) \div (2a-2b)$
   (2) $(18a^5+33a^4b+6a^3b^2-11a^2b^3+20ab^4+32b^5) \div (3a+4b)$

5. (1) Add $(4+17J) + (3-2J)$
   (2) Subtract $(16-2J) - (4+6J)$

6. (1) Multiply $(6+9J)$ $(7+3J)$
   (2) Divide $(10+62J) \div (8+2J)$

7. If a resistance of 62 ohms is connected in series with a coil with a reactance of 42 ohms and a capacitor with a reactance of 100 ohms, what is the impedance of the circuit expressed as a numerical vector?

8. Find the current in the series circuit shown at the right. Give your answer as a numerical vector.

9. Find the impedance of the circuit shown at the right. Give your answer in J-operator form.

10. Find the source voltage in the circuit shown at the right if the voltage across R_4 is 10 volts.

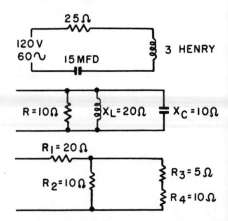

CHAPTER FOUR

Mathematics In Practical Electronics

4-1. Introduction

YOU have learned many ways of dealing with the problems involved in making ac circuit computations. You know how to lay out the resultant vectors and then measure the angles of lead or lag to determine their values. While this is satisfactory for many of the problems and circuits that you have dealt with, you will find that it will be very awkward when you start working with the precision timing circuits, filter networks, and frequency control circuits that are so important in electronics work.

Many of these difficulties can be overcome by applying the principles of trigonometry to vector solutions. In this way we are able to account for the angles formed by vectors, as well as the length of the vectors, without having to rely on any construction or measurement. While you may never have used trigonometry, or "trig" as it is usually called, it is really a very valuable mathematical tool. It is not difficult to either learn or use; in fact, it is much simpler than many of the processes you have already learned.

By studying trigonometry, you will not only learn another method of computing with vectors, but you will also learn more about the principles involved with the vectors themselves. You will see why a sine wave of alternating current is called a "sine wave" and learn why ac vectors are often called "phasors." In addition, you will learn to work with power in ac circuits and study some of the factors concerning the importance of "power factor." This knowledge of trigonometry will be of value to you throughout your career in electronics. For example, this knowledge of trigonometry is essential when working with computer equipment.

In this lesson you will also study a few short cuts that will help you speed up and simplify many of your circuit calculations. You will learn to work with significant figures and the powers of ten as well as some special tricks in using algebra. You will learn how to construct and use many different types of graphs that will enable you to present complex information clearly and precisely in a simplified form. The importance of these graphs cannot be overemphasized, because the technical texts and references which you will constantly need in your work will use this form of presentation many times. In many ways, this is the most important chapter on mathematics since you will be using and reviewing all previous material and "polishing up" the rough edges of what you have already learned.

4-2. Trigonometry

Trigonometry is the study of the mathematical relationships that exist between the sides and angles of triangles. The word trigonometry itself is derived from two Greek words which mean the measurement of angles. The origin and earliest uses of trigonometry were for measuring distances and objects by using triangles. Today surveyors and construction engineers use trigonometry for this same purpose. However, the science of trigonometry has been developed to such a point that it is now commonly used for many other purposes.

As an electronics technician, your most important use for trigonometry will be in the solution of the triangles formed by vector diagrams to determine phase relationships. Before you can actually learn to use trigonometry in this way, you must first learn some of the basic fundamentals and principles of angles, triangles, and coordinate systems.

Angles

When two straight lines meet at a point an angle is formed. Thus, when the two lines OX and OY meet at the

point 0 as shown in Fig. 4-1A, an angle is formed between the two lines. Similarly, the two lines OA and OB meeting at the point 0 in Fig. 4-1B also form an angle. The point 0, where the lines

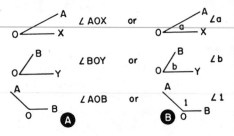

Fig. 4-2. Naming angles.

meet, is called the "vertex" of the angle, and the lines themselves are known as the sides of the angle. The angle in Fig. 4-1A is called "angle XOY" to show that it is the angle formed by lines OX and OY. Likewise, the angle in Fig. 4-1B is "angle AOB."

To save time and space, the symbol "∠" is used in mathematics to represent the word "angle." Thus, the angles in Fig. 4-2A could be designated as ∠AOX, ∠BOY, and ∠AOB. In mathematics when we are working with a large number of angles, it might be awkward to completely describe angles in this way. Instead, we could insert a letter or a number in the vertex of the angles, as shown in Fig. 4-2B, and simply call them "∠a", "∠b", or "∠1" as shown. Many times special designations are used to describe angles. For

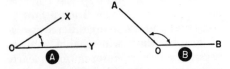

Fig. 4-1. Angles are formed when two straight lines meet.

example, we often use the Greek letter theta, θ, in electronics to designate the phase angle. This would be written, ∠θ, and if we are working with several different phase angles we would indicate them with appropriate subscripts such as ∠θ₂, ∠θ₃, or perhaps ∠θₐ and ∠θᵦ.

The size or the magnitude of an angle is a measure of the space or distance between the sides and is determined by the difference in *direction* of the sides. Notice that it is only the difference in direction of the two sides

there are three generally accepted units of measurements for angles, we will be concerned with only two of them: the degree, written (°), and the radian. To help understand these two units of measurement more thoroughly and for our study of trigonometry, let's examine angles a little more closely, especially their relationship to circular measure.

An angle should always be thought of as being generated by a line that starts at a certain initial position and rotates about the vertex of the angle

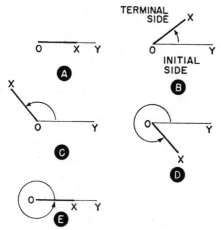

Fig. 4-3. Generation of angles.

that determines the size of an angle. The lengths of the sides do not in any way affect the size of the angle itself. You can easily see that either shortening or lengthening the sides of the angles shown in the figures will not change the size of the angles.

In working with the size or measurement of angles, as in measuring anything else, some standard unit of measurement must be chosen. While it is easy to see that an angle is either smaller or larger, or nearly the same size as another angle, this is not enough definition for the precision required in mathematics or electronics. While

until it stops at its final position. This is shown in Fig. 4-3. Consider the two straight lines: The short, heavy line OX and the lighter and longer line OY.

In Fig. 4-3A, line OX is drawn on top of line OY and no angle is formed. However, in Fig. 4-3B, an angle has been generated because the line OX has been rotated counterclockwise from its initial position on line OY. Thus, the various angles XOY in Figs. 4-3B, 4-3C, and 4-3D can be considered to be generated by the rotation of line OX from its initial position. The side of the angle that represents the original or initial position of the rotating side is known as the "initial side." The final position of the rotating side determines the size of the angle and is known as the "terminal side."

If the terminal side of the angle is rotated one complete revolution before it is stopped, the two lines are back at their original position, as shown in Fig. 4-3E. Thus, an angle is said to be generated by a line rotating about a point from one position to another. The unit of measure called the degree is based upon this generation by rotation. By definition, there are 360° in one complete revolution of the rotating side or 1° equals $\frac{1}{360}$ of a complete revolution.

As we progress with our study of angles, triangles, and trigonometry, we will find that the degree is often a very large unit of measurement. For this reason, the degree can be divided into smaller units called "minutes," written ('), and the "minute" can be further divided into units called "seconds," written ("). There are 60 minutes in one degree, and 60 seconds in each minute. Thus, the size of a certain angle might be written as 35° 46' 57" to tell us that the angle is 46 minutes and 57 seconds more than 35/360 of a revolution of the terminal side. While these minutes and seconds may seem to be ridiculously small units right now, we will soon see that they can be very important. Remember, there are 360° in one revolution, 60 minutes in each degree (360 × 60 or 21,600 minutes in a revolution), and 60 seconds in each minute (60 × 60 or 3600 seconds in a degree and 360 × 60 × 60 or 1,296,000 seconds in a revolution).

In trigonometry, we often use the decimal system instead of minutes and seconds. For example, instead of saying that an angle is 36° 30', we can write it as 36.5° because 30' is half of 60' and $\frac{1}{2}$ equals .5. In using decimals,

however, we must be very careful to remember that we are working with 60 parts to a degree. For example, 36.25° is $36\frac{1}{4}$° which is 36 and $\frac{1}{4}$ of 60, or 36° and 15'. Likewise, in converting 36° 12' to decimals, we have $36\frac{12}{60}$° = $36\frac{1}{5}$° = 36.2°. It is very easy to make errors in converting from decimals to minutes or seconds.

Now let's examine Fig. 4-3 again to start our consideration of the other unit of angular measure which we'll need: the radian. As the line OX rotates about the vertex to form the various angles shown in the figure, it must rotate or pass through every possible position from an angle of 0° or no angle at all in Fig. 4-3A to an angle of 360° or one complete revolution as shown in Fig. 4-3E. If we assume that the line OX never changes in length as it is rotating through this one revolution and place a pencil at the point X, we would find that a complete circle would be drawn by our pencil, as shown in Fig. 4-4.

Thus, we can say that since there are 360° in one revolution of side OX there are 360° in the circle. Also, since the *length* of OX has no bearing on the number of degrees in the revolution or

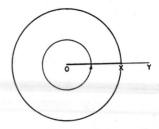

Fig. 4-4. Point X describes a complete circle in one complete revolution of terminal side OX.

in the size of the angles that could be formed by any one partial revolution, we can say that there are 360° in every circle, no matter how small or how large it may be. Changing the length of OX would change the radius of the circle and its area, but not the number of degrees in it.

Now, in a circle the size of the one shown in Fig. 4-4, if we were to mark off each degree on the circumference of the circle, the degree marks would be very close together. In fact, they would be so close together that it might be difficult to show any space between them at all if we attempted to put in all 360 marks. In such a small circle the difference between a degree or two would be insignificant as far as the linear distance between the marks is concerned.

However, suppose that we were considering a circle as large as the earth. At the equator, where it is about 25,000

called an arc. Otherwise it would simply be called a curved line, or curve. An arc that is exactly equal in length to the radius of the circle of which the arc is a part is said to be a radian. A more formal way of saying it is that a radian is an angle that, when placed with its vertex at the center of a circle, intercepts an arc equal in length to the radius of the circle. Thus, if the ∠XOY in the circle shown in Fig. 4-5A is to be equal to one radian, the length of the arc XY measured along the circumference of the circle must be equal to the radius of the circle or the sides OX or OY of the angle.

If we lay out and mark off a circle using angles that are each equal to 1

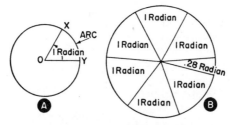

Fig. 4-5. Radian measure.

miles around the earth, there would be nearly 70 miles between the degree marks and each degree would be extremely important. In fact, even a difference of a minute (1/60 degree) would be nearly 1.2 miles. Thus, a degree can be a very small unit or a very large unit, depending on where and how it is used and the minute and second subdivisions are quite important.

The radian is a unit of measure that is based upon the length of an "arc" of a circle as compared with the radius of the circle. An "arc" is simply a part or section of the curved line that forms the circumference of a circle. An arc can be any length, but it must be a section of a true circle in order to be

radian, as shown in Fig. 4-5B, we will find that there are 6.28 radians in a circle. This must hold true for any circle regardless of its size since the length of arc intercepted by an angle of 1 radian must change directly as the radius of the circle changes. We are already familiar with the Greek letter π which we use in working with the area of circles. We know that it is a constant equal to 3.14. Therefore, we usually say that there are 2π radians in every circle since $6.28 \div 3.14 = 2$.

Many times you will want to change from radian measure to degrees, etc. Therefore, you should know how many degrees there are in a radian and how to convert from one to the other. Since there are 360° in every circle and 2π

radians in every circle, 2π radians = 360°. From this:

$$2\pi \text{ radians} = 360°$$
$$\pi \text{ radians} = 180°$$
$$1 \text{ radian} = \frac{180}{\pi}$$
$$= 57.2959$$

or approximately 57.3°. Accordingly, to change radians to degrees we would multiply the number of radians indicated by 57.3. Since 57.3 or $\frac{180}{\pi}$ is the multiplier when changing radians to degrees, we would multiply the number of degrees by $\frac{\pi}{180}$ or .01745 in order to change them to radians.

Now that we have learned something about angular measure, we can consider a few other facts concerning angles. Although we don't often stop to realize it, a straight line is really an 180° angle and is, therefore, probably the most common angle used. We can show that there are 180° in any straight line by rotating the terminal side OA of any angle such as $\angle$ AOB in Fig. 4-6 until the line AB is straight. When the line AB is a straight line, the $\angle$ AOB equals ½ a revolution of the rotating side which must be 180°.

Even though the straight line is the most common angle, the right angle is

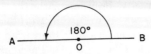

Fig. 4-6. Straight line is 180° angle.

the most important. We are already familiar with the fact that there are 90° in a right angle and that there is a system of angular measurement based on right angles. However, it is the use of the right angle in the right triangle

and its pythagorean relationships that is responsible for its greatest importance.

When two straight lines intersect each other so that four right angles are formed, the lines are said to be perpen-

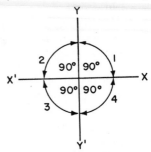

Fig. 4-7. Right angles formed when two lines are mutually perpendicular.

dicular to each other or mutually perpendicular. In Fig. 4-7, the two lines X'X and Y'Y are mutually perpendicular because angles 1, 2, 3, and 4 are all equal to 90° and are right angles. This is, of course, the basis of our coordinate systems which are used in graphs, surveying, navigation, etc. We will learn more about this a little later.

Any angle that is less than 90° is called an acute angle and any angle larger than 90° is called an obtuse angle. Two acute angles whose sum is equal to a right angle or 90° are called complementary angles. Either one of such acute angles may be called the complement of the other. Two angles whose sum is two right angles (180° or a straight line) are called supplementary angles.

Angles, of course, may be added, subtracted, multiplied, or divided, using the rules of arithmetic or algebra. We even have positive and negative angles to consider sometimes. A positive angle is generated when the terminal side is rotated counterclockwise to form the angle. If the angle is formed by the terminal side rotating clockwise it is called a negative angle. Now let's consider triangles.

Triangles

A triangle is a three-sided, closed plane figure. It is probably quite obvious what we mean by a closed, three-sided figure. However, if you have never studied geometry you may wonder what we mean by a "plane" figure. A plane figure is simply a figure that has height and width, but no depth. Thus, a triangle, a square, a circle, or any other figure that is drawn flat on a piece of paper is a plane figure. A pyramid, a cube, or a sphere are all what we call "solid" figures, whether they actually exist or whether they are drawn so that their depth is indicated. Thus, the figures in Fig.4-8A are plane figures and those in Fig.4-8B are solid figures. The study of trigonometry includes both plane and solid figures, but in your work you will need only to be familiar with trigonometry for plane figures unless you enter some very specialized field work.

Since a triangle has three sides, it must also contain three angles, as

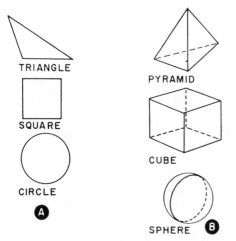

Fig. 4-8. A, Plane figures.   B, Solid figures.

shown in Fig.4-9. A triangle is named for reference purposes by naming the three vertexes of the three angles in order around the triangle. Thus, the triangle in Fig.4-9 would be called triangle ABC. It might also be called

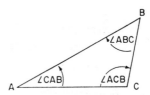

Fig. 4-9 A triangle has three angles and three sides.

triangle CBA, triangle BCA, triangle CAB, triangle BAC, or triangle ACB, depending on which vertex we start with and in which direction we go around. The mathematical symbol for a triangle is "△." Thus, the triangle in Fig. 4-9 could be written △ABC.

The sum of all the angles in a triangle is always 180°. It can never be any more or any less no matter what the size or shape of the triangle may be. This is very important in your work in trigonometry since you can always find the value of the third angle of any triangle if you know the other two.

If one of the angles of a triangle is a right angle, the triangle is called a right triangle. Accordingly, since a right triangle always has one 90° angle, the other two angles must be acute angles whose sum is also 90°. This relationship allows us find one acute angle of a right triangle if we know the other acute angle. A right triangle is shown in Fig.4-10. The fact that it is a right triangle is shown by drawing a small square at the vertex. The side of a right triangle that is opposite the right angle has been given the special name, "hypotenuse." When a right triangle is in standard position as shown in Fig.4-10, the side "a" is called the altitude and the side "b" is called the base.

Two triangles are said to be "similar" when their corresponding angles are equal. In other words, similar triangles are triangles that are identical in shape, but not necessarily in size.

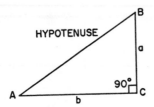

Fig. 4-10. A right triangle contains one right angle.

Thus, although the corresponding angles of similar triangles are equal, the sides are not equal. However, there is a special relationship between the sides of similar triangles that forms the basis of all trigonometry. *The corresponding sides of similar triangles are always proportional.*

For example, the triangle in Fig. 4-11A is similar to the triangle in Fig. 4-11B, because $\angle 1 = \angle a$, $\angle 2 = \angle b$, and $\angle 3 = \angle c$. If we establish a ratio between any two sides of one of the similar triangles, we will find that it is equal to the ratio established between the corresponding sides of the other similar triangle. Thus, the ratio of side AC to side CB of $\triangle ABC$ is $\dfrac{AC}{CB} = \dfrac{5''}{6''}$.

The ratio of the corresponding sides of $\triangle XYZ$ would be

$$\frac{XZ}{ZY} = \frac{10''}{12''} = \frac{5''}{6''}$$

Accordingly, we can establish a proportion from the two ratios as:

$$\frac{AC}{CB} = \frac{XZ}{ZY}$$

Also, $\dfrac{AB}{CB} = \dfrac{XY}{ZY}$ since $\dfrac{9''}{6''} = \dfrac{18''}{12''}$

and

$$\frac{AC}{AB} = \frac{XZ}{XY} \text{ since } \frac{5''}{9''} = \frac{10''}{18''}.$$

Remember, this proportionality between corresponding sides always exists when two or more triangles are similar.

Since we know that there are 180° in all triangles, we can determine whether triangles are similar by knowing only two of the angles. If two angles of one triangle equal two angles of another triangle, the third angles of the two triangles must also be equal to each other and the triangles will be similar. In the case of right triangles, the right angle of one is always equal to the right angle of another, so if one of the acute angles of one right triangle equals an acute angle of another right triangle, the two right triangles must be similar.

Now let's suppose we have two similar right triangles such as those shown in Fig. 4-12. In these triangles angle 1 and angle a are both equal to 30°. Any other right triangles that can be drawn that have one of their acute angles equal to 30° will also be similar to these right triangles. If we examine the ratios of any two of the sides of these

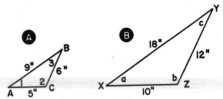

Fig. 4-11. Similar triangles have corresponding angles equal.

similar right triangles, we will discover a very important fact.

For example, the ratio of the side opposite the 30° angle, BC, to the hypotenuse, AB, of $\triangle ABC$ is equal to:

$$\frac{BC}{AB} = \frac{5''}{10''} = .5$$

Likewise, the same ratio exists for the corresponding sides of △XYZ because:

$$\frac{YZ}{XY} = \frac{10''}{20''} = .5$$

Since any other right triangle containing an acute angle of 30° must be similar to these, the ratio of the side opposite the 30° angle to the hypotenuse must always be equal to .5 for any right triangle that contains a 30° angle. Thus, we can say that the ratio of the side opposite the 30° angle to the hypotenuse of any right triangle containing a 30° angle is always equal to

$$180° - 90° - 60° = 30° \quad \text{and}$$

$$\frac{\text{side opp. 30°}}{\text{hypotenuse}} = .5 \quad \text{and}$$

$$\frac{\text{side opp. 30°}}{50} = .5 \quad \text{and}$$

$$\text{side opp. 30°} = 25$$

Now, if we were to construct a right triangle containing a 29° angle and compute the same ratio for it, we would find that it would equal .4848. Thus, any time a ratio of side opp ∠ to hypotenuse worked out to .4848, we would know that the angle would be

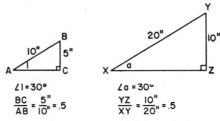

∠1 = 30°
$$\frac{BC}{AB} = \frac{5''}{10''} = .5$$

∠a = 30°
$$\frac{YZ}{XY} = \frac{10''}{20''} = .5$$

Fig. 4-12. Right triangles are similar if one acute angle equals the corresponding acute angle.

.5. Mathematically, this can be written as

$$\frac{\text{side opp. 30°}}{\text{hypotenuse}} = .5$$

and, by applying this equation, we can determine any one of the factors if one of the others is known.

If we have a right triangle where one side equals 12.5 and the hypotenuse equals 25, we can tell that the angle opposite the 12.5 side must be equal to 30° whether it is given to us or not. Then, if one of the acute angles is 30°, the other must be 60° because 30° + 60° + 90° = 180°. Or, if we know that the hypotenuse of a right triangle equals 50 and one of the angles equals 60°, we can find the value of one of the sides because

29° because the ratios of corresponding sides of similar triangles are always equal. By continuing in this way we could work out the ratios for all the possible angles that can exist in a right triangle and use these ratios to compute other unknown facts about their triangles.

This is trigonometry in its most basic form. Mathematicians have worked out ratios for all the angles it is possible to have in a right triangle and listed them in tables. These ratios are called the "trigonometric functions" of angles and can be used for computing unknown facts about similar right triangles. Since the functions are computed for all the angles that can exist, any right triangle you may have to work with will be similar to one for which the functions are listed. By using these known functions in mathematical statements, as we have just done with the 30° right triangles, we can compute all the facts about any right triangle.

Trigonometric Functions

We have seen that certain ratios can be established between two of the sides of a right triangle and that these same ratios will exist between the corresponding sides of any similar right triangle, no matter how large or how small it may be. These ratios are called the "trigonometric functions" of the

make up the angle Θ, and is called the "adjacent side." Using these special names, the six separate ratios or functions that can be established for the acute angle Θ are:

1. $\dfrac{BC}{AB}$ or $\dfrac{\text{opposite side}}{\text{hypotenuse}}$ is the function called the "Sine" of the angle Θ.

2. $\dfrac{AC}{AB}$ or $\dfrac{\text{adjacent side}}{\text{hypotenuse}}$ is the function called the "Cosine" of the angle Θ.

3. $\dfrac{BC}{AC}$ or $\dfrac{\text{opposite side}}{\text{adjacent side}}$ is the function called the "Tangent" of the angle Θ.

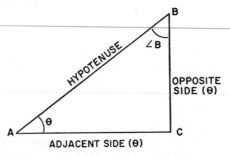

Fig. 4-13. Right triangle showing names of sides with respect to ∠Θ.

angles to which they are related. If you examine any right triangle carefully, you will see that there are six of these ratios or "functions" that can be established for each of the acute angles of the triangle. These six functions have been given special names that you must learn and thoroughly understand in order to make any practical use of trigonometry.

Let's look at the typical right triangle shown in Fig. 4-113 and consider the angle Θ at the lower left. Notice that the three sides of this right triangle have been given special names. The hypotenuse is the side opposite the right angle. The side, BC, opposite the angle Θ is called the "opposite side." The side, AC, and the hypotenuse

4. $\dfrac{AC}{BC}$ or $\dfrac{\text{adjacent side}}{\text{opposite side}}$ is the function called the "Cotangent" of the angle Θ.

5. $\dfrac{AB}{AC}$ or $\dfrac{\text{hypotenuse}}{\text{adjacent side}}$ is the function called the "Secant" of the angle Θ.

6. $\dfrac{AB}{BC}$ or $\dfrac{\text{hypotenuse}}{\text{opposite side}}$ is the function called the "Cosecant" of the angle Θ.

Although there are six of these trigonometric functions for the angle Θ, the first three are the most commonly used. In fact, if you examine them carefully, you will see that the "Cotangent" is simply the reciprocal of the "Tangent," the "Secant" is the reciprocal of the

"Cosine," and the "Cosecant" is the reciprocal of the "Sine." Since all the sides of the triangle are taken into consideration in the first three functions, Sine, Cosine, and Tangent, the reciprocal relationships expressed by the Cotangent, Secant, and Cosecant do not tell us anything really new. They just express it in a different way to provide certain conveniences for persons who work extensively with trigonometry. Since you will probably not be using trigonometry enough to make it worthwhile, you do not have to memorize the last three functions. However, it is important that the first three functions be thoroughly learned and the fact that there are three more reciprocal functions should be remembered.

These trigonometric functions are usually abbreviated as follows:

$$Sin\ \theta = \frac{Opp}{Hyp}$$

$$Cos\ \theta = \frac{Adj}{Hyp}$$

$$Tan\ \theta = \frac{Opp}{Adj}$$

$$Csc\ \theta = \frac{Hyp}{Opp}$$

$$Sec\ \theta = \frac{Hyp}{Adj}$$

$$Cot\ \theta = \frac{Adj}{Opp}$$

In addition to the angle θ in the triangle shown in Fig.4-13, we also have another acute angle. This is $\angle B$ at the top of the triangle and it is the "complement" of angle θ because $\angle\theta + \angle B$ must equal 90° in a right triangle. Angle A also has six separate ratios or functions which can be established between its sides. These six functions of

angle B are stated just the same as those for $\angle\theta$. In other words:

$$Sin\ B = \frac{Opp}{Hyp}$$

$$Cos\ B = \frac{Adj}{Hyp}$$

$$Tan\ B = \frac{Opp}{Adj},\ etc.$$

However, notice that the side *opposite* angle B is the side that was adjacent to angle θ. Likewise, the side adjacent to angle B is the side that was opposite angle θ. Thus, although the trigonometric functions of Sin, Cos, Tan, etc., are stated the same for either of the acute angles, the sides actually referred to in these functions as "opposite" and "adjacent" are different.

For this reason, even though we can simply say:

$$Sin = \frac{Opp}{Hyp},\ Cos = \frac{Adj}{Hyp},\ Tan = \frac{Opp}{Adj}$$

as a general statement of the trigonometric functions, we must express the specific angle as: $Sin\ \theta = \frac{Opp}{Hyp}$ or $Cos\ A = \frac{Adj}{Hyp}$ in order for our expression to have any specific meaning for a particular triangle. In fact, as you can see from studying the sides and angles of Fig.4-13,

$$Sin\ \theta = \frac{Opp}{Hyp} = \frac{BC}{AB}$$

but BC is adjacent to angle B, so

$$\frac{BC}{AB} = \frac{Adj}{Hyp}\ \text{or the Cos of angle B.}$$

Thus, $Sin\ \theta = \frac{BC}{AB} = Cos\ B$ and $Sin\ \theta$ must equal Cos B.

The following relationships between the functions of one acute angle and its complement can be worked out by referring to Fig. 4-13.

Angle (θ)	Sides Used	Complement (B)	
$\text{Sin } \theta =$	$\dfrac{\text{Opp}}{\text{Hyp}} = \dfrac{BC}{AB} = \dfrac{\text{Adj}}{\text{Hyp}}$	$= \text{Cos B}$	
$\text{Cos } \theta =$	$\dfrac{\text{Adj}}{\text{Hyp}} = \dfrac{AC}{AB} = \dfrac{\text{Opp}}{\text{Hyp}}$	$= \text{Sin B}$	
$\text{Tan } \theta =$	$\dfrac{\text{Opp}}{\text{Adj}} = \dfrac{BC}{AC} = \dfrac{\text{Adj}}{\text{Opp}}$	$= \text{Cot B}$	
$\text{Cot } \theta =$	$\dfrac{\text{Adj}}{\text{Opp}} = \dfrac{AC}{BC} = \dfrac{\text{Opp}}{\text{Adj}}$	$= \text{Tan B}$	
$\text{Sec } \theta =$	$\dfrac{\text{Hyp}}{\text{Adj}} = \dfrac{AB}{AC} = \dfrac{\text{Hyp}}{\text{Opp}}$	$= \text{Csc B}$	
$\text{Csc } \theta =$	$\dfrac{\text{Hyp}}{\text{Opp}} = \dfrac{AB}{BC} = \dfrac{\text{Hyp}}{\text{Adj}}$	$= \text{Sec B}$	

Tables of Functions. We mentioned earlier that mathematicians had worked out these trigonometric functions or ratios of the sides of triangles for all possible angles and listed them in tables. These are called Tables of Functions, and must be used for all work in trigonometry. Some of these Tables of Functions are very detailed, such as those used in navigation where the functions are listed in minutes and seconds for all the angles. This is necessary for this type of work because, as we have seen, even a few minutes can mean several miles when we are considering the whole earth.

However, such detailed tables require a thick book which would not be practical for most of your work in electronics. Usually, accuracy to one degree, or possibly a few tenths of a degree, will be close enough for your work with phase angles. A typical Table of Functions that is simple and

efficient is shown in Fig.4-14.This table lists the Sine, Cosine, Tangent, and Cotangent for angles from 0° through 90° in a convenient form.

The angles from 0° to 45° are listed in steps of 1° in the column marked "degrees" at the left of the table. In the next column, the sine of all the angles from 0° to 45° are listed, then the tangent, the cotangent, and the cosine of the angles in the indicated columns. You should be familiar enough with tables of this sort to find the indicated functions of the angles from 0° through 45° without any trouble. For example, to find any of the functions for an angle, say 36°, we read down the degree column until we come to 36. Then, reading to the right, the sine of 36° is .5878, the tangent is .7265, the cotangent is 1.3764, and the cosine is .8090.

Now, we have seen that the sine of an angle is equal to the cosine of its complement. That is, in Fig. 13, the $\text{Sin } \theta = \dfrac{BC}{AB} = \text{Cos A}$, as we discussed earlier. Therefore, if the sine of 36° is equal .5878, as shown in the table, this same value of .5878 must be equal to the Cosine of 54° which is the complement of 36° (36° + 54° = 90°). Likewise, the Cosine of 36°, which according to the table is .8090, must be equal to the Sine of 54°. Thus, once we have listed the functions of the angles from 0° to 45°, we automatically have a list of functions of all the angles from 0° to 90° if we remember the relationships of the functions of complementary angles.

Most tables are made so that they can be read up as well as down, like the one in Fig.4-14 Notice that we have the functions listed again, but in the reverse order at the bottom of the table. In addition, at the extreme right we have another heading marked "degrees." This we read from the bottom,

Degrees	Sine	Tangent	Cotangent	Cosine	
0	.0000	.0000	......	1.0000	90
1	.0175	.0175	57.290	.9998	89
2	.0349	.0349	28.636	.9994	88
3	.0523	.0524	19.081	.9986	87
4	.0698	.0699	14.301	.9976	86
5	.0872	.0875	11.430	.9962	85
6	.1045	.1051	9.5144	.9945	84
7	.1219	.1228	8.1443	.9925	83
8	.1392	.1405	7.1154	.9903	82
9	.1564	.1584	6.3138	.9877	81
10	.1736	.1763	5.6713	.9848	80
11	.1908	.1944	5.1446	.9816	79
12	.2079	.2126	4.7046	.9781	78
13	.2250	.2309	4.3315	.9744	77
14	.2419	.2493	4.0108	.9703	76
15	.2588	.2679	3.7321	.9659	75
16	.2756	.2867	3.4874	.9613	74
17	.2924	.3057	3.2709	.9563	73
18	.3090	.3249	3.0777	.9511	72
19	.3256	.3443	2.9042	.9455	71
20	.3420	.3640	2.7475	.9397	70
21	.3584	.3839	2.6051	.9336	69
22	.3746	.4040	2.4751	.9272	68
23	.3907	.4245	2.3559	.9205	67
24	.4067	.4452	2.2460	.9135	66
25	.4226	.4663	2.1445	.9063	65
26	.4384	.4877	2.0503	.8988	64
27	.4540	.5095	1.9626	.8910	63
28	.4695	.5317	1.8807	.8829	62
29	.4848	.5543	1.8040	.8746	61
30	.5000	.5774	1.7321	.8660	60
31	.5150	.6009	1.6643	.8572	59
32	.5299	.6249	1.6003	.8480	58
33	.5446	.6494	1.5399	.8387	57
34	.5592	.6745	1.4826	.8290	56
35	.5736	.7002	1.4281	.8192	55
36	.5878	.7265	1.3764	.8090	54
37	.6018	.7536	1.3270	.7986	53
38	.6157	.7813	1.2799	.7880	52
39	.6293	.8098	1.2349	.7771	51
40	.6428	.8391	1.1918	.7660	50
41	.6561	.8693	1.1504	.7547	49
42	.6691	.9004	1.1106	.7431	48
43	.6820	.9325	1.0724	.7314	47
44	.6947	.9657	1.0355	.7193	46
45	.7071	1.0000	1.0000	.7071	45
	Cosine	Cotangent	Tangent	Sine	Degrees

Fig. 4-14. TABLE OF FUNCTIONS

45°, up to the top, 90°, in conjunction with the function headings at the bottom. Thus, to find the Cosine of 63°, we read up the right-hand degree column to 63, then across to the extreme left to the column which is marked "Cosine" at the bottom. This shows us that Cosine 63° is .4540, Cotangent 63° is .5095, Tangent 63° is 1.9626, and Sine 63° is .8910.

Thus, Sine 63° is .8910 which is the Cosine of its complement, 27°. By studying the table, you will notice some important relationships between the various functions. The Sine of 0° is .0000, but the Cosine is 1.0000, while the Sine of 90° is 1.0000 and the Cosine is zero. Thus, the Sines of angles start from 0° and .0000 and work up to a maximum of 1.0000 at 90°. The Cosine works out exactly the opposite; it has a value of 1 at 0° and decreases until it is zero at 90°. The value of the Sine or the Cosine of an angle can never be more than 1. The Tangent also starts at 0° and .0000, but the Tangent functions have no upper limit. At 89° it is 57.290, but as you can see, it is increasing in value rapidly as it approaches this upper limit. From 89° it increases to some infinite (unmeasurable) value at 90°.

Interpolation. Although accuracy to one degree is usually satisfactory, you may occasionally want to be accurate to a fraction of a degree. You can get this additional accuracy from the Table of Functions even though it shows only whole degree steps. We do this by a process known as interpolation. Suppose we want to find the sine of an angle of 36.5°. Since it is between 36° and 37°, we know that its sine must be more than the sine of 36° and less than the sine of 37°. Therefore, we look up the sine of both 36° and 37° and proceed as follows:

First, we subtract to find the difference between the values of the sines of the two angles. Thus:

$$\begin{array}{ll} \text{Sine } 37° = & .6018 \\ -\text{ Sine } 36° = & .5878 \\ \hline \text{Difference} & .0140 \end{array}$$

Now, the angle that we are trying to find the sine for is 36.5°, which is an increase of .5° over 36°. Therefore the sine of 36.5° must be the sine of 36° plus .5 of the difference between 36° and 37°.

$$.5 \times .0140 = .00700$$

Then, .5878 (Sine 36°) plus .007 equals .5948, which is the sine of 36.5°.

To make sure that we understand this, let's try another example. What is the Sine of 28° 15'? First,

$$\begin{array}{ll} \text{Sine } 29° = & .4848 \\ -\text{ Sine } 28° = & .4695 \\ \hline \text{Difference} & .0153 \end{array}$$

Now, 28° 15' is 15/60 or .25 more than Sine 28°. Therefore:

$$.25 \times .0153 = .003825 \quad \text{and}$$
$$.4695 + .003825 = .473325$$

which is the Sine of 28° 15'. To interpolate sine functions, find the difference between the functions of the next smaller and the next larger angle. Then, multiply this difference by the amount of increase and add the product to the function of the smaller angle. The same procedure is used to interpolate tangent functions.

Interpolation of Cosine and Cotangent funtions starts the same: Find the difference between the next smaller and next larger functions and multiply this difference by the amount of increase. Now, since the values of Cosine and Cotangent become smaller as the angle becomes larger, you must subtract the product from the value of the function of the smaller angle.

Using Trigonometry

Now that we have learned some of the basic facts concerning angles and triangles, let's see how we can put them to everyday use in solving circuit problems. Working with the trigonometric functions of angles will help you to understand and remember them. For example, suppose we have the simple circuit shown in Fig.4-15.The coil has an inductive reactance of 15 ohms and is in series with a 15-ohm resistance. Neglecting the resistance of the coil itself, what is the impedance and the phase angle of the circuit?

We have already learned two ways to solve such a problem. First, we learned to construct a very accurate

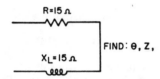

Fig. 4-15. Simple AC circuit.

vector diagram using the resistive and reactive components and then to measure the resultant impedance vector and the phase angle. While this could be done for very simple circuits, we soon discovered that the drawings became very complex and difficult to work with if the circuits became the least bit complicated. However, the greatest disadvantage in this method is that the accuracy depends on drawing neatly and accurately. Since most of us are not draftsmen or artists, it may be difficult to make a completely accurate drawing to scale and this gives a large margin for error when using this method.

Next, we learned to use the J-operator and to express a vector mathematically by using a binomial number. This eliminated the need for many of

the accurate diagrams because we could work with vectors mathematically to combine them into a final binomial representation of the resultant. Then, by using the pythagorean theorem, we could find the numerical value of this binomial representation which would give the length of the final vector. However, we still must construct a diagram and actually measure the angle of lead or lag to find the phase angle.

Using trigonometry to solve vector diagrams will eliminate the need for any construction or measurement in finding the phase angle as well as the impedance. It is also quite a bit easier than finding the square roots of numbers such as we have to do when we use the pythagorean theorem. Now, let's use trigonometry to solve the circuit shown in Fig. 4-15

The best way to begin is to lay out a simple sketch of the vectors involved. Since we are not going to make any measurements, this can be a rough diagram as shown in Fig.4-16 Here the resistance component becomes a vector that forms the base of a triangle. The reactance component becomes a vector that represents the altitude of a triangle. Since the phase angle between a pure resistance and a pure inductance is exactly 90°, these two vectors form a 90° angle. Therefore, the resultant impedance vector which we draw from the tail of the resistance vector to the head of the reactance vector becomes the hypotenuse of a right triangle. We want to know the value of the length of this impedance vector and the size of the phase angle Θ that is formed by it.

Looking at this triangle in terms of what we know about it as compared to what we want to know, we see that we know the value of the side opposite the angle Θ and the value of the side adjacent to the angle Θ. Now, we consider the trigonometric functions that we have just learned to see which one of them fits the unknown angle θ in terms of the known values. If we go

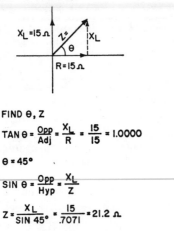

FIND θ, Z

$$TAN\ \theta = \frac{Opp}{Adj} = \frac{X_L}{R} = \frac{15}{15} = 1.0000$$

$$\theta = 45°$$

$$SIN\ \theta = \frac{Opp}{Hyp} = \frac{X_L}{Z}$$

$$Z = \frac{X_L}{SIN\ 45°} = \frac{15}{.7071} = 21.2\ \Omega$$

Fig. 4-16. Trigonometric solution to circuit in Fig. 4-15.

down the list of functions, the first one that we come to that uses the opposite and adjacent sides is the tangent. This states that

$$Tan\ \theta = \frac{Opp}{Adj}$$

If we use this function as an equation and substitute the known values, we have:

$$Tan\ \theta = \frac{Opp}{Adj} = \frac{X_L}{R} = \frac{15}{15} = 1.0000$$

This simply tells us that the tangent of the angle θ is equal to 1.0000 when the opposite side and the adjacent side are both equal to 15.

Now, we turn to the Table of Functions in Fig. 4-14 and look down the column headed "Tangent" until we come to 1.0000. Then, looking to the left, we find that this number is the tangent of an angle of 45°. Thus, the phase angle θ in our diagram must

equal 45°, because our equation states that Tan θ = 1.0000 and our Table of Functions shows us that only 45° has a tangent equal to 1.0000.

Now that we have found our phase angle, we will want to find the value of our impedance vector. We can do this quite easily now that we know the value of θ because:

$$Sin\ \theta = \frac{Opp}{Hyp} = \frac{X_L}{Z}$$

Stated in terms of Z, this becomes:

$$Z = \frac{X_L}{Sin\ \theta} = \frac{15}{Sin\ 45°}$$

Then, from the Table of Functions,

$$Sin\ 45° = .7071\ \text{and}\ Z = \frac{15}{.7071}$$

Performing the mathematics:

$$15 \div .7071 = 21.2 = Z$$

Thus, using two steps of simple algebra and arithmetic and the Table of Functions, we can find both the phase angle (45°) and the impedance (21.2Ω) for the circuit shown in Fig.4-15. By using the trigonometric functions of angles in this way, we can find the value of either of the acute angles of a right triangle if two of the sides are known, or the value of the two unknown sides if one of the sides and an acute angle are known.

Resistance in Coils. Up until now in working with ac circuits we have always neglected the resistance that exists in the windings of coils in our circuit calculations. While we can do this without being too far off for most purposes, occasionally we will want to be more accurate. This does not present any particular problem where we are given both the resistance and either the inductance or the inductive reactance of the coil, but in many practical circuits that we will want to

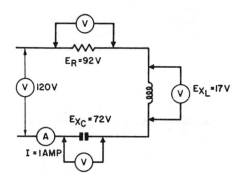

Fig. 4-17. Typical series circuit voltage measurements.

study, this information is not easy to obtain. Of course it is easy to measure the resistance of a coil with an ohm-meter, but the inductance cannot be found so easily unless we have a special meter.

However, through the use of trigonometry and standard measuring instruments, it is quite easy to determine the inductance of a coil and separate

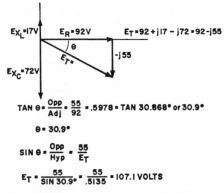

Fig. 4-18. Computation of total voltage without considering coil resistance.

the inductive reactance from the resistance. For example, consider the circuit shown in Fig.4-17.Here we have a coil, a capacitor, and a resistor in series with each other. If we measure the voltage drops across each of these units as shown, and then compute the

total voltage of the circuit, we will find that the total voltage we compute does not agree with the total voltage as indicated by measurement. Let's see why and how to overcome this difficulty.

First, computing the total voltage, E_T, without considering any possible resistance that the coil might have, we get the results shown in Fig.4-18.Drawing our rough vector diagram as shown, we have E_{X_L} of 17V as the inductive vector component, E_{X_C} of 72V as the capacitive vector component, and E_R of 92V as the resistive vector component. Mathematically, this gives us: $92 + j17 - j72$, or $92 - j55$ as our final vector stated as a binomial. Thus, E_T is the hypotenuse of a right triangle with a base of 92V and an altitude of 55V. Then, using trigonometry, we find that the phase angle Θ equals:

$$\text{Tan } \Theta = \frac{\text{Opp}}{\text{Adj}} = \frac{55}{92} = .5978$$

Therefore:

Θ = angle whose tangent is .5978

If we look in our Table of Functions, we find that we do not have a tangent of .5978 listed. But, the tangent of 30° is .5774 and the tangent of 31° is .6009. Therefore, the phase angle Θ must lie somewhere between 30° and 31° since its tangent lies between the tangent of 30° and 31°. You have learned to find the function of an angle by interpolation when it lies between two angles that are listed. A similar process is also used to find an angle when its function does not appear in the table.

First, we look up the next larger function listed and then the next smaller function listed and find their difference. Doing this, we have:

$$\text{Tan } 31° = .6009$$
$$- \text{Tan } 30° = .5774$$
$$\overline{\text{Difference} = .0235}$$

COIL RESISTANCE, R_L = 12 Ω BY MEASUREMENT
CIRCUIT & COIL AMPS, I_L = IA AS SHOWN IN FIG. 4-17

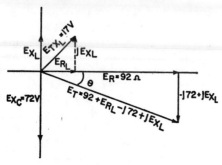

Fig. 4-19. **Vector diagram of circuit in Fig. 4-17** considering coil resistance.

Thus, the difference of 1° between 30° and 31° makes a difference of .0235 between the tangents of these two angles.

Next, if we subtract the tangent of the smaller angle (30°) from the tangent we have computed for the angle θ, we have:

$$\text{Tan } \theta = .5978$$
$$-\text{ Tan } 30° = .5774$$
$$\text{Difference} = .0204$$

Now, if a 1° increase from 30° increases the tangent by .0235, and the tangent shows an increase of .0204 from the tangent of 30°, then the angle must be 30° plus $\dfrac{.0204}{.0235}$ of 1°. Changing this fraction of $\dfrac{.0204}{.0235}$ to a decimal, we have:

$$.0204 \div .0235 = .868$$

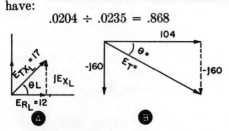

Fig. 4-20. **Trigonometric solution of vector diagram of Fig. 4-19.**

and the angle θ whose tangent is .5978 must be 30.868°. Normally, working to the nearest one tenth of a degree will be accurate enough for our purposes. Therefore, for the problem in Fig. 4-18, the phase angle θ is equal to 30.9°.

Now that we have found the angle θ, we can find the value of E_T through the function:

$$\text{Sin } \theta = \frac{\text{Opp}}{\text{Hyp}} \text{ or Hyp} = \frac{\text{Opp}}{\text{Sin } \theta}$$

or

$$E_T = \frac{55}{\text{Sin } 30.9°}$$

Since our table lists the functions in one-degree steps we must interpolate to find the sine of 30.9°. Doing this, we have:

$$\text{Sin } 31° = .5150$$
$$-\text{ Sin } 30° = .5000$$
$$\text{Difference} = .0150$$

Thus, .0150 is the difference between the sine functions of 30° and 31°. Since the angle is 30.9°, we will want only nine tenths of this difference for our sine function. Accordingly:

$$.0150 \times .9 = .01350$$

Then:
$$\text{Sin } 30° = .5000$$
$$+ .9 \times .0150 = .0135$$
$$\text{Sin } 30.9° = .5135$$

If we substitute this in our equation, we have

$$E_T = \frac{55}{\text{Sin } 30.9°}$$

$$= \frac{55}{.5135} = 107.1 \text{ volts}$$

Thus, by computation we find that E_T = 107.1 volts while the measured value for E_T as shown in the circuit of Fig. 4-17 is 120 volts. The reason for this difference is that the Q of the coil is low; therefore, the ratio of the resistance of its winding to its inductance is large. This means that the voltage E_{X_L} which we assumed to be purely inductive does not lead the current in the circuit by a full 90°. Consequently, our E_{X_L} of 17 volts is really voltage made up of $E_{R_L} + JE_{X_L}$ and cannot be written $+J17$ and added directly to our $-J72$. It must be broken down into its two components, $E_{R_L} + JE_{X_L}$. Thus, the vector diagram of our circuit must be drawn as shown in Fig.4-19,and ou voltage vector E_T must be found from:

$$E_T = E_R + E_{TX_L} - JE_{X_C} \text{ and:}$$

$$E_T = E_R + (E_{R_L} + JE_{X_L}) - JE_{X_C}$$

$$= 92 + E_{R_L} - J72 + JE_{X_L}$$

In order to work out a solution to this problem, we must know the values of both E_{R_L} and E_{X_L}. Neither the value of the resistance of the coil nor the value of its inductance is given to us. However, the chances are that if we have a meter or meters capable of reading the voltages of the circuit and the current through the circuit, as shown in Fig.4-17,we will also have an ohmmeter. With the ohmmeter we can determine the resistance of the coil, and then by computation we can find E_{R_L} and E_{X_L}.

For example, suppose we measure the resistance of the coil and find it to be 12Ω. Our circuit ammeter shows us that the current through the circuit is 1 amp. Thus,

$$E_{R_L} = I \times R_L$$

$$= 1 \times 12$$

$$= 12 \text{ volts}$$

This gives us one of our components of E_{X_L}, so our equation for E_T now becomes:

$$E_T = 92 + E_{R_L} + JE_{X_L} - j72$$

$$= 92 + 12 + JE_{X_L} - j72$$

Now, all we have left to determine is the value of JE_{X_L}.

This is where trigonometry really helps us. We have the total coil voltage drop and have been able to compute the resistance component of this total drop. Therefore, we have the value of both hypotenuse and the base of a right triangle as shown in Fig. 4-20A , and can compute the value of JE_{X_L}.

First, we list our values as:

Given: $E_{TX_L} = 17V$ Find: E_{X_L}
$I_L = 1A$
$R_L = 12Ω$

Then: $E_{TX_L} = E_{R_L} + JE_{X_L}$

and: $JE_{X_L} = E_{TX_L} - E_{R_L}$ (vectorially)

Thus: $JE_{X_L} = E_{TX_L} - (I_L \times R_L)$ (vectorially)

and: $JE_{X_L} = 17 - (1 \times 12) = 17 - 12$ (vectorially)

Now, sketching the vector diagram with 17 as the hypotenuse and 12 as the base of a right triangle as shown in Fig. 4-20A, allows us to use our trigonometry. First we will want to find the phase angle Θ_L. To do this, we use the Cosine function which is:

$$\text{Cos } \Theta = \frac{\text{Adj}}{\text{Hyp}} = \frac{E_{R_L}}{E_{TX_L}} = \frac{12}{17} = .7057$$

In checking our Table of Functions we find that there is no Cosine given as exactly .7057. While we could interpolate to find the exact value for Θ, our Cosine of .7057 is so close to .7071, which is the Cosine of 45°, that we can use the approximate value of 45° as the angle Θ_L.

Now that we know that Θ_L is equal to 45°, we can proceed to find the value of JE_{X_L} (the opposite side) by using one of the other functions. For example,

$$\text{Tan } \Theta_L = \frac{\text{Opp}}{\text{Adj}} \text{ and:}$$

$$\text{Opp} = \text{Adj} \times \text{Tan } \Theta_L$$

Substituting

$$JE_{X_L} = E_{R_L} \times \text{Tan } 45°$$
$$JE_{X_L} = 12 \times 1.0000 = 12$$

Thus, JE_{X_L}, which is the reactive component of the total coil voltage, is also equal 12 volts. Notice that we could also have used the Sine, since

$$\text{Sin } \Theta_L = \frac{\text{Opp}}{\text{Hyp}} \text{ and therefore}$$

$$\text{Opp} = \text{Sin } \Theta_L \times \text{Hyp or}$$
$$JE_{X_L} = \text{Sin } 45° \times E_{TX_L}$$
$$= .7071 \times 17 = 12 \text{ (approx.)}$$

The function used is a matter of personal choice or convenience as long as the necessary values are known.

Now, notice carefully what we have done. We have taken a voltage drop across a coil and broken it up into its resistive and reactive components. We cannot measure these components of voltage because they do not exist separately. They only exist together as a total, but the fact that this vector sum is not exactly in phase with the current tells us that it must have both of the components even though they are not measurable separately. And, in order to *compute* the circuit values accurately, we must have the values of the components themselves and not their vector sum. Since the resistance of a coil, the current through the coil, and the total voltage across the coil are all generally easy to measure with commonly available instruments, we have used these values, together with trigonometry to obtain the two components of total coil voltage.

If we have the inductance or the inductive reactance of the coil available, we can also use them to compute the value of the components. However, in practical circuits the value of the inductance or inductive reactance is often not known. Since these values cannot be measured without instruments, which are not usually available in the average shop, we have shown you how to solve the problem by a method which can almost always be achieved.

Since we now have all the values required to find E_T as shown in Fig.4-19, we can continue with our computation as shown in Fig.4-20B. We have already established the fact that:

$$E_T = E_R + E_{TX_L} - JE_{X_C}$$

By substitution:

$$E_T = E_R + (E_{R_L} + JE_{X_L}) - JE_{X_C}$$

and: $\quad E_T = 92 + 12 + J12 - J72$

Then: $\quad\quad E_T = 104 - J60$

and we can draw the vector diagram as shown in Fig.4-20B and compute the value of E_T and Θ by using trigonometry. First:

$$\text{Tan } \Theta = \frac{\text{Opp}}{\text{Adj}} = \frac{60}{104} = .5769$$

and

$$\Theta = 30° \text{ (approx.)}$$

Then:

$$\text{Sin } \Theta = \frac{\text{Opp}}{\text{Hyp}}$$

and

$$\text{Hyp} = \frac{\text{Opp}}{\text{Sin } \Theta} = \frac{60}{.5} = 120V$$

This is the value of E_T that we obtained by measurement in Fig. 4-17 and is therefore correct.

We have used a very low Q coil, $Q = \dfrac{12}{12} = 1$, to demonstrate the importance of considering the resistive component of voltage in a coil. While such a low Q coil will not be found often in practical circuits, it is still important to know how to handle these effects when they do occur. You are probably wondering now about the resistance of capacitors and if it has to be considered also. It does not. While all capacitors do have some resistance, it is never large enough to be noticed in a practical capacitor. We will get some more practice using trigonometry in circuit calculations a little later. Right now, we should learn some more basic facts about trigonometry.

Coordinate Systems

We have become used to expressing a vector as a binomial term by using the J-operator. Now that we have learned a little about trigonometry, we can also express a vector as a numerical value and an angle. For example, the voltage E_T which we computed in the last section can be expressed as a binomial: $104 - J60$ volts; or as a number and an angle: $120\underline{/-30°}$ volts. Either expression gives us a number picture of the vector and allows us to construct an accurate diagram of both the resultant vector and its components. They also allow us to compute with the vectors mathematically.

These two methods of noting vectors mathematically are given special names. The first, using a binomial such as $104 - j60$ volts is termed a "rectangular" or "cartesian" coordinate. The second, using a number and an angle such as $120\underline{/-30°}$ volts is called a "polar" coordinate. Notice that in the polar form we give the angle a negative value to show that we are measuring it in a clockwise direction from the reference to vector E_T. We could also say $120\underline{/+330°}$ volts if we measured counterclockwise from the reference line all the way around to vector E_T. Either way, the notation tells us that we have a voltage of 120V lagging the current

by 30°. The usual method is to give the angle the same sign as the corresponding j term when we use "rectangular" coordinates. Thus, a vector such as $E = 20 + j20$ volts would be written in polar form as $E = 28.3\underline{/+45°}$ volts.

Both of these methods of describing a vector or locating a point are commonly used. Measurements and computations are made either way, depending on the information desired and the equipment available. Often, when mechanical or electronic computers are used, conversions from rectangular coordinates to polar coordinates and back again are made constantly, depending on the nature of the information supplied, the type of information needed, and the equipment in the computer. While we have actually learned nearly everything about these two systems of describing a vector, our work in electronics is such that we have used them constantly without knowing some of the basic concepts of these systems of coordinates. Now is a good time to catch up on some of these basic considerations.

Rectangular Coordinates. First of all, a coordinate system is simply a standard frame of reference for describing some particular value, condition, or place. Unless we have these standard references, even simple, everyday occurrences would be difficult to explain or describe. For example, the common directions of east, north, south, or west, have no meaning unless we know what they are east or north or south from. Describing the voltage-current relationship of a circuit as 120 volts lagging a current of 1 ampere by 30° has no meaning unless we are familiar with a standard condition to compare it with. For this reason, standard reference frames have been established for universal use so that everyone will have the same means for

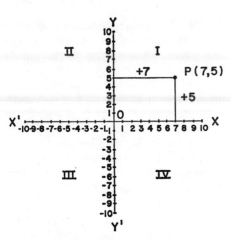

Fig. 4-21. Coordinate reference frame.

describing a situation so that everyone else can understand it.

Originally, the rectangular coordinate system was devised for giving directions in a standard manner. Since this system is so simple and so widely understood, it has been adopted for locating values and describing conditions throughout the fields of science and mathematics.

To begin with, let's call a rectangular coordinate system a device for associating points with pairs of numbers. The standard reference for this system consists of two mutually perpendicular lines, as shown in Fig. 4-21. One line is always horizontal and is labeled X'X as shown. Therefore, the other line labeled Y'Y is always vertical as shown, and the lines intersect at the point 0. We have used this device constantly in our work with vectors and it is nothing new except that we have never used these particular letters for the axes.

Now the two lines are called the coordinate axes and are said to be made up of the X axis (line X'X) and the Y axis (line Y'Y). The point 0 is called the origin. We can lay off scales along these axes to suit our particular pur-

pose, but the scale from the origin, 0, to the right along the X axis is always positive, while the scale is always negative from the origin, 0, to the left along the X axis. Likewise, the scale from the origin, 0, up toward Y is always positive and the scale down from the origin, 0, to Y' is always negative.

This reference frame consisting of the two coordinate axes serves as a means of locating any point in the plane of the axes by referring to two numbers. The two numbers completely express the position or distance of the point from the origin of the coordinate axes. For example, consider the point P in Fig. 4-21

We can completely describe its position so that anyone familiar with this system can immediately locate it by saying it lies +5 from the X axis and +7 from the Y axis. The distance of the point from the Y axis, measured along the X axis is called the "abscissa" of the point. The distance of the point from the X axis measured by the scale on the Y axis is called the "ordinate" of the point. These two numbers, each with their proper algebraic sign, are called the "coordinates" of the point. In writing the coordinates of a point, the abscissa is written first and the ordinate second. Thus, we would write the coordinates of the point P in Fig. 4-21 as "the coordinates of P are (7, 5)."

The coordinate axes divide the area into four sections, or quadrants as they are called. These quadrants are numbered in Fig. 4-21 by the Roman numerals I, II, III, IV. Notice that a point must have two positive coordinates to lie in the first quadrant and two negative coordinates to lie in the third quadrant. A point in the second quadrant must have a negative abscissa and a positive ordinate, while a point in the fourth quadrant has a positive abscissa and a negative ordinate.

This system of referring to a point by its coordinate is sometimes called the "Cartesian" coordinate system in honor of the French mathematician Descartes. It is also called the "rectangular" coordinate system because a rectangular figure is drawn when the points are completely located.

In electronics work, we use this standard coordinate reference frame constantly, but we usually use some other method of labeling the coordinate axes. However, regardless of the symbols we may use, the quadrant designations always remain the same, the signs of the scales are always the same, and we always consider the positive section of the X axis as the starting point or reference line. When the frame is assigned a degree system of reference, 0° is always at X, 90° at Y, 180° at X', and 270° at Y'. While most of our work will lie in the first and fourth quadrants, which is all we need to represent vectors consisting of coordinates using positive resistance, +JX, and −JX, we will have some occasion to get into the second and third quadrants.

Polar Coordinates. As we have seen in studying ac circuits and trigonometry, we can use degrees to designate the points in the standard coordinate reference frame as shown in Fig. 4-22.Thus, we can also locate a point P accurately and clearly by saying it is 10 units from the "0" of the graph and a line connecting the point "P" with "0" forms an angle of 45° with the positive X axis, as shown in Fig.4-22.This would be written 10/+45° to show the length of a line from the origin, 0, to the point as 10 units; and the displacement of the line from 0° (measured counterclockwise) as /+45°. Thus, saying point P is 10/+45° would describe the location of the point in terms of "polar" coordinates. We call this the "polar" coordinate system be-

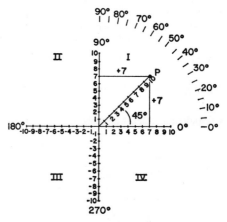

POINT P = 10 /+45° (POLAR)
POINT P = +7, +7 (RECTANGULAR)

Fig. 4-22. Reference frame for polar coordinates.

cause of its use in reference to the poles of the earth for navigation and surveying. Remember, a negative sign is used for angles generated or measured from 0° in a clockwise direction.

Coordinate Conversion. The point P in Fig. 4-22 can be completely described or located by using either polar coordinates or rectangular coordinates. Therefore, we may often wish to convert polar coordinates to rectangular coordinates and vice versa. We can do this quite easily by using the fundamentals of trigonometry.

For example, suppose we wish to refer to the point P in Fig. 4-23 in rectangular coordinates so that it can be combined with other points that are also expressed as rectangular coordinates. Here the point P is expressed in polar form as an impedance vector and a phase angle, and would be written as $Z = 20/+60°$. To convert this impedance vector to its rectangular coordinates, we would express it as a resistance ± reactance.

Now, the resistance component would be the adjacent side of $\angle \theta$ and the reactive component would always be the opposite side of $\angle\Theta$ and represent the $\pm$ j term. Accordingly:

$$\text{Cos }\Theta = \frac{\text{Adj}}{\text{Hyp}} \text{ or Adj} = \text{Hyp} \times \text{Cos }\Theta$$

Substituting: $R = Z \text{ Cos }\Theta$

Likewise: $\text{Sin }\Theta = \dfrac{\text{Opp}}{\text{Hyp}}$ or

$$\text{Opp} = \text{Hyp} \times \text{Sin }\Theta$$

Substituting: $X = Z \text{ Sin }\Theta$

Then, since: $Z = R \pm JX$

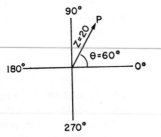

Fig. 4-23. Converting polar coordinates to rectangular coordinates.

We can substitute:

$$Z = Z \text{ Cos }\Theta \pm J(Z \text{ Sin }\Theta)$$

Or: $Z = Z (\text{Cos }\Theta \pm J\text{Sin }\Theta)$

Thus, by applying this equation, we can convert any polar coordinates to rectangular coordinates.

In Fig. 4-23, we would have:

$$Z = Z (\text{Cos }\Theta \pm J\text{Sin }\Theta)$$

Substituting:

$$Z = 20 (\text{Cos } 60 + J\text{Sin } 60)$$

From our tables:

$$Z = 20 (.5 + J866)$$

and:

$$Z = 10 + J17.32$$

would express

$$Z = 20\underline{/+60°}$$

in rectangular coordinates.

For example, to convert the rectangular coordinates of an impedance, $Z = 250 - j100\Omega$ to polar coordinates we have in three steps:

$$\text{Tan }\Theta = \frac{\text{Opp}}{\text{Adj}}$$

Substituting: $\text{Tan }\Theta = \dfrac{-JX}{R}$

$$= \frac{-100}{250} = -.4$$

and from our tables:

$$\Theta = -21.8°$$

(Θ is negative because JX was negative).

Then: $\text{Sin }\Theta = \dfrac{\text{Opp}}{\text{Hyp}}$

Or: $\text{Hyp} = \dfrac{\text{Opp}}{\text{Sin }\Theta}$

Substituting: $Z = \dfrac{-JX}{\text{Sin }\Theta} = \dfrac{100}{\text{Sin } 21.8°}$

$$= \frac{100}{.3714} = 269\Omega$$

Accordingly: $Z = 269\underline{/-21.8°}\Omega$ in polar coordinates.

Notice that once we found Θ, we could have also used $\text{Cos }\Theta = \dfrac{\text{Adj}}{\text{Hyp}}$ instead of $\text{Sin }\Theta = \dfrac{\text{Opp}}{\text{Hyp}}$ since the necessary values are all available. However, our answer would still have worked out to the same value of $269\underline{/-21.8°}\Omega$.

Phasors and Sine Waves

In the lessons on alternating currents you learned that an alternating current is sinusoidal in nature. In other words, the various values of current and voltage generated by an alternating current source describe what is called a sine wave that continuously repeats itself periodically. However, we have never discussed just what a sine wave really is nor why ac current values produce it.

Additionally, in your first introduction to vectors, we mentioned that the vectors we were using in ac circuit calculations were not really considered to be vectors at all by electronics engineers. Instead, they are really "phasors" in the most accurate technical sense. This is due to the fact that vectors are used to express force as a magnitude and direction, while phasors represent sine-wave values with respect to time or phase.

Since many of you learned to work with vectors in high school or college physics, and since vectors and phasors can be treated the same in circuit computations, we have continued to call these phasors "vectors" and to apply many of the standard principles for vector solutions in our circuit calculations.

However, many modern engineering texts are beginning to refer to electrical vectors as phasors and we should be familiar with why they really are phasors. We will not change our methods of working with them and we will continue to call them vectors. But, this will be a good time to examine both the sine wave and electrical vectors in greater detail.

Angles Greater Than 90°. In studying trigonometry, we have considered the functions of angles only up to 90°. However, we can have angles of any magnitude, depending on where the terminal side of an angle stops and on how many complete revolutions it makes in generating the angles. In our study of sine waves, we will need to consider the functions of all the possible angles up to 360°.

To begin with, let's consider the sine of the acute angle Θ shown in Fig. 4-24A. Since this ∠Θ is equal to 30°, the sine of Θ is equal to the ratio of the length of the opposite side over the hypotenuse which always works out to .5. Now let's consider the angle Θ shown in Fig. 4-24B. This angle Θ is equal to 150° which is larger than 90° and so cannot be one of the angles in a right triangle. We know that the trigonometric functions are based on the

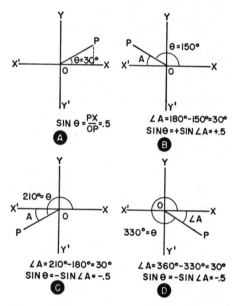

Fig. 4-24. Sines of angles greater than 90°.

sides and angles of right triangles. Yet, the ∠Θ = 150° is considered to have a sine function, even though it cannot be part of a right triangle. In fact, the sine of 150° is .5, just the same as the sine of 30°.

To see how this is determined, we must consider what is known as the "associated acute angle" of the angle Θ. First of all, an angle is said to be in *standard position* when its *initial* side coincides with the *positive* side of the X axis of the standard coordinate reference frame, regardless of where · its terminal side may be. Thus, the $\angle\theta$ = 150° in Fig. 4-24B is in standard position. Now, the *associated acute angle* of any angle θ larger than 90° is the acute angle which the *terminal side* of the angle makes with the *X axis* when the angle θ is in *standard position*. Since $\angle\theta = 150°$ in Fig. 4-24B is by definition in standard position, $\angle A$ is its associated acute angle.

Now, $\angle A$ is the supplement of $\angle\theta$, and therefore $\angle A = 180° - \angle\theta$ (150°) or 30° in Fig.4-24B. In Fig.4-24C we have another angle θ which is equal to 210°. Its associated acute angle is $\angle A$ in Fig.4-24C because, by definition, the associated acute angle is the acute angle formed between the terminal side and the X axis. Since θ equals 210°, and since the $\angle X'OX$ is equal to 180°, the $\angle A$ in Fig.4-24C must be equal to 210° - 180° or $\angle A = 30°$ again.

In Fig.4-24D, we show still another angle θ. This time $\angle\theta = 330°$ and its associated acute angle, $\angle A$, must equal 360° - 330° or 30° once again. Remember, the associated acute angle always lies between the terminal side of $\angle\theta$ and the X axis as shown in Fig. 4-24. Notice that from this definition, $\angle\theta$ in Fig. 4-24A is really its own associated acute angle.

There is a trigonometric statement which says: "the function of any angle greater than 90° is equal to plus or minus the function of its associated acute angle." This simply means that the 150° $\angle$ has the same sine as its associated acute $\angle$, which is $\angle A$. Since $\angle A$ is 30°, the sine of the 150° $\angle$ is the same as the sine of the 30° angle. Likewise, the sine of 210° is equal to the sine of 30° except that it is negative, and the sine of 330° is also equal to the sine of 30° except that it is negative.

In this fashion, the sine of any angle

greater than 90° may be determined by finding the value of the function of its associated acute angle and affixing a plus or minus sign, depending on the quadrant in which the terminal side of the angle lies.

As you have probably already guessed, all the other functions can also exist for any angle greater than 90°. The rules for the sine function all apply to the other functions as well. Thus, the Cosine of $\angle\theta = 252°$ as shown in Fig. 4-25A is equal to minus the Cosine of 72° or $-.3090$ because 72° is the associated acute angle of 252°. Likewise, the tangent of $\angle\theta = 305°$ is equal to minus the tangent of 55° or -1.4281 as shown in Fig. 4-25B.

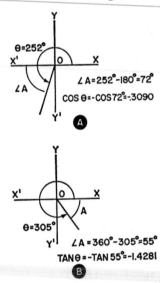

Fig. 4-25. All functions exist for all angles.

Now let's consider the sign of the functions in the different quadrants. In the first quadrant all six functions are positive. In the second quadrant, the sine and cosecant are positive, all other functions are negative. In the third quadrant the tangent and its reciprocal, the cotangent, are positive and the other functions are negative. In the fourth quadrant the cosine and secant are positive and the other four functions are negative.

To see why the functions have these signs look at Fig. 4-26. First consider that the X-X' axis and the Y-Y' axis divide the figure into four quadrants. A line drawn from the Y-Y' axis along or parallel to the X axis is considered positive if it is drawn to the right, and negative if it is drawn to the left. Similarly, a line drawn from the X-X' axis along or parallel to the Y axis is positive if it is drawn upwards and negative if it is drawn down below the X-X' axis.

Now look at angle θ in Fig. 4-26A. Side a is positive because it is drawn above the X-X' axis, and side b is also positive because it is drawn to the right of the Y-Y' axis. The hypotenuse of the triangle is always considered positive and therefore the functions are as follows:

$$\text{Sin } \theta = \frac{+a}{+c}$$

$$\text{Cos } \theta = \frac{+b}{+c}$$

$$\text{Tan } \theta = \frac{+a}{+b}$$

$$\text{Cot } \theta = \frac{+b}{+a}$$

$$\text{Sec } \theta = \frac{+c}{+b}$$

$$\text{Cosec } \theta = \frac{+c}{+a}$$

In each case we have a plus term divided by another plus term, so the result in each case is positive.

Now look at Fig. 4-26B and consider the second quadrant. Again we are interested in angle θ. The functions

are equal to functions of the supplementary angle Φ (Greek capital letter Phi) which is always positive. The hypotenuse c is always positive. Side a which is parallel to the Y axis and drawn above the X-X' axis is positive. Side b which is parallel to the X axis is drawn to the left of the Y-Y' axis and is therefore negative. So now the functions are as follows:

$$\text{Sin } \theta = \quad \text{Sin } \Phi \quad = \frac{+a}{+c}$$

$$\text{Cos } \theta = - \text{ Cos } \Phi \quad = \frac{-b}{+c}$$

$$\text{Tan } \theta = - \text{ Tan } \Phi \quad = \frac{+a}{-b}$$

$$\text{Cot } \theta = - \text{ Cot } \Phi \quad = \frac{-b}{+a}$$

$$\text{Sec } \theta = - \text{ Sec } \Phi \quad = \frac{+c}{-b}$$

$$\text{Csc } \theta = \quad \text{Csc } \Phi = \frac{+c}{+a}$$

From this you can see that the Sin and Cosec will be positive because you have a plus term divided by another plus term and the other four functions negative because in each of these expressions there is one plus term and one negative term.

Now look at θ in the third quadrant shown in Fig. 4-26C. The hypotenuse c is positive, but now both a and b are negative. Therefore:

$$\text{Sin } \theta = - \text{ Sin } \Phi \quad = \frac{-a}{+c}$$

$$\text{Cos } \theta = - \text{ Cos } \Phi \quad = \frac{-b}{+c}$$

$$\text{Tan } \theta = \quad \text{Tan } \Phi \quad = \frac{-a}{-b}$$

$$\text{Cot } \theta = - \text{ Cot } \Phi \quad = \frac{-b}{-a}$$

$$\text{Sec } \Theta - \text{Sec } \Phi = \frac{+c}{-b}$$

$$\text{Csc } \Theta = \text{Csc } \Phi = \frac{+c}{-a}$$

In the case of the Tan and Cot functions you have a minus term divided by a minus term which gives you a plus result so the tangent and cotangent are positive in the third quadrant and all other terms are negative.

Now look at Θ in the fourth quadrant as shown in Fig. 4-26D. Again c is positive. Side b will also be positive, but side a is negative. Therefore:

$$\text{Sin } \Theta = - \text{Sin } \Phi = \frac{-a}{+c}$$

$$\text{Cos } \Theta = \text{Cos } \Phi = \frac{+b}{+c}$$

$$\text{Tan } \Theta = - \text{Tan } \Phi = \frac{-a}{+b}$$

$$\text{Cot } \Theta = - \text{Cot } \Phi = \frac{+b}{-a}$$

$$\text{Sec } \Theta = \text{Sec } \Phi = \frac{+c}{+b}$$

$$\text{Csc } \Theta = - \text{Csc } \Phi = \frac{+c}{-a}$$

Thus Cos and Sec are positive and the other four functions negative in the fourth quadrant.

The Sine Wave. Now that we have learned how to determine the sine of any angle up to 360°, we are ready to continue with the definition of a sine curve. A sine curve is really just a graph of all the sines of all the angles up to 360° that repeats itself periodically. Since there are an infinite number of angles that can be generated between 0° and 360° if we consider all the possible stopping points of the terminal side, there will also be an infinite number of sine functions to plot a curve. Therefore, we will simply choose angles in 15° steps from 0° to 360° and plot their functions. Further, we will round off the sine functions of these angles to two decimal places because this is as accurate as we will be able to plot them if we keep the graph to a reasonable size.

Now let's examine and list the sine functions of the angles, starting with $\angle \Theta = 0°$. When Θ equals zero, there is no angle or opposite side, so the opposite side when $\angle \Theta$ equals 0° must also be zero. Therefore, since $\text{Sin } \Theta = \frac{\text{Opp}}{\text{Hyp}}$, $\text{Sin } \Theta = \frac{0}{\text{Hyp}}$ when $\angle \Theta = 0°$, so $\text{Sin } \Theta$ must equal 0. Therefore, our

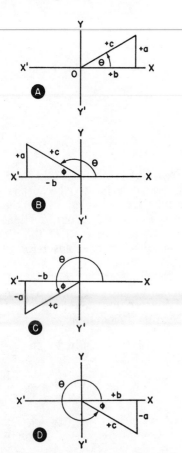

Fig. 4-26. Determining the signs of the functions in the four quadrants.

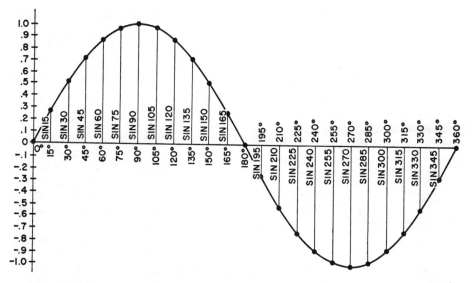

Fig. 4-27. Graphical plot of the sines of angles in 15° steps from 0° to 360°.

list of functions begins with:

$$\theta = 0°, \text{Sin } \theta = 0$$

Next, we have seen that the ratio of Opp/Hyp is always equal to the sine of the ∠θ as listed in the tables no matter what the relative lengths of the sides of the right triangle may be. Therefore, you can use the tables directly to make a list of the sine functions of all the angles you wish to use.

The next step is to lay out a graph as shown in Fig.4-27. Here we have laid out a base line on the X axis and marked it in 15° steps from 0° to 360°. Next, we have laid out the numbers from 0 to 1.0 in steps of .1 vertically in the positive direction along the Y axis and the numbers from 0 to −1.0 in steps of −.1 in the negative direction along the Y axis. At each step of 15° along the X axis, we have plotted the appropriate value of the sine of the angle indicated in terms of the numbers located on the Y axis. Thus, we have a graph of *various values* of the Y values of the sines of all the angles indicated

along the X axis. This is generally called a graph of Y = Sin X.

When these points are joined together with a smooth curve, they form a curve representing the sines of all the angles between 0° and 360° and therefore this is called a sine curve or sometimes a sine wave. We can consider the terminal side of the angles generated to form the sine curve as a rotating vector, as shown in Fig.4-28. This rotating vector generates the angles and consequently the functions of the angles indicated by the sine curve. If sin θ = $\frac{\text{Opp}}{\text{Hyp}}$, and Hyp (rotating vector) equals

1 unit, then sin $\theta = \frac{\text{Opp}}{1} = \text{Opp}$. Thus, if we let this vector equal 1″, 1′, 1 volt, or any other unity value, the sine functions generated will be equal to the length of the perpendiculars, which will also equal the actual value of the sine functions as listed in the tables.

Notice that as the vector starts from 0°, the function is zero; as it passes

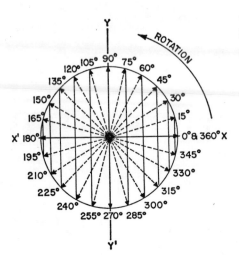

Fig. 4-28. **Diagram of rotating vector generating sine functions shown in the sine curve of Fig. 27.**

tion as shown in Fig.4-29A, the instantaneous value of voltage at a rotation of 15° would be 2.7 volts, 5 volts at 30°, 7.1 volts at 45°, etc. If we were to measure all these instantaneous voltages at steps of each 15° of angular rotation of the basic armature in a standard magnetic field from 0° through 360° we would obtain a sine wave graph similar to the one in Fig.4-27.This is why an ac voltage is said to vary sinusoidally, and is called a sine wave.

If the armature continues to rotate again and again at the same speed, the sine wave voltage will repeat itself indefinitely. We will get a complete 0° − 360° sine wave during each complete revolution or period, so the sine wave is called a periodic repetition of the same functions.

Phase Relationships. We have seen how the voltage generated by the rotating armature describes a sine wave just as the sine functions of the rotating vector describe the sine curve of the angles it passes through. Now suppose we have two generators represented by rotating vectors, as shown in Fig.4-30. They are exactly the same except that when one armature is passing through 90° the other is passing through zero

through 90° the maximum function is generated, and then at 180° the function is again zero, then maximum in the negative direction at 270°, and back again to no function at 360°. Notice also that the value of the function changes most rapidly when the vector is rotating through 0°, 180°, and 360°. This rotating vector can be compared to the rotation of the armature of a basic ac generator as shown in Fig. 4-29.

As the armature moves parallel to the lines of force as shown in Fig.4-29A, no voltage will be generated. As it moves at right angles to the lines of force as in Fig.4-29B, the maximum number of lines of force will be cut and the maximum voltage will be generated. While it is moving from its position shown in Fig.4-29A to that shown in Fig.4-29B, the voltage generated will increase from zero to maximum in proportion to the sine of its instantaneous angular position. Thus, if we consider the maximum voltage as 10 volts at 90° of rotation as shown in Fig.4-29B, and zero voltage as zero volts at 0° of rota-

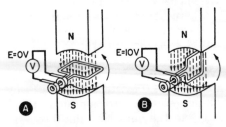

Fig. 4-29. **Generator armature can be compared to rotating vector in Fig. 28.**

degrees. The sine wave outputs of the two generators are superimposed on each other as shown by the solid and dotted sine waves in Fig.4-31.

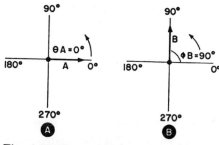

Fig. 4-30. Two generators represented by rotating vectors. A shows instantaneous value of Sin θ A to be zero. B shows instantaneous value of Sin θ B to be maximum at the same instant.

As you can easily see, these voltage sine waves are generated 90° out of phase with each other just as the vectors are 90° out of phase. Thus, the rotating vectors represent the relative phase of the two sine waves and are called phasors. By applying the principles of trigonometry to the angle generated by one of the phasors, we can determine the instantaneous value of voltage generated for any position of the phasor if we know its value at Sin θ = 1.

Thus, if at Sin θ = 1, or 90°, the phasor produces a voltage of 120 volts, then at ∠θ = 30, the instantaneous value of voltage generated will equal Sin θ = $\frac{\text{Opp}}{\text{Hyp}}$. And, Hyp = Phasor length at Sin θ = 1, therefore Hyp = 120. Then, Sin θ = $\frac{\text{Opp}}{120}$ and θ = 30°, therefore Sin 30° or .5 = $\frac{\text{Opp}}{120}$ and Opp = 120 × .5 = 60 volts of instantaneous voltage. In this way phasors can be used to represent the instantaneous values of all the sine wave voltages occurring across circuit components at any instant.

Phasors can be expressed in rectangular coordinates as well as polar coordinates. All the principles of the parallelogram measurement method for solving vector diagrams can be applied to phasors. Similarly, the J-operator and trigonometry can be used in the solution of phasor problems. Consequently, we shall continue to call our phasors "vectors" in this course. Remember, however, that although a phasor can perhaps be considered as a special type of vector as is done in most older texts, a vector cannot be considered to be a phasor.

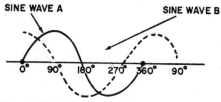

Fig. 4-31. Sine waves generated by two identical phasors operating 90° apart.

Trigonometry in AC Circuits

We have seen in an earlier part of this lesson how trigonometry can be used in simple ac circuit calculation. Now let's look at a more complicated circuit, such as the one shown in Fig. 4-32, to see how what we have learned about vector diagrams, the J-operator, algebra, and trigonometry can best be

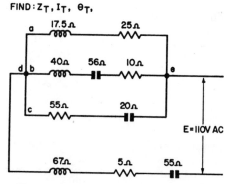

Fig. 4-32. Series parallel AC circuit.

used in circuit calculations. This is a series-parallel circuit with the various values given as shown in the diagram. We are asked to find the total impedance Z_T, the total current I_T, and the final phase angle Θ_T.

First, we will want to find the impedance of the three parallel branches, a, b, and c, which we can do as follows:

$$Z_a = R + JX_L = 25 + J17.5\Omega$$

$$\text{Tan } \Theta_a = \frac{\text{Opp}}{\text{Adj}} = \frac{X_{La}}{R_a} = \frac{17.5}{25} = .700$$

$$\Theta_a = 35°$$

Then: $\text{Sin } \Theta_a = \dfrac{\text{Opp}}{\text{Hyp}} = \dfrac{X_{La}}{Z_a}$ or

$$Z_a = \frac{X_{La}}{\text{Sin } \Theta_a} = \frac{17.5}{\text{Sin } 35°}$$

$$= \frac{17.5}{.574} = 30.5\Omega$$

Thus: $Z_a = 30.5\underline{/35°}\Omega$

Next: $Z_b = R + JX_L - JX_c$
$$= 10 + J40 - J56$$
$$= 10 - J16$$

$$\text{Tan } \Theta_b = \frac{\text{Opp}}{\text{Adj}} = \frac{X_b}{R_b}$$

$$= \frac{-16}{10} = -1.6$$

$$\Theta_b = -58°$$

Then: $\text{Sin } \Theta_b = \dfrac{\text{Opp}}{\text{Hyp}} = \dfrac{X_b}{Z_b}$ or

$$Z_b = \frac{X_b}{\text{Sin } \Theta_b} = \frac{-16}{\text{Sin } -58°}$$

$$= \frac{-16}{-.848} = 18.9\Omega$$

Thus: $Z_b = 18.9\ \underline{/-58°}$

Next: $Z_c = R - JX_c = 55 - J20$

$$\text{Tan } \Theta_c = \frac{\text{Opp}}{\text{Adj}} = \frac{-20}{55} = -.364$$

$$\Theta_c = -20°$$

Then: $\text{Sin } \Theta_c = \dfrac{\text{Opp}}{\text{Hyp}} = \dfrac{X_c}{Z_c}$ or

$$Z_c = \frac{X_c}{\text{Sin } \Theta_c} = \frac{-20}{\text{Sin } -20}$$

$$= \frac{-20}{-.342} = 58.5\Omega$$

Thus: $Z_c = 58.5\underline{/-20°}\Omega$

Now assume a voltage between d and e and find I for each branch as follows:

$$I_a = \frac{E_{de}}{Z_a} = \frac{100}{30.5\underline{/35°}} = 3.28\underline{/-35°}a$$

$$I_b = \frac{E_{de}}{Z_b} = \frac{100}{18.9\underline{/-58°}} = 5.3\underline{/58°}a$$

$$I_c = \frac{E_{de}}{Z_c} = \frac{100}{58.5\underline{/-20°}} = 1.71\underline{/20°}a$$

Note: When you divide by an angle you simply change the sign of the angle in the divisor and add it to the angle in the numerator. The numerator in this case is actually $100\underline{/0°}$.

Now: Convert branch currents I_a, I_b, and I_c from polar to rectangular coordinates for easy addition as follows:

$$I_a = I_a (\text{Cos } \Theta_a + J\text{Sin } \Theta_a)$$
$$= 3.28 (\text{Cos } -35° + J \text{Sin } -35°)$$
$$= 3.28 (.8192 - J.5736)$$
$$= 2.69 - J1.88 \text{ amps}$$

$(-35°$ lies in the fourth quadrant and therefore $\text{Cos} -35°$ is positive and $\text{Sin} -35°$ is negative. This explains why the resistive term is positive and the reactive term is negative.)

$$I_b = I_b (\text{Cos } \Theta_b + J\text{Sin } \Theta_b)$$
$$= 5.3 (\text{Cos } 58° + J\text{Sin } 58°)$$
$$= 5.3 (.5299 + J8480)$$
$$= 2.81 + J4.5 \text{ amps}$$

$$I_c = I_c (\text{Cos } \Theta + J\text{Sin } \Theta_c)$$
$$= 1.71 (\text{Cos } 20° + J\text{Sin } 20°)$$
$$= 1.71 (.9397 + J.3420)$$

$$= 1.61 + J585 \text{ amps}$$

Now, $I_{de} = I_a + I_b + I_c$

and: $I_a = 2.69 - J1.88$

$I_b = 2.81 + J4.5$

$I_c = 1.61 + J.585$

and $I_{de} = 7.11 + J3.205$

Now: $\text{Tan } \Theta_{de} = \dfrac{\text{Opp}}{\text{Adj}} = \dfrac{I_{de_x}}{I_{de_r}}$

$$= \dfrac{3.2}{7.11} = .45$$

$$\Theta_{de} = 24.2°$$

Then I_{de} in polar form:

$$\text{Sin } \Theta_{de} = \dfrac{\text{Opp}}{\text{Hyp}} = \dfrac{I_{de_x}}{I_{de}} \text{ or } I_{de} = \dfrac{I_{de_x}}{\text{Sin } \Theta_{de}}$$

Then: $I_{de} = \dfrac{I_{de_x}}{\text{Sin } \Theta_{de}} = \dfrac{3.2}{\text{Sin } 24.2}$

$$= \dfrac{3.2}{.4099} = 7.8$$

Then: $I_{de} = 7.8 \underline{/24.2°} \text{ amps}$

Now: $Z_{de} = \dfrac{E_{de}}{I_{de}} = \dfrac{100}{7.8 \underline{/24.2°}}$

$$= 12.8 \underline{/-24.2°} \Omega$$

Converting Z_{de} to rectangular coordinates:

$$Z_{de} = Z_{de} (\text{Cos } \Theta_{de} + J\text{Sin } \Theta_{de})$$

$$= 12.8 (\text{Cos } - 24.2°$$

$$+ J\text{Sin } - 24.2°)$$

$$= 12.8 (.9114 - J4099)$$

$$= 11.7 - J5.25 \Omega$$

Now combining:

$$Z_T = Z_{de} + J67\Omega - J55\Omega + 5\Omega$$

$$= 11.7\Omega + 5\Omega - J5.25\Omega$$

$$+ J67\Omega - J55\Omega$$

$$= 16.7 + J6.75$$

Then: $\text{Tan } \Theta_T = \dfrac{\text{Opp}}{\text{Adj}} = \dfrac{6.75}{16.7} = .404$

$$\Theta_T = 22°$$

Converting Z_T to polar form:

$$\text{Sin } \Theta_T = \dfrac{\text{Opp}}{\text{Hyp}} = \dfrac{X_T}{Z_T} \text{ or}$$

$$Z_T = \dfrac{X_T}{\text{Sin } \Theta_T} = \dfrac{6.75}{\text{Sin } 22°}$$

$$= \dfrac{6.75}{.3746} = 18.\Omega$$

$$= 18 \underline{/22°} \Omega$$

Then: $I_T = \dfrac{E_T}{Z_T} = \dfrac{110 \underline{/0°}}{18 \underline{/22°}}$

$$= 6.11 \underline{/-22°} \text{ amps}$$

With this as a typical example of using trigonometry in ac circuits, try some of the problems you solved using the J-operator and the Pythagorean theorem in the previous chapters.

Power in AC Circuits. Up until now we have never considered power in ac circuits because we have not had a simple method of finding it. In a purely resistive circuit, where the current and voltage are in phase, the power is equal to the voltage times the current as it is in a dc circuit. In a purely reactive circuit where there is no resistance whatsoever, power is alternately stored up by the reactive elements and then returned to the line. Such a circuit can exist only in theory, of course, because practical circuits always have some resistance. However, oscillatory tank circuits, do come fairly close to being resistance-free and, consequently, small properly timed surges of current can keep them going indefinitely.

Thus, we can say that the resistive elements of a circuit consume the only power expended. Let's see what this means in terms of the circuit we have just studied. If we construct the resultant vector diagram of the circuit from $\Theta_T = 22°$, $Z_T = 18\Omega$, we have a vector $Z_T = 18 \underline{/22°}$ as shown in Fig. 4-33. The reactive component of this impedance JX_T is shown, and the resistive component is equal to R_T as shown. The resistive component is equal to 16.7Ω, while the reactive component is 6.75Ω as we discovered while solving for Z_T.

Now, if the resistive component is all that consumes power, the power must be equal to $E_R \times I$ since only the resistive component of voltage forces current through the resistance to consume power. However, in the circuit we have just solved, we are not given the value of E_R, nor did we find it in any of our computations. However, if we lay out a vector representing the conditions of our circuit, we have a vector of the total voltage E_T of 110V leading the current vector, which we have taken as our reference vector, by 22°. We can find E_R now by using

$$\text{Cos } \theta = \frac{\text{Adj}}{\text{Hyp}} = \frac{E_R}{E_T} \text{ and } E_R = E_T \text{ Cos } \theta.$$

Now, if $P = E_R \times I$ equals the power expended and $E_R = E_T \text{ Cos } \theta$

By substitution: $P = E_T \text{ Cos } \theta \, I$
or $P = EI \text{ Cos } \theta$

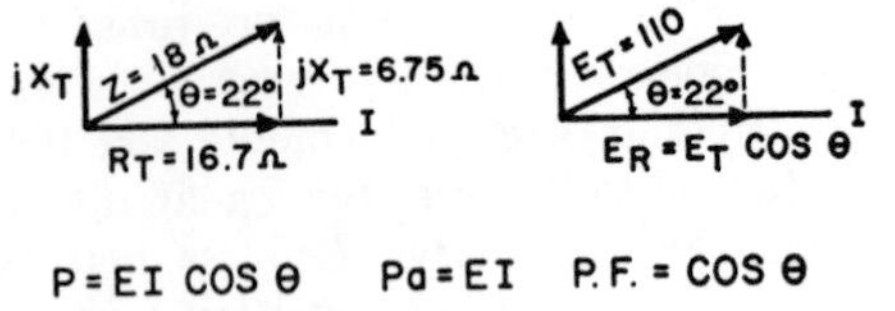

P = EI COS θ   Pa = EI   P.F. = COS θ

Fig. 4-33. Vector representation of power factor.

Then, substituting known values:

$$P = 110 \times 6.11 \times \text{Cos } 22°$$
$$= 110 \times 6.11 \times .9272$$
$$= 623 \text{ watts}$$

This is the power actually consumed by the circuit.

Now, in ac circuits we have another value of power which is called the apparent power. This is simply the product of E_T and I_T without considering their relative instantaneous values at any particular moment. Thus, in the circuit we have just solved, the apparent power is simply 110×6.11 or 672.1VA. The apparent power in a circuit is designated as P_a to separate it from the true power P which does take into consideration the relative instantaneous values of E and I through multiplication by Cos θ.

Now, we have another situation in ac power that must be considered. This is the power factor PF which is the ratio of the true power P to the apparent power P_a. Mathematically, this is stated: $PF = \dfrac{P}{P_a}$.

If $PF = \dfrac{P}{P_a}$, then:

$$PF = \frac{EI \text{ Cos } \theta}{EI} = \text{Cos } \theta$$

and the power factor can be found from PF = Cos θ. In the circuit we have just computed, PF = .927 lagging because the current lags the voltage by 22°. Power factor is also expressed as a percentage, 92.7%.

There are other formulas for power and power factor in ac circuits, but these are the most common. Since the formula $P = I^2R$ uses only resistance and current, it will also give us the true power. Here we are not multiplying the effective values of current by an effective value of voltage without considering their relative instantaneous values. We are simply squaring the effective value of current and multiplying it by the total resistive component of Z. Thus, $P = I^2R$ for our circuit gives us

$$6.11^2 \times 16.7 = 623 \text{ watts,}$$

which is true power.

We can also write another formula for power factor: If $PF = \dfrac{P}{P_a}$ and

$$P = I^2R \text{ and } P_a = EI$$

Then: $\quad PF = \dfrac{I^2R}{EI} = \dfrac{IR}{E}$

But, $\quad E = IZ$, so $PF = \dfrac{IR}{IZ} = \dfrac{R}{Z}$

Therefore, $PF = \dfrac{R}{Z}$. However, $\dfrac{R}{Z}$ is just another way of saying Cos θ, because

$$\text{Cos } \theta = \frac{\text{Adj}}{\text{Hyp}} = \frac{R}{Z}$$

It also should be noted that true power $P = PF \times P_a$ because $PF = \dfrac{R}{Z}$ or Cos θ and $P_a = EI$, and our first formula for power was $P = EI$ Cos θ. Any of the relationships may be used, and if you remember that $P_a = EI$ and $P = EI \times PF$, $PF = $ Cos θ, you can use algebra and trigonometry to work out the other formulas.

Although you will not become an expert in the science of trigonometry from what you have learned in this lesson, you have covered most of the basic fundamentals and their application in electronics. You should be able to handle nearly every problem that you will come in contact with if you have understood these concepts of elementary trigonometry. Like any other math, trig requires a lot of practice to become familiar with it.

4-3. Computing Short Cuts

Many simple calculations in electronics can become quite tedious because of the size of the numbers involved. Take the case of finding the plate current of a tube by measuring the voltage drop across the plate load resistor. Assuming there is a 7.0-volt drop across a 22,000-ohm resistor, what is the current? Ohm's Law tells us that we divide the voltage by the resistance to get the current. This is simple enough, but look at the arithmetic involved:

```
          .00031818
22000)7.00000000
      6 6000
        40000
        22000
       180000
       176000
        40000
        22000
       180000
       176000
         4000
```

There are five digits in the divisor, nine in the dividend, and eight in the quotient. No matter how many places there are in the quotient, there will still be a remainder with either four or five digits in it.

Practically speaking, a lot of needless work was done in performing this division. This operation could have been made much simpler. For one thing, the quotient was carried three decimal places too many. The second simplification is to get rid of those three zeros in the divisor. When these things are done, your division looks like this:

```
       .31
22)7.00
   6 6
     40
     22
     18
```

Admittedly, the quotients obtained by these two divisions have their decimal points in different places. However, the method that was used to get rid of the three zeros in the second divisor also shows us how to shift the decimal point in the second quotient.

How to take the unnecessary work out of practical calculations will be the subject of this section of the chapter. There are two parts to this section: One is concerned with the number of digits that should be used in any arithmetic operation; the other is how to get rid of zeros whose only purpose is to locate the decimal point.

The rules that you will learn in this section are not only labor-saving tricks, they greatly reduce the possibility of mistakes. Everyone makes mistakes in arithmetic. The more marks you have to make on a piece of paper in order to solve a problem, the more likely you are to make a mistake. By using no more figures than are absolutely necessary, you can reduce the likelihood of an incorrect answer.

Exponential Numbers

Many of the numbers used in science represent either very large or very small quantities. The field of electronics is no exception. In many cases, the majority of the digits in the numbers are zeros. These zeros serve only to locate the decimal point. They are necessary but very inconvenient to work with.

Mathematicians working in the different fields of science have developed another way of writing these numbers that makes it unnecessary to write a lot of zeros. At the same time, it is very easy to keep track of the number of zeros. The method is simply to express the number as the product of two factors. One factor, called the digit factor, contains the significant digits (this term is explained later in this section). The other factor, called the exponential factor, is a whole numbered power of 10 which properly locates the decimal point. This method of writing large and small numbers is sometimes called the scientific method of expressing numbers.

As examples, let's use the resistance and current values in the sample division earlier in this section. The resistance was 22,000 ohms. Using the two-factor method, this number is expressed as 2.2×10^4. The current was found to be .000318. This would be written using exponential numbers as 3.18×10^{-4}. To show that these new figures are correct, we can multiply them out. 10^4 is 10,000; multiply this by 2.2 and we get 22,000. 10^{-4} is .0001; multiply this by 3.18 and we get .000318.

Conversion from one system of expressing a number to the other is very simple and involves only determining the correct power of 10. One rule tells the whole story: The power of 10 is given by the number of places the decimal point must be moved to obtain the digit factor. Moving the decimal point to the left gives a positive exponent; moving the decimal point to the right gives a negative exponent. For convenience, the digit factor is usually written with only one digit to the left of the decimal point.

Here are some examples: Convert 473,000 to exponential form. The decimal point in the digit factor will come between the 4 and the 7; this is five places to the left, giving an exponent of $+5$. The digit factor is then 4.73 and the exponential factor is 10^5. The complete expression is 4.73×10^5. Convert 6,720,000. The decimal point moves six places to the left, giving 6.72×10^6. Convert .000706. The decimal point moves to the right four places making the exponent -4. The complete expression is 7.06×10^{-4}. Convert .0000000123. The decimal point moves eight places to the right giving 1.23×10^{-8}.

Converting the number back is just as easy: Move the decimal point as many places as the power of 10 shown by the exponent. If the exponent is positive, move the decimal point to the right; if the exponent is negative, move the decimal point to the left. After this conversion, every place must be shown. If the decimal point is moved more places than are occupied by digits in the digit factor, fill in the blank places with zeros.

To convert 3.14×10^{-2}, we must move the decimal point to the left two places. There is only one place in the digit factor to the left of the decimal point so that we must add a zero to the left of the 3. This results in .0314. To convert 3.14×10^2, the decimal point must move two places to the right. This time there are digits in the digit factor for each place moved over and then no zeros are added. 3.14×10^2 is equal to 314.

As simple as this system is for general use, it is even easier to make conversions in electronics. Many times it is not even necessary to count the number of decimal places. Our method of giving the values of voltage and current, and of components, has the digits all counted for us. You seldom see 1,500,000 ohms written out in full; instead, it is written 1.5M or 1.5 meg. Either way it means 1.5 million. One million is equal to 10^6, so as soon as you see the expression megohm, you know that the exponential factor is 10^6.

There are a number of other common methods of indicating size in the name of a unit. For instance, 1 kilocycle is 1000 or 10^3 cycles; 1K ohm means 1 kilohm or 10^3 ohms. The prefix "kil" or "kilo" immediately tells you that the exponential factor is 10^3. Similarly, 1 milliampere is 1/1000 of an ampere; 1 millihenry is 1/1000 of a henry; 1 millivolt is 1/1000 of a volt, etc. 1/1000 is $\frac{1}{10^3}$ or 10^{-3}. The prefix "milli" is just another way of writing 10^{-3}. In the same way, "micro" means 1/1,000,000 or 10^{-6}. "Micro-micro" means one millionth of a millionth or 10^{-12}. Basic units such as volts, amperes, henries, etc., have an exponential factor of 10^0 or 1.

Multiplication and Division. Exponential numbers are at their best for multiplication and division. It is in these operations that they save the most amount of work. These operations are actually performed in two parts. The indicated operation is performed on the digit factors and then on the exponential factors. As an example, suppose a calculation called for multiplying $.0022 \times 670 \times 3.14$. Converting and grouping digits gives $(2.2 \times 6.70 \times 3.14) \times (10^{-3} \times 10^2 \times 10^0)$. First multiply the digit factors together and you get 46.2836. Next, you multiply the exponential factors by adding the exponents algebraically; $-3 + 2 + 0 = -1$. Combining the two factors you get 46.2836×10^{-1}. This result can be simplified even more by moving the decimal point in the digit factor one place to the left giving $4.62836 \times 10^1 \times 10^{-1}$. Now the two exponents cancel leaving 4.62836 as the final answer.

Division is just as easy. For example, divide .0572 by .0026. Converting and grouping gives

$$(5.72 \div 2.6) \times (10^{-2} \div 10^{-3}).$$

$5.72 \div 2.6 = 2.2$. The division of the exponential factor is performed by subtracting the exponent of the divisor (-3) from the exponent in the dividend (-2).

$$-2 - (-3) = -2 + 3 = 1$$

The complete quotient of this division is 2.2×10^1 or 22. The same basic procedures are followed for operations with combined multiplications and divisions. As an example, take

$$(22,000 \div 80) \times (.032 \div 308) \times 7$$

Fig. 4-34 shows how this is set up and solved.

Power and Roots. Raising a number to a power is a special form of multiplication; taking a root is a special form of division. As in multiplication and division, we must perform the indicated operation on the digit factor and treat the exponential factor separately. An exponential number is raised to a power by multiplying the exponents. You can see that this will give the correct answer by considering the following:

$$10 \times 10 = 10^2$$
$$10 \times 10 \times 10 = 10^3$$

and therefore

$$10^2 \times 10^2 \times 10^2 = (10^2)^3$$

But we know that

$$10^2 \times 10^2 \times 10^2 = 10^{2+2+2} = 10^6$$
$$(10^2)^3 = 10^{2 \times 3} = 10^6$$

Extracting the root is the reverse of raising to a power. A root of an exponential number is taken by dividing the exponent by the digit indicating the root, 2 for square root, 3 for cube root, etc. Suppose you want the square root of 10^6. Dividing the exponent 6 by 2

gives 10^3. We know that $10^3 \times 10^3 = 10^6$ which shows that dividing the exponent by the root gives the correct result.

We know from arithmetic that $6 \div 2$ is the same as $6 \times \frac{1}{2}$. Thus, $\sqrt{10^6}$ may be written as $(10^6)^{1/2}$. Fractional exponents indicate that roots must be

$$22000 = 2.2 \times 10^4$$
$$80 = 8.0 \times 10^1$$
$$.032 = 3.2 \times 10^{-2}$$
$$308 = 3.08 \times 10^2$$
$$7 = 7 \times 10^0$$

$$\left(\frac{2.2}{8.0} \times \frac{3.2}{3.08} \times 7\right) \left(\frac{10^4}{10^1} \times \frac{10^{-2}}{10^2} \times 10^0\right)$$

$$= \frac{2.2 \times 3.2 \times 7}{8.0 \times 3.08} \times \frac{10^4 \times 10^{-2} \times 10^0}{10^1 \times 10^2}$$

$$= \frac{49.28}{24.64} \times \frac{10^2}{10^3} = 2 \times 10^{-1} = .2$$

Fig. 4-34. Solving combined multiplication-division problems using exponential numbers.

taken. When this method of indicating the roots is used, square root is handled as the 1/2 power, cube root as the 1/3 power, and so on. The square root of 10^6 could be written as $10^{\frac{6}{2}}$. The square root of 10^3 would be written as $10^{\frac{3}{2}}$.

At the beginning of this section, you learned that the exponent of 10 in an exponential number must be a whole number. This can lead to a slight complication when taking roots. Consider taking the square root of 8.1×10^3. We would write this as $\sqrt{8.1} \times 10^{\frac{3}{2}}$. But our exponential number system does not allow fractional or decimal exponents. In order to extract the square root of 8.1×10^3, we must have an exponent that is divisible by 2. We get this by increasing or decreasing the exponent and moving the decimal point in the digit factor accordingly.

$$8.1 \times 10^3$$
$$= 81 \times 10^2$$

$$= .81 \times 10^4$$

The square root of 81×10^2 is 9×10; the square root of $.81 \times 10^4$ is $.9 \times 10^2$. Both of these roots convert to 90 in the decimal system. 8.1×10^3 converts to 8100, the square root of which is 90; and you can see that we have obtained the correct result. To extract the cube root, the exponent of 10 must be made divisible by 3; the exponent for a fourth root must be divisible by 4, etc.

Addition and Subtraction. There is nothing to be gained in converting decimal numbers into exponential numbers for addition and subtraction. However, addition and subtraction may occur as part of a calculation when exponential numbers are used to simplify multiplication and division. When addition and subtraction are indicated, you must remember that you can only add and subtract exponential numbers having the same power of 10. The reason for this is quite simple. For example, $160 + 16 = 176$. But we can write 160 as 1.6×10^2 and 16 as 1.6×10. If we simply add $1.6 + 1.6$, we get 3.2 which will not be the correct answer for $160 + 16$ regardless of whether we multiply it by 10 or 10^2. If we first change the numbers so that we have the same power of 10, then we will get the correct answer. For example, $160 = 16.0 \times 10$, and $16 = 1.6 \times 10$. Then,

$$16 \times 10 + 1.6 \times 10$$
$$= 17.6 \times 10 = 176$$

As you can see, the use of exponential numbers greatly simplifies multiplication and division when working with large numbers having many zeros adjacent to the decimal point and on either side of it. Still greater simplification can be obtained when some of the digits in a number like 4.62836 can be dropped. This is possible when we are working with measured values. In most practical work, it is seldom necessary to use more than four digits in any factor. The rules for dropping digits from a number which has been obtained by a measurement are the next subject that we take up.

Significant Figures

When you took arithmetic in grade school, the teacher probably listed numbers like 67,530, 4156, 873, and told you to "round them off" to the nearest thousand or hundred or ten. You did this sort of thing for homework two or three nights and that was the end of it. The next and last time you did this was on a test. Well, that time wasn't wasted; studying significant figures is just learning when to round off and how much.

The term "significant" is used here in a dictionary sense: "having a meaning." In working with significant figures, you retain only those figures which have meaning and drop all others by "rounding off." The use of significant figures applies only to numbers which are connected in some way with measurements.

The figures that you used when studying mathematics were considered exact. 1 was 1, and 2 was 2. Each digit meant exactly what it said; not almost or approximately, or a little more or less. This is not true of numbers that are obtained by measurement. There is always a certain amount of estimating or guesswork in taking any measurement. The first step in using significant figures is to properly record the results of the measurement. This means putting down meaningful figures in a manner that shows how exact the measurement was.

Fig.4-35 shows a scale with two arrows along the bottom edge. We can consider that the scale is used to show the position of pointers represented by the arrows. The scale is divided into four major units and each of these units is subdivided into ten parts. Suppose we wanted to read the position of arrow A.

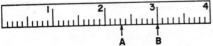

Fig. 4-35. Scale for showing use of significant figures in recording a measurement.

Arrow A lies between two and three units so the first figure is 2. Since the arrow is slightly past the third mark following the 2, the second figure is .3. Two figures are all that can be read directly from the scale marks. We must estimate the third digit by mentally dividing the space between the scale marks into ten parts. Then we must decide which of these ten parts the arrow is nearest. For arrow A this gives 3 as the third digit.

Perhaps you disagree with the reading of 2.33. Maybe you think the reading should be 2.32 or 2.34. Perhaps it should. The last digit is an estimate, not an exact figure. Because it is an estimate, different observers will record different values for this digit. However, if each observer reads the scale carefully, the readings should span only three digits; in this case, .02, .03, and .04. This is what you are saying when you record any measurement. Only the right-hand digit is an estimate and the error in reading is not more than ±1 in the right-hand figure.

Perhaps you think the arrow is exactly one-quarter of the way between 2.3 and 2.4; in other words, the reading should be 2.3¼. However, a mixed decimal and fraction is awkward to use. Since ¼ = .25, why not record the reading as 2.325? Because this gives misleading information. To anyone using this figure, it means that you could tell

the difference between 2.324, 2.325, and 2.326. Obviously you cannot, so 2.325 should not be recorded. You could, however, record 2.3¼. This indicates that you could tell the difference between 2.3, 2.3¼, and 2.3½. It also says that no attempt was made to read the scale any closer than one-quarter of the smallest division. Therefore, rather than use a mixed decimal and fraction, it is better to estimate so that you will have only three digits.

What about the reading of arrow B? It appears to be exactly on the "3" line. How should this be recorded? If it is recorded as just 3, it indicates only that the reading is nearer to 3 than to 2 or 4. If it is recorded as 3.0, it means nearer to 3 than to 2.9 or 3.1. The correct way to record this is as 3.00. The two zeros to the right of the decimal point say that the scale can be read to 1/100 of a unit. 3.000 would be wrong because you cannot read the scale to thousandths. Even when a pointer falls directly on a scale mark, you cannot assume a more precise reading than at any other point on the scale.

Each of the readings, 2.33 and 3.00, has three digits. Therefore, we say that they have three significant figures. If we had read the scale only to the nearest scale mark, the readings would have been 2.3 and 3.0 with two significant figures each.

Zeros in a decimal number may or may not be significant depending on where they are in the number. .00678 has only three significant figures. The two zeros between the decimal point and the 6 are not considered significant. .0067800 has five significant figures. The two zeros between the decimal point and the 6 are not significant, but the two zeros following the 8 are. If these last two digits had not been significant, they should not have been written; since they were written, you must assume that the measurement could be made to five figures.

Numbers like 22,000 create a problem. The "2's" are significant, but what about the zeros? As the number is written you cannot tell how many significant figures it has. Unless there is some note with the data, you must assume only two significant figures. However, if this were written as an exponential number, there would be no uncertainty. 2.2×10^4 has two significant figures. 2.20×10^4 has three significant figures. This is another advantage of exponential numbers; only significant figures appear in the digit factor.

Rules for Significant Figures. For convenience the rules for using significant figures will be listed by number. Then, examples of the application of the rules will be shown. In the examples, the rules that apply will be shown by number.

1. Only one uncertain figure should be recorded in giving the numerical value of any measured quantity. The uncertainty of the last figure will be ± 1 unless otherwise stated.

2. In addition and subtraction with significant figures, keep only as many decimals as are given in the number having the fewest decimals.

3. When multiplying and dividing, retain enough figures in each factor so that no factor has a greater uncertainty than the factor with the least number of significant digits.

4. When dropping non-significant digits by rounding off, increase the most right-hand retained figure by 1, if the figure to its right is 5 or greater.

5. Products and quotients should be rounded off so that the uncertainty is the same as that of the factor with the least number of significant figures.

Now some examples: Add $14.16 +$ $.0078 + 1.234$. The least number of decimal places is 2, so the last two numbers must be rounded off to two decimal places (Rule 2). .0078 becomes .01, and 1.234 becomes 1.23 (Rule 4). The sum is 15.40 (not 15.4). Since there were two decimal places in the numbers added, there must be two decimal places in their sum. (Common sense.)

Multiply $14.16 \times .0078 \times 1.234$. .0078 has the least number of significant figures, 2, and an uncertainty of 1 part in 78. The other two factors must be rounded off. 14.16 rounded off to three figures becomes 14.2 (Rule 4) with an uncertainty of one part in 142. Rounded off to two figures it becomes 14 with an uncertainty of one part in 14. This uncertainty is much greater than one part in 78, so three significant figures must be used (Rule 3). 1.234 rounds off to 1.23 with an uncertainty of one part in 123. The product of $14.2 \times .0078$ is .11076; we round this off to .111 (Rule 5, Rule 4). $.111 \times 1.23 = .13653$ which when rounded off becomes .137 (Rule 5, Rule 4).

What effect does this rounding off have on the accuracy of the calculation? None. If we had not rounded off any of the figures, the final product would have been .136292832. If we had not rounded off .11076, the final answer would have been .1362348. Both of these numbers round off to .136. Our answer was .137, just one unit greater. Since the last digit has an uncertainty of ± 1, we can say the three answers were practically identical. By rounding off we have saved a lot of needless work without any loss of accuracy.

Multiply 19.7×9.81. Both numbers have the same number of significant figures. However, the larger number can be rounded without loss of accuracy. 19.7 has an uncertainty of one part in 197 or about .5%. 9.81 has an uncertainty of one part in 981 or about 1/10%. Rounding off 9.81 gives 9.8 with an uncertainty of one part in 98 or about 1%. This is much closer to the uncertainty of 19.7. The product without rounding off is 193.257; if 9.81 is rounded off to 9.8, the product is 193.06. Rounded to three figures, the answers are the same. It is apparent that Rule 4 can be modified at times to say that the percentage uncertainty of two factors should be nearly the same. It is hard to state this as a fixed rule and give exact values of how much the uncertainties can differ, but it does show how the use of common sense fits in with significant figures.

It is seldom necessary to use more than three significant figures in electronics. Except for precision parts, tolerances range from ±1% to ±20%; a good service meter has an accuracy of ±2% for voltage and current and ±5% for resistance. Keep the accuracy of your instruments and the tolerances of your parts in mind when performing calculations. Do not carry a lot of meaningless digits. Three significant figures are accurate enough for all but the most exacting laboratory work. Two significant digits are enough when using ±20% parts.

4-4. Graphs

A graph is a picture that shows the effect of changes in one variable on a second variable. They are very common in electronics literature since they provide a simple means to describe circuit operations, to illustrate equations and formulas, to show relationships when no formulas exist, and as a means of displaying the results of experiments.

Graphs are not new to you; you studied them in grade school. They are commonly used in newspapers to show economic trends. Although the same things could be shown with columns of figures, the line on a graph puts the idea over much better. It is hard to visualize trends or patterns from a column of figures, but a line on a graph lays the pattern out in front of you in a way that is easy to grasp.

Using Graphs

The most common type of graph is drawn on paper ruled with uniformly spaced horizontal and vertical lines. This type of paper is known as rectilinear, or "cross-section," or just "plain" graph paper. Cross-section paper is available with many different line spacings, but 4, 5, 10, and 20 lines per inch are the most common.

The data for plotting graphs may be obtained by measurements of both quantities. Or the data may be obtained by repeated solutions of a formula. A graph with two plots obtained in the latter manner is shown in Fig. 4-36. This graph shows the voltage across a 75-ohm resistor and the power dissipated in it for different values of current.

Fig. 4-36 was plotted by assuming different values for the current and calculating the corresponding voltage drops and power dissipations using the formulas shown. Since the calculated values of voltage and power depend on the assumed values of the current, voltage and power are called the "dependent variables." The current could be given any desired value and changed at will, so current is called the "independent variable." Following custom, the dependent variable is scaled along the vertical axis, and the independent variable is scaled along the horizontal axis.

Several important things about graphs are illustrated here. Both scales are labeled to show the quantity they represent, and the units in which that quantity is measured. The values

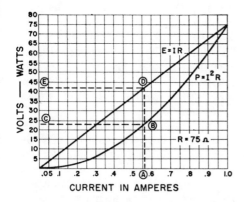

Fig. 4-36. Change in voltage across, and power in, a 75-ohm resistor as current changes.

assigned to each division of the scales are marked along them. Note that the two scales are not equally divided; one division of the horizontal scale is equal to .05 units and one division on the vertical scale equals 5 units. Each plot is labeled with the formula used to obtain the data. The formulas also serve as titles, telling what the graph shows. The value of the resistance used in the calculation completes the labeling. All the information needed to use or identify this graph appears upon it. Nothing is left to memory or imagination. Without this information no graph is complete.

Graphs like Fig.4-36 are frequently made up to avoid repeated computations. For example, suppose you are checking the effect of changing tube voltages on the output of an amplifier. You are measuring the output with an ammeter in series with the 75-ohm load of the amplifier. In order to avoid making a very large number of calculations of voltage and power, you have constructed this graph. Now you can obtain the voltage and power for each value of current without having to work out each solution with pencil and paper.

The dashed lines on Fig.4-36 show how the voltage and power for a current of .56 ampere would be read from the graph. Starting at .56 (point A) on the horizontal scale, trace upward to the intersection with the power curve (point B). Then trace over to the vertical scale and read 23 watts at point C. The .56 line intersects the voltage line at D. Tracing over to the vertical scale from D gives 42 volts at point E. The same graph could be used to determine the current for a specific power. You would simply reverse the procedure and start at the required power on the vertical scale. Then trace over to the power curve and down to the horizontal scale to read current.

It actually takes longer to tell how to read values from a graph than it takes to do it. The dashed lines which were drawn on Fig.4-36 are not necessary in practice. They were used here only to demonstrate the procedure. With a little practice you will find that you can do the reading right at the curve without tracing to the scales. Try to determine the voltage drop and the power dissipation for the following currents: .72, .23, .07, and .48. What current is necessary for 60 watts, 36 watts, 7 watts, and 53 watts? Remember when reading the scale of a graph that, since an estimate is involved, all the rules for significant figures apply. You can check your readings by using the formulas to calculate the values.

Slope. One look at a graph can tell you a great deal about the way the dependent variable changes with changes in the independent variable. You have only to glance at Fig.4-36 to know that voltage drop and power dissipation do not change in the same way with changes in current. The graph of voltage against current is a straight line. The increase in voltage for a given increase in current is the same at every

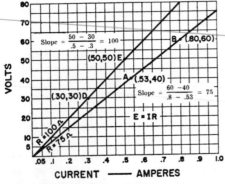

Fig. 4-37. Determining the slope of a line.

point on the line. An increase of .1 ampere always produces an increase of 7.5 volts; an increase of .2 ampere always produces an increase of 15 volts. These relationships hold true no matter what value the current has at the start.

A special name is given to the rate at which the dependent variable changes with changes in the independent variable. This rate of change is called the slope. The slope is determined by dividing the span of the dependent variable over a section of the line by the span of the independent variable over the same section. Two examples of slope calculation are shown in Fig.

4-37. The two lines on this graph are plots of voltage against current for two different values of resistance. The slope of the line, R = 75 ohms, was calculated for the section between point A (.53, 40) and point B (.80, 60). The span of current is equal to the scale reading of B minus A. The value of B, .80, minus the value of A, .53, is equal to .27 ampere. On the vertical scale, the reading of B is 60. We subtract the reading of A on the vertical scale, 40, from B (60) to obtain the voltage span, which is 20. Dividing the voltage span by the current span gives 20 ÷ .27 = 75. The slope of the R = 75 ohms line is 75. The slope of the R = 100 ohms line is calculated between point D (.30, 30) and point E (.50, 50). The slope is (50 − 30) ÷ (.50 − .30) which works out to be 100.

You have undoubtedly already noticed that in both the examples of slope calculation the slope was numerically equal to the value of the resistance used in the formula which was plotted. Whenever the dependent variable is equal to the independent variable multiplied by a constant, the slope will always be equal to the constant. It is also true that the graph of the relationship will always be a straight line on rectilinear graph paper. Because the graph is a straight line, the relationship is said to be linear and the formula which expresses the relationship is called a linear equation.

The slope of a straight line is constant; that is, the slope is the same for all parts of the line. This is not true for all graphs. Unless the graph is a straight line on rectilinear paper, the slope will be different at different parts of the curve. In other words, the value of the slope depends on the value of the independent variable. Because the slope is continually changing, we must

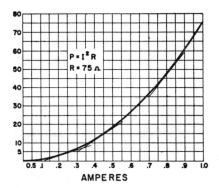

Fig. 4-38. Determining the slope of a non-linear graph.

use a slightly different method to determine it. Fig. 4-38 shows how the slope of a curved line on a graph is obtained. First, it is necessary to draw a line tangent to the curve at the point at which the value of the slope is desired. (A tangent line is a line which touches the curve at only one point.) Three such tangent lines are shown on the curve. One is tangent at the point (.20, 3.0), another at (.40, 12), and the third at (.80, 48). The slope of the tangent lines is determined the same way as the slope of a straight line graph. The slope of the curve at the point where the tangent line touches it is the same as the slope of the line.

It is obvious that each of the three tangent lines has a different slope. It is also apparent that the slope is least when the current is least. As the current increases, the slope of the curve becomes greater. From a practical viewpoint this means that, when the current is low, a small change in current results in only a small change in power, but when the current is large, a small change in current results in a large change in power. This type of curve will always result when the dependent variable is directly proportional to the square of the independent variable. Because the graph of the

formula is not a straight line on rectilinear paper, the formula is said to be a nonlinear equation.

Another common nonlinear curve results when the dependent variable is proportional to the square root of the independent variable. The curve of the formula $E = \sqrt{PR}$ for determining the voltage drop across a 75-ohm resistor for a given power dissipation is

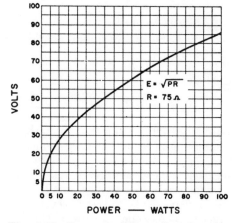

Fig. 4-39. Curve resulting when dependent variable is proportional to square-root of independent variable.

shown in Fig. 4-39. This curve has a high initial slope which decreases as the value of the independent variable becomes larger.

A third common nonlinear curve is shown in Fig. 4-40. This is the plot of current against resistance for a constant voltage drop.

The tangent to the curve at one point is also drawn in. Two points, A (2, 30) and B (8, 8) are marked on the tangent line and are used to determine the slope. In determining the span of the dependent variable, the value of the dependent variable at the point nearer Y-Y′ axis is always subtracted from the value of the dependent variable at the farther point.

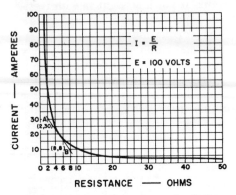

Fig. 4-40. Curve of a reciprocal relation.

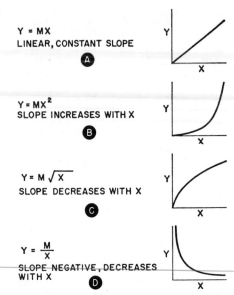

Fig. 4-41. Four common equations and their curves.

Here we have

$$(8 - 30) \div (8 - 2) = \frac{-22}{6} = -3.66$$

This curve differs from the others that you have studied in that it has a negative slope. The practical meaning of a negative slope is simply that the dependent variable becomes smaller as the independent variable becomes larger. The slope of this curve is greatest for small values of the independent variable, and least for high values. This curve shape and negative slope are characteristic of the graph of any equation in which the dependent variable is inversely proportional to the independent variable.

Each of the four types of formulas you are likely to use has its own characteristic graph curve. These curves show the way the dependent variable changes when the independent variable changes. The slope of the curves gives a numerical value to the rate of change. Fig. 4-41 summarizes the four types of equations and their curves. In the equations X stands for the independent variable, Y for the dependent variable, and M for the factor of proportionality. Remember the general characteristics of the curve of each equation; they are a big help in visualizing the relationship expressed in a formula.

Types of Graph Paper

Common rectilinear graph paper is best for showing the relationship between variables. However, it is not always the easiest type to use. An accurate graph of some formulas can be obtained only by plotting a large number of points. It is difficult to read values from a curve when the curve is nearly parallel to either the horizontal or vertical grid lines. The uncertainty of readings near the low end of either scale is much greater than the un-

Fig. 4-42. Comparison of linear and logarithmic scales.

certainty near the high end.

The plotting and reading of graphs can be made much easier by using graph paper which has special scales. There are many special types of graph paper for use in science, engineering and business. Three of these types are common in electronics.

Logarithmic. Most of the disadvantages of rectilinear paper can be overcome by plotting the logarithms of the variables instead of the variables themselves. To avoid having to look up the logarithms of every number, a special type of graph paper is used. The scales on this paper are laid out so that the distance of each number from the lower left corner is proportional to the logarithm of the number. Fig. 4-42 shows rectilinear and logarithmic scales side by side for comparison. The numbers on the rectilinear scale are ten times the logarithm of the numbers opposite them on the logarithmic scale. Notice in particular that there is no "0" on the logarithmic scale. There is no logarithm for zero.

In order to extend the scale from 10 to 100, it is necessary only to repeat the 1 to 10 scale to the right of the 10. For numbers less than 1, it would be necessary to add additional 1 to 10 scales to the left of 1. Each complete 1 to 10 scale along an axis is called a cycle. Logarithmic graph paper is described by the number of cycles along the horizontal and vertical scales. The chart on which Fig. 4-43 is drawn is called "1 × 2 cycle."

One big advantage of logarithmic graph paper is that the uncertainty in reading numbers from the scale is the same at both ends of a cycle. The low end of the cycle can be read to three significant figures; the upper end of the cycle can be read to two significant figures. In both cases the uncertainty is about 1 part in 100. This is very

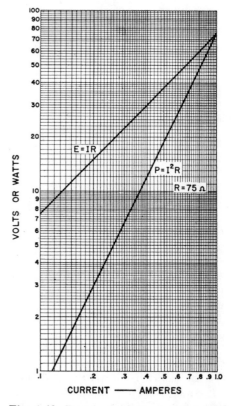

Fig. 4-43. Power against current and voltage against current plotted on logarithmic paper.

important when a graph is used as an aid to computation.

Another advantage of logarithmic scales is shown in Fig. 4-43 The two lines on this graph are plots of the same relationships that gave one straight line and one curved line in Fig. 4-36. Both the voltage and the power plots are straight lines on this type of paper. In fact, all four of the typical equations in Fig. 4-41 are straight lines when plotted on logarithmic paper. This greatly simplifies the work of plotting. No more than three points need be calculated. (Actually two points are enough; the third is just a check.)

While it is much easier to plot and

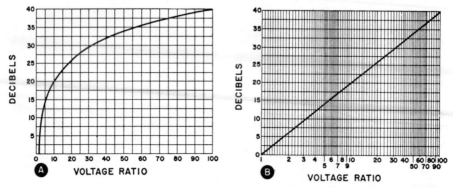

Fig. 4-44. Plots of voltage ratio against decibels.   A, Rectilinear; B, Semi-logarithmic.

read values from graphs on logarithmic paper, these plots have two big disadvantages. They do not show the exact manner in which changes in one variable affect the value of the other variable. Furthermore, you cannot determine the slope except in the case of the linear equation ($y = mx$).

A second disadvantage is the fact that there is no zero on the scales. On the 1 × 2 cycle paper used here, currents below .1 ampere, voltage drops below 7.5 volts, and powers below 1 watt do not show. If these lines had been plotted on 2 × 3 cycle paper, the lowest values would have been .01 ampere, .75 volt, and .1 watt. However, no matter how many cycles were used, zero would not appear.

Semi-logarithmic Paper. Another type of special graph paper has a logarithmic scale on one axis and a linear scale on the other. The logarithmic scale may have from 1 to 5 cycles; the linear scale may have any convenient number of lines. The most common are 10 or 20 lines to the inch. One use for this type of paper is to obtain a straight line plot of an equation in which one variable is proportional to the logarithm of the other. Another use is where a large range of numbers must be covered on one scale.

A linear scale would not show details on the low end, whereas a logarithmic scale would open up the low end and make all parts equally readable.

Two plots of a logarithmic relationship between variables are shown in Fig.4-44. Fig.4-44A shows the plot of

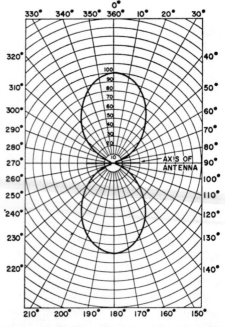

Fig. 4-45. Polar plot of antenna field strength.

voltage ratio against decibels on recti-linear paper. At least 20 points must be calculated and marked to get a smooth plot. Even then the graph is very difficult to read below 15 on the voltage ratio scale. Fig.4-44B shows the same relationship plotted on semi-logarithmic paper. It can be drawn with only three calculations, and can be read with equal ease on all parts of the line.

Polar Graphs. A third type of special graph paper is laid out in polar coordinates. Points are located by means of radial lines marked in degrees and a series of circles with common centers which show the distance along the radials. This paper is used when you want to show the radiation patterns of antennas, loudspeakers, light sources, and other forms of energy transmitters. A polar plot is used for this type of graph since it gives a pattern of direction in space that is immediately apparent. Fig.4-45 is an example of a graph plotted on polar coordinate paper. The graph shows the radiation pattern of an ideal quarter-wavelength antenna in free space. The distance of the points along the radials is proportional to the field strength in percent of the field strength in the direction of maximum radiation.

4-5. Practice Problems

The only way you can be sure that you completely understand what you have learned about mathematics is to put your knowledge to use in solving problems. A few problems will tell you whether you understand the mathematics, but you must continue to solve more and more difficult problems if you are to remember what you learn. There is no substitute for practice in math.

In this section of the lesson, there are several practical problems in electronics for you to solve. The answers to these problems are given so that you will be able to tell whether you are solving them correctly. If your answers do not agree with those shown, check your work carefully step by step. Often one small error early in a problem can completely change the result. Be especially careful in manipulating signed numbers and in looking up numbers in tables: Little mistakes in these areas can destroy the results of an otherwise perfect solution.

1. In the right triangle shown in Fig. 4-46 , Side X is equal to 25 ohms and Side R is equal to 76.0 ohms. What does Side Z equal?
ANS: 80.0 ohms.
2. In the triangle shown in Fig.4-46, if Side Z equals 45 and $\angle \theta$ equals 45°, what does Side X equal?

Fig. 4-46. A right triangle.

ANS: X = 31.8
3. What is the sine of 345°?
ANS: −.2588
4. Find $\angle \theta$ if Cos $\angle A$ = .4415.

ANS: 26.2°

5. If the voltage of an ac circuit is leading the current by 35.8°, what is the power factor of the circuit?

ANS: .812 or 81.2%

6. If the total voltage applied to the circuit discussed in Problem 5 is 220 volts and the current through the circuit is 1.79 amps, what is the true power consumed by the circuit?

ANS: 320 watts

7. If the impedance of a circuit can be described as: $Z = 5\underline{/36.9°}\,\Omega$ in polar coordinates, how would you express it in rectangular coordinates?

ANS: $Z = 4 + j3\Omega$

8. A choke coil draws 2 amps of current when it is connected across 110V dc. When connected to 110V, 60 cycles, ac, the current drawn is .25 amp. What is the resistance of the coil and the inductive reactance of the coil?

ANS: $R = 55\Omega$, $X_L = 437\Omega$

9. The following 60-cycle impedances are connected in series: $Z_1 = 3-j6\Omega$, $Z_2 = 10 + j19\Omega$, $Z_3 = 2-j7\Omega$, $Z_4 = 5 + j14\Omega$. What is the impedance of the circuit in polar coordinates?

ANS: $28.2\underline{/45°}\,\Omega$

10. In the circuit described in Problem 9, what value of capacitance would we have to add to the circuit to make the power factor 70.7% leading?

ANS: 66.3μf

11. A supply of 220 volts ac is applied to an impedance of $Z_a = 55\underline{/40°}\,\Omega$ in parallel with an impedance of $Z_b = 71\underline{/-36°}\,\Omega$. What is the power consumed in Z_b?

ANS: 552 watts.

12. Perform the following division and give the answer to three significant figures.

$$\frac{1}{6.28 \times 1550 \times 10^3 \times 452 \times 10^{-7}}$$

ANS: 2.27×10^{-3}

13. Divide .0058 × .000983 by .0000071.

ANS: 8.03×10^{-1}

14. An angle is equal to 3 radians. What does it measure in degrees?

ANS: 171.9°

15. How many degrees are there in 1.7 radians?

ANS: 97.4°

16. Convert 15.6° to radians.

ANS: .272 radians

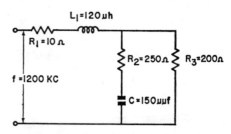

17. In the circuit shown in Fig.4-47, what is the total impedance?

ANS: $890\underline{/77.6°}\,\Omega$

Fig. 4-47. A series parallel circuit.

4-6. Review Problems

1. Give the sines of the following angles: 23°, −47.5°, 290°, 163°, 215°.

2. Convert 12 + J10.8 to polar coordinates.

3. Convert 30/−50.5° to rectangular coordinates.

4. What are the power factors of circuits having the following impedances: 67.1/68°; 123/−84°; .015/72°; 1.49/60°; 15.1 − j7.7?

5. What is the impedance in polar coordinates at 60 cycles of the circuit at the right?

.6 h   63Ω   6ufd 33Ω   1h   4.6Ω

6. What is the current through the circuit at the right? Give your answer in polar form.

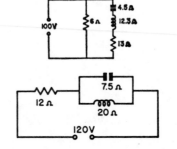

100V   6Ω   4.5Ω 12.3Ω 13Ω

7. What is the power dissipated in the circuit at the right?

12 Ω   7.5 Ω   20 Ω   120V

8. Express as exponential numbers: 57 mmf, 10 megohms, .16 microsecond, 26.7K ohms, 4503 kc.

9. Solve the following problem and express your answer as an exponential number with the correct number of significant figures:

$$\frac{.0073(14.689 - 3.2)}{569} \times \frac{117 \times 9.64}{.00857} =$$

10. Sketch graphs, as in Fig. 4-41, for capacitive reactance with capacity as the independent variable, and inductive reactance with inductance as the independent variable. Label the axes.

CHAPTER FIVE

Binary Arithmetic
And Boolean Algebra

5-1. Introduction

MILITARY installations, weather stations, insurance companies, and banks, to name but a few, handle tremendous amounts of data each day. To be useful, this data must be processed quickly and accurately. Furthermore, in our rapidly expanding scientific investigations, we need increasingly faster methods for carrying out complex calculations. To meet these requirements, high speed electronic digital computers were developed.

What is a digital computer? In general, it is an arrangement of electronic circuits and auxiliary equipment. Its functions are to solve mathematical problems with definite, individually distinct quantities, and to provide direct, numerical, finite solutions. It also selects and correlates parts of the data. For complex problems, such as differential equations, data must be reduced to fundamental relations in arithmetic, the only mathematics a digital computer can handle.

The first electronic arithmetic calculating machine built was ENIAC (Electronic Numerical Integrator and Computer). In this machine, electronic circuits replace mechanical and electromechanical devices for storage and computations to attain very high operational speeds. The only moving parts were in the input and output mechanisms. Although ENIAC was completed at the University of Pennsylvania in the summer of 1946, it soon became obsolete with the advance of superior machines, such as the IBM Selective Sequence Calculator, the Harvard Mark III, SEAC, BINAC, UNIVAC, and EDVAC.

EDVAC (Electronic Discrete Variable Arithmetic Computer), for example, had higher computing speed than ENIAC. Although EDVAC was physically smaller, it had much greater power as a computing instrument. One improvement was that data and instructions were represented within the machine in the binary scale (scale of 2), a system with only two possible stable conditions.

Adoption of the binary system to represent information in EDVAC was a move to utilize the binary nature of electronic components and circuits which constitute the calculating machine. Although we deal with different amounts of voltages and currents in circuits, generally we can say that a circuit is either conducting or not conducting. These two extremes are representative of bistable operations since only one condition can exist at a time. In application, bistable circuits, such as flip-flops, can be used for static storage of information and for the control of switching operations.

Recognition and use of the bistable nature of electronic elements was a major advance in electronic technology. Although bistable elements in suitable combinations could be used to calculate in the decimal number system, EDVAC's inventors held a different view. They believed that if binary elements were to be used at all, a true binary machine would be most efficient and would provide higher speed operation. To solve the problem of decimal to binary conversion and vice versa, specialized computer input and output devices have been developed.

Because the binary system is the "language" of most digital systems, our first step in understanding such systems is to learn the language. Thus, in this chapter you will study the concepts of the binary numbers and how these concepts are used.

In addition to learning the language of digital computers, you will also study how the computer "thinks." The computer must store and remember data presented to it. It can make a choice based on previous results. In solving problems, it must perform long chains of operations and determine if the individual and the final solutions are correct. Finally, it determines when one problem is finished and when to start the next. To perform these functions, digital computers and digital systems must have logical sequence of operations built into their circuits. The arrangement of these circuits is based on the fundamentals of logical algebra, known as Boolean algebra.

We will start our discussion with the binary number system. However, we will orient you first into this world of two states through the familiar decimal system. We have ten fingers for ten digits, but we also have our hands to represent two digits.

5-2. Binary Numbers

A number system is an orderly system of symbols used for making quantitative measurements. Man probably began counting by using his fingers as a reference. This reference is now called a "base," (technically called "radix"). With ten fingers, man started to count to the "base ten." Through years of development, he expanded the limited counting range of his fingers to include larger values. The Hindus and Arabs started our decimal system, in which numbers larger than or equal to ten were written with the ten basic digit symbols, 0 through 9, but were arranged in different positions. For example, two thousand six hundred and seven is written as 2,607 where 2 stands for two thousand, 6 for six hundred, 0 for no or absence of tens, and 7 for seven units. Likewise, man provided methods to denote numbers that were smaller than one by using fractions. For instance, one quarter of one can be written as .25 or 1/4. Since the decimal number system has become a part of our everyday living, we take the decimal system for granted and forget the existence of other number systems.

However, if we examine a desk ruler, we see there are twelve inches to a foot. This length measuring system is a duodecimal system, or has a radix of 12. A measuring cup contains eight ounces to make an octonary (eight) system. But for computers, radices of two, three, five, eight, and ten have been used so far. Their technical terms are binary, ternary, quinary, octonary, and decimal, respectively. Nevertheless, except for the recently developed ternary system in the Soviet Union, the others are direct or coded binary systems in which the counters, for example, are basically binary units.

In the binary system just as in the decimal system, we need symbols to represent quantities to simplify handling of the binary numbers. As far as the quantities are concerned, if everyone uses the same symbol for a particular quantity, confusion of symbols will not exist. We shall continue to use Hindu-Arabic symbols, "0" for zero and "1" for one. These are the only two quantities in the binary system.

On paper we use these two symbols, 0 and 1, but for computers other symbols are frequently used; two such symbols are 999999 and 0011, which are computer zeros.

The reason for the adoption of such symbols depends to a large extent upon the nature and purpose of the particular computer under consideration. Factors such as reliability of operation, ability to detect errors once they occur, and savings in components create problems in the design of computers. Fortunately, since these adopted symbols do not alter the function of the computer to any extent, we will not concern ourselves with the symbol changes.

Writing Binary Numbers

Before going into binary numbers, let us first review and further explore the "positional" method of decimal numbers. Suppose we have seven hundred and twenty-five. We can write it symbolically as 725 where 7 designates seven "hundreds," 2 designates two "tens," and 5 designates five "units." Another way of writing 725 from its definition is 700 + 20 + 5. Using powers of ten or the radix 10, we can expand 725 to $(7 \times 10^2) + (2 \times 10^1) + (5 \times 10^0)$. The symbols, 7, 2, and 5 are digit values but the exponential terms, powers of the radix 10, are the positional values. (Notice, however, that each position is 10 times larger in value than the previous position starting from the first digit at the right; 10 is 10×10^0, where $10^0 = 1$, 100 is 10×10^1, for instance.) Here, we can see that the digits in a position indicate a particular value, the digit's value *times* the *value* of the *position*. Hence, 7 in the "hundreds" place is 7×10^2, 7×100, or 700.

In the binary number system, as in the decimal number system, the numbers can be written with the positional method of notation. Because the binary number system has only two digit symbols, 0 and 1, we must write our binary numbers in terms of these symbols. A typical number is 1101 (read, "one, one, zero, one") or $(1101)_2$, where the subscript 2 specifies the radix of the number system.

By applying the positional method, we can rewrite 1101 as

$$(1 \times 2^3) + (1 \times 2^2) + (0 \times 2^1) + (1 \times 2^0).$$

Here we have replaced the base of the exponential terms of the positional values from 10 in the decimal system to 2 because the binary system has a radix of 2. When we expand the powers of 2 in this example, we get

$$(1 \times 8) + (1 \times 4) + (0 \times 2) + (1 \times 1)$$

Notice that $2^0 = 1$. Thus, the positional values of a binary number, starting from the right digit of a number, is always a power of 2; that is, $2^0, 2^1, 2^2, 2^3, 2^4, \ldots$, or expanded to $1, 2, 4, 8, 16, \ldots$, as many terms as necessary. Each position to the left of a digit in a binary number has twice the positional value of that digit.

We can simplify the expression

by remembering that any number multiplied by 1 is the number itself, and any number multiplied by zero is zero. Thus, the expression

$$(1 \times 2^3) + (1 \times 2^2) + (0 \times 2^1) + (1 \times 2^0).$$

can be simplified to

$$2^3 + 2^2 + 1$$

A few more examples will aid in understanding the method of forming binary numbers. This time we will leave out the zero digits because you know that any number multiplied by zero equals zero.

$$\text{Binary } 11010 = 2^4 + 2^3 + 2^1$$
$$= 16 + 8 + 2$$

$$(11)_2 = 2^1 + 2^0$$
$$= 2 + 1$$

For negative binary numbers,

$$\text{Binary } -101 = -(2^2 + 2^0)$$
$$\text{Binary } -101 = -(4 + 1)$$

$$\begin{aligned}(-111111)_2 &= -(2^5 + 2^4 + 2^3 + \\ &= \quad 2^2 + 2^1 + 2^0) \\ &= -(32 + 16 + 8 + \\ &= \quad 4 + 1)\end{aligned}$$

We have been discussing whole numbers. Now let's see how we express fractions or numbers that are smaller than the magnitude of whole numbers.

Fractions

There are two ways of expressing quantities which cannot be written as whole numbers. Quantities which may be represented as a fraction are called rational, and those which cannot be represented as a fraction are called irrational. Examples of rational numbers are

¼ and 2/3; examples of irrational numbers are $\sqrt{2}$ and π. (In case you were taught to use 22/7 as the value of π, let us say here that 22/7 is an approximate value. $22/7 = 3.1428...$; $\pi = 3.1416$.)

A computer cannot handle fractions as such, but by extending the number system to include terms involving negative powers of 2, fractions may be represented to any degree of accuracy.

You will recall that in the decimal system

$$2^{-1} = \frac{1}{2^1} = \frac{1}{2},$$

$$2^{-2} = \frac{1}{2^2} = \frac{1}{4}, \text{ etc.}$$

To express fractions using the binary system, a period or point is placed between the digit in the 2^0 position and the digit in the 2^{-1} position. This point is called the decimal point in the decimal system and, appropriately, the binary point in the binary system. The position values are read from *left* to *right* on the right side of the binary point.

Example:

binary: $0.1 = 2^{-1}$

$$= \frac{1}{2} \text{ or } = 0.5$$

With our knowledge of writing binary whole numbers and fractions, we can also write a mixed number; that is, one having both a whole number and a fraction.

Example:

$$(1101.101)_2 = 2^3 + 2^2 + 2^0 + 2^{-1} + 2^{-3}$$

$$= 2^3 + 2^2 + 2^0 + \frac{1}{2^1} + \frac{1}{2^3}$$

$$= 8 + 4 + 1 + \frac{1}{2} + \frac{1}{8}$$

or in decimals

$$= 8 + 4 + 1 + 0.5 + 0.125$$

Conversion of Binary to Decimal

To convert any binary number to a decimal number, we can multiply each binary digit by the decimal equivalent of its corresponding power of 2 and add the products.

In Table 5-1 you will find a list of positive and negative powers of 2 and their decimal equivalents. Both fractional and decimal equivalents are shown for the negative powers of 2. This table will help you primarily in converting between decimal and binary.

Table 5-1 lists only the powers of 2 between 2^{10} and 2^{-10}. It can be extended easily in either direction. For instance, to determine the value of 2^{11}, simply multiply the value of 2^{10} by 2.

$$1024 \times 2 = 2048 = 2^{11}.$$

To find the value of 2^{12}, multiply 2048 by 2.

$$2048 \times 2 = 4096 = 2^{12}.$$

To extend the table in the negative power direction, multiply the denominators (numbers below the horizontal line) of the fractions by 2 to obtain the fractional form or

Table 5-1

Powers of 2	Decimal Equivalent
2^{10}	1024
2^9	512
2^8	256
2^7	128
2^6	64
2^5	32
2^4	16
2^3	8
2^2	4
2^1	2
2^0	1
2^{-1}	$\frac{1}{2} = 0.5$
2^{-2}	$\frac{1}{4} = 0.25$
2^{-3}	$\frac{1}{8} = 0.125$
2^{-4}	$\frac{1}{16} = 0.0625$
2^{-5}	$\frac{1}{32} = 0.03125$
2^{-6}	$\frac{1}{64} = 0.015625$
2^{-7}	$\frac{1}{128} = 0.0078125$
2^{-8}	$\frac{1}{256} = 0.00390625$
2^{-9}	$\frac{1}{512} = 0.001953125$
2^{-10}	$\frac{1}{1024} = 0.0009765625$

$$\frac{1}{1024 \times 2} = \frac{1}{2048} = 2^{-11}$$

$$\frac{1}{2048 \times 2} = \frac{1}{4096} = 2^{-12}$$

$$\frac{.0009765625}{2} = .00048828125 = 2^{-11}$$

$$\frac{.00048828125}{2} = .000244140625 = 2^{-12}$$

Table 5-2 and 5-3 are for conversion by tables. Table 5-2 gives numbers from 0 to 33 expressed in the decimal system and their equivalents in the binary system. Table

Table 5-2

Decimal	Binary
0	0
1	1
2	10
3	11
4	100
5	101
6	110
7	111
8	1000
9	1001
10	1010
11	1011
12	1100
13	1101
14	1110
15	1111
16	10000
17	10001
18	10010
19	10011
20	10100
21	10101
22	10110
23	10111
24	11000
25	11001
26	11010
27	11011
28	11100
29	11101
30	11110
31	11111
32	100000
33	100001

divide the decimal form by 2 to obtain the decimal form.

Examples:

$$\frac{1}{1024} = 2^{-10}$$

Table 5-3

Decimal	Binary
$\dfrac{1}{16} = 0.0625$	0.0001
$\dfrac{1}{8} = 0.125$	0.0010
$\dfrac{3}{16} = 0.1875$	0.0011
$\dfrac{1}{4} = 0.25$	0.0100
$\dfrac{5}{16} = 0.3125$	0.0101
$\dfrac{3}{8} = 0.375$	0.0110
$\dfrac{7}{16} = 0.4375$	0.0111
$\dfrac{1}{2} = 0.5$	0.1000
$\dfrac{9}{16} = 0.5625$	0.1001
$\dfrac{5}{8} = 0.625$	0.1010
$\dfrac{11}{16} = 0.6875$	0.1011
$\dfrac{3}{4} = 0.75$	0.1100
$\dfrac{13}{16} = 0.8125$	0.1101
$\dfrac{7}{8} = 0.875$	0.1110
$\dfrac{15}{16} = 0.9375$	0.1111

5-3 gives rational fractions from 1/16 to 15/16 in the decimal system and their equivalents in the binary system. However, these tables have only limited applications for large scale conversion.

A few examples will illustrate some of the more common methods of performing the binary to decimal conversion.

1. List from right to left the successive powers of 2 as follows:

$$64 \quad 32 \quad 16 \quad 8 \quad 4 \quad 2 \quad 1$$

and under each power put down the associated binary digit. The equivalent decimal number is obtained by adding up those powers that have "1" beneath them. For example, given $(110101)_2$, find its decimal equivalent.

Solution:

$$\begin{array}{cccccc} 32 & 16 & 8 & 4 & 2 & 1 \\ \hline 1 & 1 & 0 & 1 & 0 & 1 \end{array}$$

Decimal equivalent $= 32 + 16 + 4$
$$+ 1$$
$$= 53$$

2. Another way of finding the answer is as follows: Multiply the digit farthest to the *left* by 2 and to this product add the second digit from the left. Multiply the result of the first calculations by 2 and add to this product the third digit from the left. Continue this procedure of multiplication and addition until the binary point is reached. The result of the last calculations is the decimal equivalent of the binary number.

Now, let us apply this second method of conversion to $(110101)_2$.

Solution:
$$\begin{aligned} 1 \times 2 + 1 &= 3 \\ 3 \times 2 + 0 &= 6 \\ 6 \times 2 + 1 &= 13 \\ 13 \times 2 + 0 &= 26 \\ 26 \times 2 + 1 &= 53 \end{aligned}$$

Decimal equivalent = 53.

3. We have already used the following method in our explanation of the formation of binary numbers. However, we will solve our example $(110101)_2$ again to show a third method for finding the decimal equivalent of a binary number.

Solution: $2^5 + 2^4 + 2^2 + 2^0$
$= 32 + 16 + 4 + 1 = 53$
Decimal equivalent = 53.

This method of binary to decimal conversion is also very adaptable to binary fractions. For example, find the decimal equivalent of $(.110101)_2$.

Solution: $2^{-1} + 2^{-2} + 2^{-4} + 2^{-6}$

$$= \frac{1}{2} + \frac{1}{4} + \frac{1}{16} + \frac{1}{64}$$

$$= \frac{53}{64}$$

or $= .5 + .25 + .0625 +$
$.015625$

$= .828125$

Decimal equivalent $= \dfrac{53}{64} = 0.828125$.

The following example will show the conversion of a binary mixed number.

Given binary 1101.01, find the decimal equivalent.

Solution: $2^3 + 2^2 + 2^0 + 2^{-2}$

$$= 8 + 4 + 1 + \frac{1}{4}$$

$$= 13\frac{1}{4} = 13.25.$$

Decimal equivalent
$$= 13\frac{1}{4} = 13.25.$$

Conversion of Decimal to Binary

We are used to thinking of numbers and quantities and doing arithmetic in the decimal system. On the other hand, electronic computers work in the binary system. To allow the digital computer to understand its human operators, we must be able to convert numbers from decimal to binary.

To convert a decimal integer to a binary number, we must divide the decimal integer repeatedly by 2 until the quotient is 0. The remainders that result from these divisions are the digits of the required binary number in order *from right to left.*

Example 1: Convert decimal 100 to binary.

Division	Remainder
$\dfrac{100}{2} = 50$	0
$\dfrac{50}{2} = 25$	0
$\dfrac{25}{2} = 12$	1
$\dfrac{12}{2} = 6$	0
$\dfrac{6}{2} = 3$	0
$\dfrac{3}{2} = 1$	1
$\dfrac{1}{2} = 0$	1

Hence, $(100)_{10}$ in the decimal system is the same as $(1100100)_2$.

Example 2: Convert decimal 33 to binary.

Division	Remainder
$\dfrac{33}{2} = 16$	1
$\dfrac{16}{2} = 8$	0
$\dfrac{8}{2} = 4$	0
$\dfrac{4}{2} = 2$	0
$\dfrac{2}{2} = 1$	0
$\dfrac{1}{2} = 0$	1

Thus, 33 in the decimal system is the same as binary 100001.

To convert a decimal fraction to a binary number, we must *multiply* the decimal fraction repeatedly by 2. In each step of multiplication, double only the fractional part of the preceding product. In each multiplication, if a "carry" into the units column occurs, the corresponding binary digit is 1; otherwise, the binary digit is 0. The required binary digits, in order *from left to right*, are obtained from top to bottom of the units column.

Example 3: Convert decimal 0.40625 to binary.

Units Column	Multiplication
	.40625
	×2
0	(0).81250
	×2
1 ←	(1).62500
	×2
1 ←	(1).25000
	×2
0	(0).50000
	×2
1 ←	(1).00000

Here decimal 0.40625 is equal to binary 0.01101.

The process of repeated multiplication will terminate, as in the preceding example, if the given decimal fraction has an *exact* binary equivalent; otherwise, the multiplication process can be continued until the desired number of digits is obtained.

Example 4: Convert decimal 0.30125 to binary to twelve significant binary digits.

Units Column	Multiplication
	.30125
	×2
0	(0).60250
	×2
1 ←	(1).20500
	×2
0	(0).41000
	×2
0	.(0).82000
	×2
1 ←	(1).64000
	×2
1 ←	(1).28000
	×2
0	(0).56000

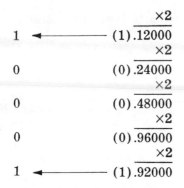

Therefore, decimal 0.30125 is the same as binary 0.010011010001 to twelve binary places.

A decimal mixed number is converted to binary in two steps. First the whole part, to the left of the decimal point, is converted by successive division. Then, the fractional part is converted by successive multiplications. Notice that in making both these conversions, the binary digits are obtained in an order that starts at the binary point going to the left for a whole number and to the right for a fraction or the fractional part of a mixed number.

This method of converting decimal numbers to their binary equivalent is probably the fastest. However, you must remember two procedures to make the conversion. Unless you make this conversion often, you may find the following method easier to remember.

To use this method, you must either refer to or make up a table of powers of 2 like Table 5-1. The following example of converting decimal 45 to its binary equivalent will show you how this second methods works.

First, check the decimal number against the table of powers of 2 to find the largest power of 2 the decimal number contains. In our example, 45 is between 32 and 64, so 2^5 is the largest power of 2 contained in 45. From this we know that there will be six binary digits. The left-hand digit is 1. Next, subtract 32 from 45 and compare the remainder with 2^4. If the difference is larger than 2^4, the second digit from the left is a 1. In this case, the difference between 45 and 32 is 13 (smaller than 2^4) so that the second digit from the left is 0. Subtract the decimal equivalent of 2^3 from the difference of the first subtraction. In other words, subtract 8 from 13. Because 13 is larger than 2^3, the third digit is 1. Continue this operation until all binary digits have been obtained. The example is carried out below.

$$
\begin{array}{rl}
45 & \\
-\ 32 & 2^5 \\
\hline
13 & \\
-\ 8 & 2^3 \\
\hline
5 & \\
-\ 4 & 2^2 \\
\hline
1 & = 2^0
\end{array}
$$

The binary equivalent is 101101.

Example: Convert decimal .768 to binary. Remember that for fractions you read the positional value from *left to right* from the binary point.

$$
\begin{array}{rl}
.768 & \\
-\ .5 & 2^{-1} \\
\hline
.268 & \\
-\ .25 & 2^{-2} \\
\hline
.018 & \\
-\ .015625 & 2^{-6} \\
\hline
etc. & etc.
\end{array}
$$

Therefore decimal .768 is binary .110001 to six significant binary digits.

5-3. Binary Arithmetic Operations

Addition and subtraction of numbers of any radix can be accomplished by a process of simple counting; that is by adding "counts" to one number while at the same time subtracting "counts" from another number. For instance, in addition, the sum of the two numbers is obtained when the second number is reduced to zero. However, a much faster and generally more satisfactory method is to add and subtract digits of corresponding orders or positions separately and to adjust the results of the individual digit sums and differences according to rules of carrying and borrowing, which we will describe. We are used to adding three or more numbers together whenever a sum is required. However, it has been found more practical for machine computations to handle only two numbers at a time. Three numbers would be added by adding the third to the sum of the first two. Because ordinary subtraction methods usually involve only two numbers at a time, machine subtraction involves no new ideas in this respect.

In computers, addition and subtraction are executed in parallel or serially, by the manner in which numbers are transmitted from one place to another. One method involves the use of a separate channel or wire for each digit of the number and all digits are transmitted simultaneously "in parallel." The other method uses only one channel or wire, and the digits are transmitted one at a time "serially" on this channel. For parallel operation, separate devices are required for addition and subtraction of each digit in the numbers involved. For serial operation, only one such device is necessary to process the digits one at a time: thus, the same device is used for all digits.

The advantage of parallel operation is that higher computation speeds are possible, and the advantage of serial operations is that less equipment is required. Both parallel and serial binary computers have been built, but their distinct advantages do not justify conclusions on the superiority of one type over the other.

The basic rules for addition and subtraction of binary digits are the same for serial as for parallel operation.

Addition

The principles of addition used in calculations with binary numbers are the same as those used with decimal numbers. The fundamental arithmetic operations with positive binary integers, or whole numbers, are given in this section. Corresponding decimal values are included with each example. Table 5-4 gives the basic rules for binary addition.

In addition, there are technical names given to the quantities involved. You know that the sum is the result of an addition and that the "carries" are digits to be carried to higher orders. The quantity to be added by another is called the "augend." The other quantity to be added to the augend is called the "addend."

TABLE 5-4

Basic Rules of Binary Addition
$1 + 1 = 10$
$0 + 0 = 0$
$0 + 1 = 1$
$1 + 1 + 1 = 11$

In binary notation, a unit in any column is equivalent to two units in the next column to the right while in a decimal system, a unit in any column is equivalent to ten units in the next column to the right. When the sum of two digits in any column equals binary 10 (this is read "one, zero"), the 1 is carried to the next column to the left.

Example 1: Add binary 1110 to binary 1011.

Adding the columns from right to left,

	binary	decimal
carries	1 1 1	
augend	1011	11
addend	+1110	+14
sum	11001	25

Example 2: Add binary 100111 to binary 110101.

Adding the columns from right to left,

	binary	decimal
carries	1 111	1
	110101	53
	+ 100111	+39
	1011100	92

Example 3: Add $(101011)_2$ to $(10111000)_2$.

	binary	decimal
carries	1 1 1	1
	10111000	184
	+ 101011	+ 43
	11100011	227

Subtraction

Subtraction is the reverse of addition. It is used to find how much one number differs from another. You will learn two methods of binary subtraction: direct subtraction, and subtraction by adding the complement.

Table 5-5 gives the basic rules for direct binary subtraction. With this method, whenever the opera-

TABLE 5-5

Basic Rules of Binary Subtraction
$0 - 0 = 0$
$1 - 0 = 1$
$0 - 1 = 10 - 1 = 1$ (and a borrow)
$1 - 1 = 0$

tion 0–1 occurs, it is replaced by 10–1 by borrowing 1 from the next column on the left.

Example: Subtract 111 from 1101 by direct subtraction.

	binary	decimal
	1101	13
	− 111	− 7
	110	6

In this subtraction, the first step is to subtract 1 from 1 in the first column at the right; the result is 0. The next step is to subtract 1 from 0, which you do by borrowing the 1 to the left of 0. Now the problem is to subtract 1 from 10, and the answer is 1. The third step is to subtract 1 from 0 again, because the 1 in the third column is now a 0 after we borrowed it in the preceding step. We must borrow from the fourth column from the right to perform this subtraction, so once again we have 1 from 10; the answer is 1. The verious steps in the problem can be shown as

binary

```
borrows          10  10
minuend         1 1 0 1
subtrahend    −   1 1 1
                ─────────
difference        1 1 0
```

The "borrows" in the preceding example were easily made because there was always a "1" in the next column to the left. Suppose there had been a "0" in this position. Obviously, we can't borrow a "1" that isn't there. In order to borrow, we'll have to get a "1" in that position. We do this by borrowing the next "1" to the left and changing each "0" in between to "1".

As an example, subtract binary 111 from binary 1100.

```
binary     decimal
1100         12
− 111       − 7
────        ────
 101          5
```

In this subtraction the first step is to subtract 1 from 0 which we must do by borrowing. However, since there is not a 1 in the column immediately to the left, we cannot borrow a 1 from this column. Instead we must borrow the 1 from the third column to the left and change each 0 in between to a 1. Thus after borrowing, we have a 0

in the third column, a 1 in the second and 10 in the first. Now subtracting 1 from 10 gives us 1. In the second column, 1 from 1 gives us 0. In the third column, to subtract 1 from 0 we must borrow 1 from the fourth column and subtract 1 from 10 to get 1. The various steps in the problem can be shown.

```
borrows         10  1  10
minuend        1 1 0 0
subtrahend   −   1 1 1
               ─────────
difference       1 0 1
```

As a third example, subtract 11111 from 1011000.

```
1 0 1 1 0 0 0
−   1 1 1 1 1
─────────────
  1 1 1 0 0 1
```

The various steps in the subtraction can be shown as:

```
borrows        1 10 10 1  10
minuend      1 0 1 1 0 0 0
subtrahend −     1 1 1 1 1
             ───────────────
               1 1 1 0 0 1
```

However, most electronic computers do not use the direct subtraction method. Computer designers have found that subtraction is easier and simpler to perform by a roundabout method known as the addition of the complement.

Subtraction by Addition of the Complement. The complement of a number in computer work is defined as the amount that must be added to that number to give the smallest number having one more digit than the machine can handle. Because we must subtract to find a complement, there is no point in using this method for subtraction in the decimal system. However, subtraction by addition of the complement is actually much easier in the binary system than by direct subtraction.

In order to subtract by "addition of the complement," we first obtain the complement of the subtrahend, the number which is to be subtracted. This complement is then added to the minuend, the number from which the subtrahend is to be subtracted. The result of this addition gives the difference between the two numbers.

The complement of a binary number is obtained by subtracting that number from the largest number that the machine can hold and adding 1 to the difference. For instance, suppose we have a computer that can carry eight digits. The largest number it can hold has a "1" in each of the eight digit places. To find the complement of 10101010, we subtract 10101010 from 11111111 and add 1 to the right-hand digit.

$$\begin{array}{l} 11111111 \quad \text{largest computer no.} \\ -10101010 \quad \text{number} \\ \hline 01010101 \\ + \qquad 1 \\ \hline 01010110 \quad \text{complement} \end{array}$$

Pay particular attention to the direct subtraction. You will see that the result of the subtraction is the same number we would get if we replaced all the 1's in the original number with 0's and replaced all the original 0's with 1's. Hence, this gives us a simpler way to perform the subtraction. Replace all 1's in the original number with 0's, and replace all 0's in the original number with 1's. This process is very easy to do in a computer, much

easier in fact than performing direct subtraction. This is one of the reasons why subtraction is performed by addition of the complement in many computers.

There will always be as many digits in the complement of a number as the machine can hold. The complement of 111 in a 3-digit computer would be

$$000 + 1 = 001$$

In a 6-digit computer the number would be 000111 and its complement would be

$$111000 + 1 = 111001$$

To subtract 101 from 10001 in a 5-digit machine we first express the subtrahend 101 in five digits as 00101 and then obtain the complement of 00101. This becomes

$$\begin{array}{l} 00101 \quad \text{subtrahend} \\ 11010 \\ + \quad 1 \\ \hline 11011 \quad \text{complement} \end{array}$$

add the complement to 10001

$$\begin{array}{l} 10001 \\ + 11011 \\ \hline \cancel{1} \ 01100 \end{array}$$

The first five digits, from right to left are the correct answer. The carry to the sixth digit, which we have crossed off in the example will not appear in the answer because the machine can handle only five digits. This crossed off digit is called an "over-flow."

Let us do the same problem as it would appear in an 8-digit computer. Subtract 00000101 from 00010001. Complementing first by changing 1's to 0's and 0's to 1's, then by adding 1:

00000101   subtrahend

11111010
+   1
_____

11111011   complement

Add the complement to 00010001:

00010001
+11111011
_____

✗ 00001100

Another advantage of performing a subtraction in this way appears when we subtract a number from a smaller number and get a negative answer. In direct subtraction we always subtract the smaller number from the larger. If the subtrahend is larger than the minuend, a minus sign is put in front of the answer.

For example, subtract 101 from 10001.

10001
−   101
_____

01100

Subtract 10001 from 101.

−10001
+   101
_____

−01100

In the preceding example, the magnitudes of the two numbers must be compared before performing direct subtraction so that the smaller is always subtracted from the larger. When subtraction is performed by adding the complement, the numbers need not be compared.

Subtract 10001 from 101 on a 5-digit machine. Complementing 10001 and adding to 101.

10001   subtrahend

01110
+   1
_____

01111   complement

101   minuend
+01111
_____

10100   sum of subtraction by addition of complement

There is no overflow to the sixth place. This tells us that the answer will be negative, and that we must complement the sum to get the correct answer.

10100   sum
01011
+   1
_____

−01100   negative complement of sum

This is exactly the same answer we obtained by direct subtraction.

All the foregoing examples have been worked using the "2's complement" method. A possible simplification in the use of complements, particularly in the construction of computers is to use the "1's complement." The 1's complement of a binary number is the number that must be added to it to obtain the largest number the machine will hold. It is obtained by merely interchanging the 1's and 0's of a number.

As an example of using the 1's complement we will subtract 101 from 10001 carrying five digits.

00101   subtrahend

11010   1's complement
+10001   minuend
_____

101011

The overflow to the sixth place is added as a "carry" to the first place.

$$\begin{array}{r} 101011 \\ + \quad \llcorner\!\!\longrightarrow 1 \\ \hline 01100 \end{array}$$

Using the extra digit in this way is called an "end-round carry."

Next, let's subtract 10001 from 101 using the 1's complement in 5 digits.

10001	subtrahend
01110	1's complement
+00101	minuend

$$\overline{+10011}$$

Without a "carry" in the sixth digit place we must obtain the 1's complement again to get the correct answer, and the answer is negative.

10011
−01100   1's complement

In the case of a negative minuend, methods of machine subtraction vary from one computer to another. For our purpose, we can add the two quantities to get a negative result.

The Binary Point in Addition and Subtraction. All the examples of addition and subtraction that you have studied so far have involved only whole numbers. Exactly the same methods are used when we are dealing with fractions and mixed numbers. However, we must arrange the numbers so that the binary points are directly beneath one another.

As an example of addition in binary mixed numbers, let's add 111.1 to 1100.11.

$$\begin{array}{r} 10100.01 \\ + \quad 111.1 \\ \hline 10100.01 \end{array}$$

Next, let's perform the direct subtraction of 111.1 from 10100.01:

$$\begin{array}{r} 10100.01 \\ - \quad 111.1 \\ \hline 1100.11 \end{array}$$

We can perform this same subtraction using the 1's complement in seven digits by writing the subtrahend in seven digits before complementing it. We must add 0's both to the right and to the left of the binary point so that we have five digits to the left and two digits to the right of the point.

00111.10	subtrahend
11000.01	1's complement
+10100.01	minuend

101100.10
   $\llcorner\!\!\longrightarrow +1$ end-round carry
—————
01100.11

Multiplication

In multiplication, the member to be multiplied is called the multiplicand. The multiplier is the number that multiplies the multiplicand. The result of a multiplication is called the product.

The binary multiplication table is shown in Table 5-6. With the relations shown in Table 5-6 we can do binary multiplication. Notice that the product is equal to 1 only if the multiplicand and the multiplier are both equal to 1.

The simplicity of binary multiplication is due principally to the fact that the product of two digits has only one digit. Because the product of 1 and some number is the number itself, and the product of 0 and some number is 0, either 0 or the multiplicand itself becomes the product.

Example: Multiply binary 1111 (decimal 15) by binary 10 (decimal 2).

binary		decimal
1111	multiplicand	15
× 10	multiplier	× 2
0000 ⎱	partial	30
1111 ⎰	products	
11110	product	

When the multiplier has three or more digits, adding the partial products in binary numbers can be a task. When you add two or three binary digits of 1, the sum can be $(10)_2$ or $(11)_2$ which has two digits to produce a carry to the next higher order. For four to seven binary digits, the sum can be from $(100)_2$ to $(111)_2$. These sums have three digits, resulting in carries to the next two higher orders. With our customary way of adding partial products, the digits in the partial products are added one column at a time, starting at the right. This operation is more difficult in the binary system than in the decimal system.

binary	
1111	multiplicand
×1101	multiplier
1111	A ⎱
0000	B ⎰ partial
1111	C ⎰ products
1111	D ⎰
11000011	product

TABLE 5-6

Basic Rules of Binary Multiplication		
Multiplicand	Multiplier	Product
1	1	1
1	0	0
0	1	0
0	0	0

decimal
15
×13
45
15
195

When you add the partial products in the fourth column from the right, you have three 1 digits and a carry from the next lower order. The sum is $(100)_2$ which has a carry to the sixth column. The fifth column produces a carry as well. As a result, the sixth column has two 1 digits and two carries from lower orders. The sum here is $(100)_2$ to provide a carry to the eighth column. The handling of multiple-digit carries, although elementary in principle, is an awkward process to execute mentally without error. The problem arises in our last example involving the two four-digit binary numbers 1111 and 1101 even though the numbers correspond with the relatively small decimal numbers 15 and 13, respectively.

The difficulty may be overcome by adding only one partial product at a time so that the carries are kept to one digit only. Although this method requires the recording of several intermediate sums, it is a simplification because the carries in each addition are small. This process, called accumulation, is used almost universally in digital computers.

To illustrate the process, we will perform the previous multiplication by accumulation.

$$\begin{array}{ll} 1111 & \text{multiplicand} \\ \times 1101 & \text{multiplier} \\ \hline 1111 & \text{partial product A} \\ 0000 & \text{partial product B} \\ \hline 1111 & \text{first sum} \\ 1111 & \text{partial product C} \\ \hline 1001011 & \text{second sum} \\ 1111 & \text{partial product D} \\ \hline 11000011 & \text{final sum} \end{array}$$

binary

$$\begin{array}{r} 1\ 0\ 1\ 1.0\ 1\ 1 \\ \times 1\ 1\ 0.1\ 1 \\ \hline 1\ 0\ 1\ 1\ 0\ 1\ 1 \\ 1\ 0\ 1\ 1\ 0\ 1\ 1 \\ \hline 1\ 0\ 0\ 0\ 1\ 0\ 0\ 0\ 1 \\ 1\ 0\ 1\ 1\ 0\ 1\ 1 \\ \hline 1\ 1\ 1\ 1\ 1\ 0\ 1\ 0\ 0\ 1 \\ 1\ 0\ 1\ 1\ 0\ 1\ 1 \\ \hline 1\ 0\ 0\ 1\ 1\ 0\ 0.1\ 1\ 0\ 0\ 1 \end{array}$$

decimal

$$\begin{array}{r} 1\ 1.3\ 7\ 5 \\ \times 6.7\ 5 \\ \hline 5\ 6\ 8\ 7\ 5 \\ 7\ 9\ 6\ 2\ 5 \\ 6\ 8\ 2\ 5\ 0 \\ \hline 7\ 6.7\ 8\ 1\ 2\ 5 \end{array}$$

If one or both of the factors entering into a multiplication are negative, the multiplication may be carried out in the same manner described, provided that the numbers involved are not in complement form. To get the sign of the product, we need only to compare the signs of the two factors. The product will be positive when the signs are alike, negative when the signs are different.

The Binary Point in Multiplication. In the foregoing examples the binary point in the multiplier was directly beneath the binary point in the multiplicand because we used whole numbers only. Just as in decimal multiplication, however, the binary points need not be in line. To illustrate the location of the binary point in multiplication we will multiply $(1011.011)_2$ by $(110.11)_2$ by the fixed point method.

Here you can see that we have not aligned the binary points before multiplying. Also, we have omitted the partial products that are equal to zero by simply shifting the next product containing 1's the necessary number of places to the left. This operation is familiar to you from decimal multiplication.

To locate the binary point in the answer, we simply add the number of places to the right of the binary point in the multiplicand and in the multiplier. This total is the number of places to the right of the binary point in the answer.

In the last example, we have two places to the right of the binary point in the multiplier, and three in the multiplicand. So there must be five $(2 + 3 = 5)$ places to the right of the binary point in the answer. This is exactly the same procedure you use to locate the decimal point.

The digital computer, unfortunately, cannot easily locate a binary point in this way. Therefore, a more systematic method, called the "floating-point," is frequently used. It involves shifting the binary point to the extreme left in both multiplier and multiplicand. This places all the digits in each number to the right of the binary point. The correct location of the binary point is then attached to each digit number in the form of a power of 2 which, when multiplied by the number, will yield the original number with the binary point in its proper position.

For example, the binary number 110.11 can be written as $.11011 \times 2^3$. This is the same as $.11011 \times 1000$ in binary notation because $(1000)_2$ is equal to 2^3. The multiplication of these two figures produces the original number.

$$.1\ 1\ 0\ 1\ 1$$
$$\times 1\ 0\ 0\ 0$$
$$\overline{1\ 1\ 0.1\ 1\ 0\ 0\ 0}$$

Similarly, binary number 1011.011 can be written as $.1011011 \times 2^4$.

Multiplication of these two numbers in the last example can now be handled as two separate products: the product of the binary digits, and the product of the exponential terms containing powers of 2.

$$.1\ 0\ 1\ 1\ 0\ 1\ 1 \quad 2^4$$
$$\times .1\ 1\ 0\ 1\ 1 \times 2^3$$
$$\overline{.1\ 0\ 0\ 1\ 1\ 0\ 0\ 1\ 1\ 0\ 0\ 1 \quad 2^7}$$

The binary product here has the same digits as in our earlier multiplication of these two numbers except that we have twelve places to the right of the binary point. The powers of 2 are multiplied by adding their exponents. Our final answer is $.100110011001 \times 2^7$, or

$$.1\ 0\ 0\ 1\ 1\ 0\ 0\ 1\ 1\ 0\ 0\ 1$$
$$\times 1\ 0\ 0\ 0\ 0\ 0\ 0\ 0$$
$$\overline{1\ 0\ 0\ 1\ 1\ 0\ 0.1\ 1\ 0\ 0\ 1\ 0\ 0\ 0\ 0\ 0\ 0\ 0}$$

After dropping the insignificant, meaningless 0's to the right of the binary point, the answer takes on the familiar form 1001100.11001.

In the computer, each number has two separate parts:

Binary Digits		Power of 2
1011011	and	10000
11011	and	1000

The machine computes the product of the binary digits, always assuming that the binary point is to the extreme left. It then computes the product of the powers of 2 represented by binary numbers. Finally, it multiplies the two products to locate the binary point.

This type of numerical representation is not new to you. You will recall a similar way in the powers-of-ten method of notation. Both the multiplier and multiplicand can be expressed in the form X.XXX multiplied by some power of 10. For example, 11.375 would be 1.1375×10^1, and 6.75 would be 6.75×10^0. The digit numbers can then be multiplied directly to get 7.678125. The exponential factors can be multiplied by adding their exponents; that is, $10^1 \times 10^0 = 10 (1 + 0) = 10^1$. Thus, the answer would be 7.678125×10^1, or 76.78125. The only difference from binary representation is that it is customary to leave one digit to the left of the decimal point in the decimal number.

Division

In division, three numbers are involved. One number is the result of an arithmetical operation of the other two. Because division can be considered, with restrictions, as the reverse of multiplication, we can learn division by comparing the two arithmetical operations.

In multiplication, the multiplicand and the multiplier are given, and the problem is to find the product. In division, the dividend, the quantity to be divided, and the divisor, the quantity divided into the dividend, are given, and the problem is to find the quotient, the result of a division. Suppose we want to work a multiplication problem backwards; we would use the product as the dividend. However, multiplier implies a meaning that the multiplicand is repeatedly added to itself for as many times as the number in the multiplier. Therefore, in a reverse multiplication, we want to find the number of times the multiplicand must be repeatedly subtracted from the product to get the multiplier. Then, the multiplier must be the quotient, and the multiplicand must be the divisor. This comparison is usually understood in ordinary computation. However, a computer performs all calculations. Lack of distinction results in the use of multipliers as divisors when a computer is instructed to work multiplication backwards, as in checking solutions.

To perform binary division, the divisor must be repeatedly sub-

tracted from the dividend with appropriate shifts to obtain the binary quotient. We make successive subtractions of the divisor from appropriate columns of the dividend.

Examples:

1. Divide 1101001 by 10101

binary

```
                    101    quotient
                 ─────────
divisor 10101) 1101001    dividend
               10101
               ─────
                01010
                00000
                ─────
                10101
                10101
                ─────
                00000    remainder
```

decimal

```
          5
21) 105
    105
    ───
    000
```

2. Divide 11000011 by 1101

binary

```
                    1111   quotient
                 ──────────
divisor 1101) 11000011    dividend
              1101
              ─────
              10110
              1101
              ─────
              10011
              1101
              ─────
               1101
               1101
               ────
               0000    remainder
```

decimal

$$\begin{array}{r} 15 \\ 13\overline{)195} \\ 13 \\ \hline 65 \\ 65 \\ \hline 00 \end{array}$$

The Binary Point in Division. The fixed point method of locating a decimal point in decimal division applies to the binary point in similar operation. Also, we can use the floating-point method.

The floating-point method in division is different from the floating-point in multiplication. In multiplication, disregarding the exponential terms, the binary point always falls to the left of the digits and the point is to the left of the product. The answer to a problem is obtained by multiplying the digits of a floating-point multiplication and the product of the exponential terms.

In division, the divisor and the dividend can be expressed as digits to the right of the binary point multiplied by an appropriate power of 2. Following the division, the binary point will be automatically placed to the left of the digits in the quotient by the computer. This is erroneous because the binary point is actually between the first and the second digit at the left of the quotient. To illustrate this situation, let us solve a division problem with floating-point notation, in the manner of a computer.

Divide 1101101.1 by 1100

With the floating-point method, the binary point is automatically placed to the left of a number. The dividend and the divisor become

$$.11011011 \times 2^7$$

and .1100 × 2^4, respectively. In floating-point computers, the binary points will be dropped automatically. Thus, division of the digits is as follows:

$$\begin{array}{r} 1001001 \\ 1100\overline{)11011011} \\ 1100 \\ \hline 1101 \\ 1100 \\ \hline 1100 \\ 1100 \\ \hline 0 \end{array}$$

At the end of the division, the computer automatically places the binary point at the left and the significant digits of the quotient become .1001001.

The computer then calculates the quotient of the terms in powers of 2 by subtracting their components.

$$2^7 \div 2^4 = 2^{(7-4)} = 2^3 = (1000)_2$$

The answer to our example would be the quotient digits with the binary point at the left times the quotient of the exponential terms.

$$.1001001 \times (2^3)_{10}$$
$$= .1001001 \times 1000$$
$$= 100.1001$$

Now, if we solve the problem with fixed point division, we get

$$
\begin{array}{r}
1001.001 \\
\hline
1100)\,1101101.100 \\
\underline{1100} \\
1101 \\
\underline{1101} \\
1100 \\
\underline{1100} \\
0
\end{array}
$$

The quotient here is true but $(10)_2$ times larger than the one obtained by using the floating-point method. We can shift the binary point in floating-point operation one place to the right so that the answer would be correct. More conveniently, however, we can add 1 to the difference of the exponents in the powers of 2 terms. Hence, in our example the powers will be

$$(7 - 4) + 1 = 3 + 1 = 4$$

Then, the answer by the floating-point method would be

$$.1001001 \times 2^4 = .1001001 \times 10000$$
$$= 1001.001$$

Bits and Words

In binary or coded binary computer, a number is represented by a train or a series of electrical pulses. The individual pulses (or absence of pulses) represent, respectively, the 1 or 0 digits in the binary representation of the number. For example, the pulse train of Fig. 5-1 represents the binary number 1101010 which in decimal notation is 106. Note that the digits are read from right to left. In a similar way the instructions which must be conveyed from place to place are also transmitted in the form of a train of pulses. Actually, then, a waveform representing a number is indistinguishable from a waveform representing an instruction. Since, however, numbers are sent only to the arithmetic portion of the computer and orders only to the control portion, no difficulty arises from this situation.

In a pulse train, as shown in Fig. 5-1, the individual pulses are referred to as "bits," while the entire pulse train is referred to as a "word." Thus, the pulse train representing 11101011 is an eight-bit word. ("Bit" is a contraction of binary digit.)

Figures 5-2A and B are shown as typical pulse trains representing, respectively, the decimal numbers 13 and 10. Pulse trains representing the sum, 23, and the difference, 3, are shown in C and D of the figure.

Here we can see that the reason for the binary member system as the language of digital computers lies in the ease of representing electronically binary words. In computer electronics, the circuit does not have to sense the amount of voltage. The circuit only needs to tell whether a signal is present or not, or in some cases the polarity of the signal. If the decimal system were used, the circuits would not only have to detect the presence of

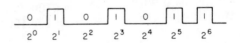

Fig. 5-1 A seven bit word.

a signal but also would have to measure the signal amplitude and to operate according to the amplitude.

Some common examples of physical binary representations are discussed here. A particular location on a punched card either has a hole or not. An electronic switch is either on or off. A transistor is either conducting or cut off. A track on magnetic tape either has a change in magnetization at a given point or does not. The magnetic core is magnetized either in one direction or the other. In each case the device has only two possible stable conditions. These two stable conditions are called "mutually exclusive" since only one condition can exist at a time. The digit value

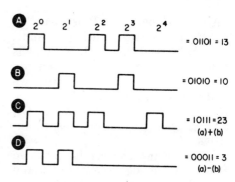

Fig. 5-2. Typical pulse train representations.

"zero" is assigned to one of these conditions and the digit value "one" to the other. The circuits of the digital systems are arranged to act on combinations of the two states according to the rules of binary arithmetic and Boolean Algebra.

5-4 Boolean Algebra

Boolean algebra obtained its name from George Boole, a nineteenth century philosopher, who was the first man to investigate this form of mathematical analysis of logic. The adaptability of this form of algebra to switching circuits found in controllers and computers was first pointed out in 1938. Since that time the increase in the use of and interest in Boolean algebra has followed the rapid development of switching circuits. As a result of these studies of Boolean algebra, we found that the most complex switching circuits could be built or implemented by using combinations of a few simple basic circuits called logic blocks. The study of Boolean algebra as applied to digital computers is the study of these circuits and the rules for combining them.

Boolean algebra is a very simple algebra. It has only two different quantities or values, 0 and 1. When used in switching circuits, "0" indicates an open circuit and "1" indicates a closed circuit. However, algebraic operations in Boolean Algebra bear little resemblance to the algebraic operations in ordinary algebra, although in some instances the rules for performing these operations are the same.

Basic Operations

In Boolean algebra, the addition sign $(+)$ is assigned the meaning "OR," and the multiplication sign $(\times)$ is assigned the meaning

"AND." Thus, A + B is read "A OR B" and is called the logical sum; A × B is read "A AND B" and is called the logical product. Remembering that the two quantities we will deal with are 0 and 1, let's see the results from performing OR and AND operations on these quantities.

Logical Sum. The results obtained from various logical sums of 0 and 1 are:

$$0 + 0 = 0$$
$$0 + 1 = 1$$
$$1 + 1 = 1$$

These equations are read as follows: "zero OR zero equals zero"; "zero OR one equals one"; and "one OR one equals one."

The above equations are the only three possible numerical operations using the logical sum. You might feel the urge to arrive at a sum of "2" for the last operation. If you use the terminology, "1 OR 1 equals 1" for expressions of this type, you will soon overcome this difficulty.

The simple circuit in Fig. 5-3 is known as an OR circuit. The two inputs and the output are so related that the output is present when either of the inputs is present or when both inputs are present. Switches A and B are the inputs and lamp C is the output. If either switch A or switch B is closed or if both switches are closed, the lamp is on; but if both switches are open, the lamp is off. The relation between the inputs and the output can be expressed as A + B = C.

For either switch, 1 repreesnts the closed condition and 0 represents the open condition. Also, for the lamp, 1 represents the on condition and 0 represents the off condition. If A is closed and B is open, C is on. Symbolically, if A = 1 and B = 0, then C = 1. The equation A + B = C becomes 1 + 0 = 1. If A and B are both closed, the lamp is again on; A + B = C becomes 1 + 1 = 1. Notice that closing both switches does not cause the lamp to light any brighter than with only one switch closed. Hence, when A and B are both equal 1, the net result is the same as when either is equal 1; that is, C is equal 1. If A and B are both open, the lamp is off; A + B = C becomes 0 + 0 = 0.

Logical Product. The results obttained from various logical products of 0 and 1 are:

$$0 \times 0 = 0$$
$$0 \times 1 = 0$$
$$1 \times 1 = 1$$

These equations are read "zero AND zero equals zero"; "zero AND one equals zero"; and "one AND one equals one." These expressions are also called the "AND" function.

The equations just shown are the only three possible numerical operations involving the logical product. The values obtained from the logical product are similar to those obtained through familiar mathematical operations. Therefore, you should not experience any difficulty

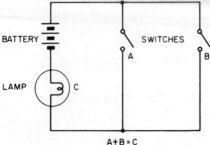

BATTERY

LAMP

SWITCHES

A

B

C

A+B=C

Fig. 5-3. Basic OR Circuit.

in performing this particular Boolean operation.

A switching circuit whose output can be described as the logical product of its inputs is shown in Fig. 5-4. As you might expect, it is called an AND circuit. The two inputs and the output are so related that the output is present only when both

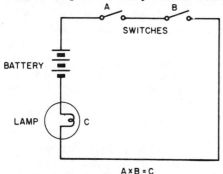

$$A \times B = C$$

Fig. 5-4. Basic AND circuit.

inputs are present at the same time. If both switches A and B are closed, lamp C is on; otherwise C is off. This relation between inputs and output can be expressed accurately by the equation $A \times B = C$, or simply $AB = C$.

With both switches closed, lamp C is on; $A = 1$, $B = 1$, and $C = 1$. The equation $AB = C$ then becomes $1 \times 1 = 1$. If A is closed and B is open, C is off. Since $A = 1$, $B = 0$ and $C = 0$, the equation $A \times B = C$ becomes $1 \times 0 = 0$. If both A and B are open, C is off; and $A \times B = C$ becomes $0 \times 0 = 0$.

Logical Complement. Another function that is important in Boolean Algebra is the complement, or NOT function, denoted by the symbol A' or $\overline{A}$. This symbol is read "NOT A" to denote the opposite of A. If A has the value 0, $\overline{A}$ must be equal 1 since that is the only other value it can have.

A switching circuit which accomplishes the "NOT" operation is shown in Fig. 5-5A. A two-position switch is the input and lamp C is the output. In Fig. 5-5A, the lamp is out when the switch is set at position A. If the switch is set at $\overline{A}$, the lamp is on. Since A. is equivalent to 0, $\overline{A}$ is 1.

In Fig. 5-5B, the input to the switch is connected to A. This reverses the value of A and $\overline{A}$, making A equal to 1 and $\overline{A}$ equal to 0.

If we perform the operations of the logical sum and logical product

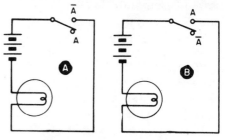

Fig. 5-5. Basic NOT circuit.

using the NOT function, we find that the following relationships are true whether A is 1 or 0.

$$A + \overline{A} = 1$$
$$A \times \overline{A} = 0$$
$$(\overline{\overline{A}}) = \overline{\overline{A}} = A,$$

where $(\overline{\overline{A}})$ reads "NOT the value NOT A" and $\overline{\overline{A}}$ reads "NOT NOT the value A."

An additional relationship also holds. If $A = B$, then $\overline{A} = \overline{B}$.

The three logical operations — sum, product, and complement — are the basic rules of Boolean algebra. However, some additional information must be known about the combination of Boolean symbols before algebraic operations can be successfully performed.

Laws of Combination

As in ordinary algebra, there are fundamental equations of operation for Boolean algebra. These fundamental equations are called the laws of combination. Most of the laws are valid for both Boolean and ordinary algebra, but a few are peculiar to Boolean algebra only. The laws are:

Laws of Tautology:

$$A + A = A$$
$$A \times A = A$$

Laws of Commutation:

$$A + B = B + A$$
$$A \times B = B \times A$$

Laws of Association:

$$(A + B) + C = A + (B + C)$$
$$= A + B + C$$
$$(A \times B) \times C = A \times (B \times C)$$
$$= A \times B \times C$$

Laws of Distribution:

$$A \times (B + C) = (A \times B) + (A \times C)$$
$$(A + B) \times (A + C) = A + (B \times C)$$

Laws of Dualization: (also known as De Morgan's theorem or inversion formulas)

$$\overline{A \times B} = \overline{A} + \overline{B}$$
$$\overline{A \times B} = \overline{A} + \overline{B}$$

Laws of Absorption:

$$A + (A \times B) = A$$
$$A \times (A + B) = A$$

There is an additional set of relations which you will find quite useful in Boolean algebra. Although the validity of these relations is obvious, their application to Boolean operations frequently is not. For this reason, you should be sure to examine them carefully.

$$A + 1 = 1$$
$$A + 0 = A$$
$$A \times 1 = A$$
$$A \times 0 = 0$$

The laws of tautology, commutation, association, absorption, and the first law of distribution should be easily acceptable with your knowledge of the logical operations of Boolean algebra and your familiarity with ordinary algebra. If there is any doubt in your mind, try substituting 1's and 0's for the letter symbols and solve both sides of the equation. You will see that the equation balances ($1 = 1$, or $0 = 0$). You may also draw simple switching circuits to prove these laws.

Second Law of Distribution. The second law of distribution can also be proved valid by substitution. However, the algebraic relation between the left and right sides of the equation is not immediately obvious, so we will perform an algebraic transformation to show that it is valid. The equation is

$$(A + B) \times (A + C) = A + (B \times C)$$

As in ordinary algebra, we can operate the two expressions in parenthesis on the left to get

$$A \times (A + C) + B \times (A + C)$$
$$= A + (B \times C)$$

Expanding the left-hand term, we get

$$A \times A + A \times C + A \times B + B \times C$$
$$= A + (B \times C).$$

From our second law of tautology, we see that $A \times A = A$. Thus, our equation becomes

$$A + A \times B + A \times C + B \times C$$
$$= A + (B \times C).$$

From the first law of distribution,

$$A \times (1 + B + C) + B \times C$$
$$= A + (B \times C).$$

Making use of the relation $A + 1 = 1$, $(1 + B$ in this case), we get

$$A \times (1 + C) + B \times C$$
$$= A + (B \times C).$$

Again using the relation $A + 1 = 1$, $(1 + C$ in this case) we arrive at

$$A \times 1 + B \times C = A + (B \times C).$$

Because $A \times 1 = A$, then

$$A + B \times C = A + (B \times C).$$

Thus, the second law of distribution can be verified algebraically by substitution.

To further clarify this algebraic operation, we will examine two simple switching networks. The network in Fig. 5-6A duplicates the logical function of the left side of equation $(A + B) \times (A + C) = A + (B \times C)$ The network in Fig. 5-6B duplicates the function of the right side. When $A = 1$, $B = 0$, and $C = 0$, both switches A are closed in Fig. 5-6A and switches B and C are open. This produces an output from the network. The same switch conditions in Fig. 5-6B will also produce an output, so, for the given values of A, B, and C, the networks function identically.

For the values $A = 0$, $B = 1$ and $C = 1$, switches B and C are closed in both networks, producing an output from each. Here again the function of the two networks is the same.

When all three switches are closed, an output is again produced from both networks. This corresponds with the values $A = 1$, $B = 1$,

and $C = 1$. Similarly, combinations $A = 1$, $B = 1$, $C = 0$, and $A = 1$, $B = 0$, $C = 1$ will also produce outputs from both networks.

The five switch combinations we have considered are the only combinations which will produce an output from either circuit. You can prove this to yourself by checking the networks with the three remaining possible switch combinations, 6 through 8, given in Table 5-7. This type of table is commonly

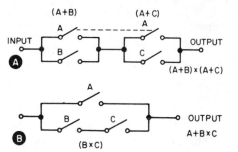

Fig. 5-6. Switching networks for (A + B) × (A + C), A; and A + B × C, B.

known as a "truth table" because the truth value of any combination of the involved variables A, B, and C can be determined from it. Truth tables are frequently used as a type of logical link between a Boolean expression and its corresponding switching network.

First Law of Dualization. In examining the first law of dualization, $\overline{A \times B} = \overline{A} + \overline{B}$, you must remember that $\overline{AB}$ or $\overline{A \times B}$ is "NOT (A AND B)" which means that the value of "A AND B" should be found *before* complementing. For example, if $A = 1$ and $B = 0$, the law becomes

TABLE 5-7

	A	B	C	A + B × C	(A + B) × (A + C)
1	1	0	0	1	1
2	0	1	1	1	1
3	1	1	1	1	1
4	1	1	0	1	1
5	1	0	1	1	1
6	0	1	0	0	0
7	0	0	1	0	0
8	0	0	0	0	0

$$\overline{1 \times 0} = \overline{1} + \overline{0}.$$

The logic product on the left is simply 0. Thus, our equation takes the form:

$$\overline{0} = \overline{1} + \overline{0},$$

or

$$1 = 0 + 1.$$

This relation is, of course, valid.

The switching network which corresponds with the right side of the equation is shown in Fig. 5-7. However, we cannot duplicate the left side of the equation with a switching network, although electronic circuits can overcome this difficulty. We can see the usefulness of Boolean algebra in getting alternative solutions of a particular switching network to work out other possible practical circuits. Undoubtedly, you need a sound knowledge of Boolean algebra to do the transformation.

As an exercise, you might try setting up a truth table for A, B, $\overline{A}$, $\overline{B}$, $\overline{A} + \overline{B}$, and $\overline{AB}$ to describe the operation of the two networks. Keep in mind that when the switches are in the positions shown, A = 1 and B = 1, while $\overline{A} = 0$, $\overline{B} = 0$, and $\overline{AB}$ = 0.

Second Law of Dualization. The second law of dualization may be stated in this way: "(NOT A AND NOT B) equals NOT (A OR B)." This indicates that the complement of A AND the complement of B equals the complement of A OR B. As in the first law of dualization, the value of A OR B must be found prior to complementing, because a bar across the top of the entire expression means that inversion takes place after solving the quantity. To clarify this we can substitute the truth values of 1 and 0 into the equation.

For A = 1 and B = 1:

$$\overline{1} \times \overline{1} = \overline{1 + 1}.$$

The left side becomes 0 × 0, or 0, and the right side becomes $\overline{1}$ since

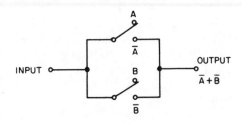

Fig. 5-7. Switching network for $\overline{A} + \overline{B}$.

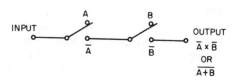

Fig. 5-8. Switching network for $\overline{A} \times \overline{B}$ and $\overline{A + B}$.

$1 + 1 = 1$. This reduces our equation to

$$0 = \overline{1}, \text{or } 0 = 0.$$

$$A + B.$$

Similarly, for $A = 0$ and $B = 0$,

$$\overline{0} \times \overline{0} = \overline{0 + 0}.$$

This becomes

$$1 \times 1 = \overline{0} \text{ or } 1 = 1.$$

For the case $A = 1$ and $B = 0$

$$\overline{1} \times \overline{0} = \overline{1 + 0}$$

$$0 \times 1 = \overline{1 + 0}$$

$$0 = \overline{1 + 0}.$$

We know that $1 + 0 = 1$ so we can make this substitution in our equation.

$$0 = \overline{1}, \text{or } 0 = 0.$$

The switching network which produces both the Boolean functions $\overline{A} \times \overline{B}$ and $\overline{A + B}$ is shown in Fig. 5-8. Table 5-8 is the corresponding truth table for the network and the equation.

For our purposes, further manipulation of Boolean expressions is unnecessary. If you understand the logical operations OR, AND, and NOT, and laws of combination, you can manipulate the logical functions of the circuits used in digital computers.

TABLE 5-8

A	B	$\overline{A}$	$\overline{B}$	$\overline{A} \times \overline{B}$	$\overline{A + B}$
1	1	0	0	0	0
1	0	0	1	0	0
0	1	1	0	0	0
0	0	1	1	1	1

5-5. Logical Circuits

Each of the three logical operations, sum, product, and complement, is performed electronically in a digital computer. The circuits that perform these operations are referred to as logical circuits because each provides a relationship between the inputs and the output which corresponds with one of the Boolean operations. The involved binary 1's and 0's can be represented by pulses of different amplitudes or polarities, or by the presence or absence of pulses. Fre-

quently, a level, such as the output of a flip-flop is also used to represent a binary digit.

Diode and vacuum tube circuits with outputs which depend upon the presence or absence of the various inputs are all of the coincidence type. A gate input and a signal input is necessary simultaneously to produce an output. The gate input effectively opens the gate to allow the signal to pass through. This type of operation is very much like the logical AND function since the gate input and the signal input are necessary to produce an output. Hence, gates of this type are called AND gates.

A circuit which produces an output when one or more of the inputs are applied is called an OR gate in keeping with logical terminology. Similarly, a circuit which inverts the input is called a NOT circuit, or simply an inverter.

There are four other common computer circuits that perform very useful logical operations. These are the inhibitor circuit, called the "INHIBIT gate," the "EXCLUSIVELY OR gate," the "NOR gate," and the "Sheffer Stroke circuit," popularly called the "STROKE gate."

The seven basic logic circuits can be combined to perform all the Boolean operations you studied earlier and, through these operations, to solve practically any type of mathematical problem. When the problem is complex, a computer with a large number of individual logic circuits may be necessary. Although the schematic diagram of such a system is correspondingly large, it simply consists of many of the basic circuit diagrams with the proper connections between them. This fact allows digital computer circuit diagrams to be simplified through the use of systems of logic symbols, each representing a particular type of logic circuit. There is one symbol for an AND gate, another for a NOT circuit, and so on. By replacing each logic circuit in the diagram with its corresponding logic symbol, both the size and the complexity of the diagram can be reduced considerably. The resultant drawing is referred to, quite

appropriately, as a "logic diagram." Logic diagrams are so useful that computer engineers generally use them instead of schematic diagrams in the design of new computing systems.

As you examine the following logic circuits, you will find illustrations of some of the more popular logic symbols used to represent them. Throughout this chapter we will use one particular symbol for each logic circuit. The symbols we have chosen will be identified in the groups of popular symbols. Our choice was made on the basis of clarity and current usage in commercial and military computer and digital control system diagrams, and in the latest editions of technical manuals and reference texts. We feel that familiarity with the logical symbols we have chosen will best familiarize you with the interpretation and use of logic diagrams in general. However, you should examine the other logic symbols carefully because you can expect to encounter several entirely different symbol systems in your work with modern digital systems.

Basic Circuits

The circuits which produced the functions OR, AND, and NOT may be considered basic circuits for two reasons. First, their logical functions are the most elementary found in Boolean algebra; and second, proper combinations of these circuits will produce any of the other logical functions, as you will see later on. This may be already evident to you if you consider that the only three operations employed in any of the Boolean equations you have seen are OR, AND, and NOT. A great many of the modern digital computers use OR-AND-NOT combinations to form their internal circuitry. Mathematical and control systems composed of this type of logic circuitry have proved both versatile and dependable in all types of digital operations. Familiarity with the electrical operation and logical function of circuits of this type is one of the keys used to analyze the operation of all digital computers and control systems.

Let's begin our study of logical circuits with a look at the simplest of the logical gate circuits, the OR gate.

OR Gate. The OR gate is a logic circuit which has an output when any one or any combination of its inputs is present, but no output when all of its inputs are absent. The gate acts as a buffer or mixing circuit between a number of pulse sources with the same polarity and a common load. The interaction of the pulse sources on each other is kept at a minimum by the gate.

A solid state diode OR gate with three inputs is shown in Fig. 5-9A. This particular gate is called a positive OR gate because only positive pulses will pass through it to satisfy the OR relationship. In the static condition the output is held at a negative level by a portion of bias voltage -V dropped across R_4. The current which causes the voltage drop flows through R_4 into each of the diode branches. The current path in the branch containing CR_1 is typical of all three branches, so we will examine that branch only.

After leaving R_4, current flows through CR_1, R_1, and low-impedance source A to ground. The small

forward resistance of CR_1 and the negligible internal impedance of the pulse source may be disregarded. The branch then becomes part of a voltage divider composed of R_1 and R_4. The other two branches are electrically the same as input branch A and in parallel with it, so that the entire gate may

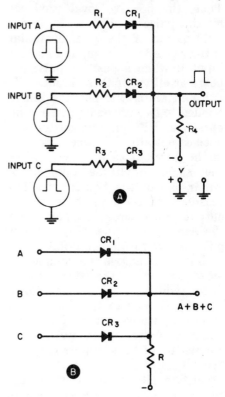

Fig. 5-9. Diode OR gate.

be thought of as a simple unidirectional voltage divider composed of R_1, R_2, and R_3 in parallel, and R_4 in series with them. The parallel resistance of R_1, R_2, and R_3 is small compared with that of R_4, so the portion of voltage -V which appears across the network, and thus at the output, is correspondingly small.

When a positive pulse is applied to input A, current in that branch increases sharply. The voltage dropped across R_4 also increases to place the junction of CR_1 and R_4 positive with respect to ground. This places a reverse bias on diodes CR_2 and CR_3, stopping current through input branches B and C. Thus, the positive level produced by the pulse applied to R_1 is the total output of the gate. A similar output appears for input B or for input C when a positive pulse appears at either of these inputs.

Equal amplitude positive pulses applied to two of the inputs, say inputs A and B simultaneously, produce essentially the same output as in the previous case for a pulse of the same amplitude applied to either one of the two inputs. The reason that the amplitude of the output pulse across R_4 has about the same amplitude of the input pulse is due to the negligibly small voltage drop across the conducting diode and series resistor. Hence, little additional current flows through R_4 due to the application of the additional pulse. The same situation exists when pulses are applied to all three inputs simultaneously.

Customarily, diode gates are represented without the pulse sources and without the input resistors, as shown in Fig. 5-9B. Zero impedance between each input and ground is assumed in this case. Furthermore, a positive input pulse is said to "pass through the input diode," since it instantaneously appears at the output when applied to an input. For example, "positive input A passes through CR_1" would indicate that the pulse at input A

produces a simultaneous output. The Boolean OR relation $A + B + C$ describes the output of the gate.

Diode OR gates are the most common type found in modern digital systems. Their low cost, small size, stability, and reliability naturally make them the most desirable choice. One disadvantage with solid state diode OR gates is that a reverse biased diode passes a small reverse current. With a large number of inputs, when one input is used, other input branches form a parallel circuit to shunt the output resistor. The output pulse reduces amplitude. Consequently, an OR gate of this type seldom has more than five inputs. If more inputs are necessary, several OR gates are tied together with their output connected to the inputs of another OR gate to improve reliability. However, both vacuum tube and transistor OR gates have been used successfully, although their comparatively high cost has almost completely eliminated them from present competition. A typical vacuum tube OR gate with two inputs is shown in Fig. 5-10A. With a circuit of this type, a negative pulse represents a binary 1.

Thus, the circuit is generally referred to as a "negative OR gate." The tube is used as a cathode follower to prevent the inversion of the negative input pulses which would occur if the output were taken from the plate circuit. The current in the tube used here can be cut off with a negative pulse on either of the active grids.

In the static condition, both grids are biased so that the tube is conducting. However, conduction is limited to the point where a nega-

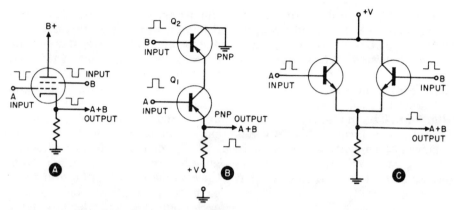

Fig. 5-10. Typical transistor and vacuum tube OR gates.

tive pulse on either grid will cut the tube off completely. Thus, a negative pulse on either grid or both grids produces a negative output pulse.

The positive OR gate in Fig. 5-10B uses two normally-conducting PNP transistors in series, with Q_1 functioning as an "emitter follower". (This is a term commonly applied to the transistor equivalent of a cathode follower.) Remember that for conduction the base of a PNP transistor must be negative with respect to the emitter. A positive pulse on the base of either or both transistors violates this condition by driving the base relatively positive. Conduction through the transistors stops and a positive pulse appears at the output.

Fig. 5-10C shows a positive OR gate made up of two NPN transistors as emitter followers in parallel. The transistors are normally cut off, but a positive pulse on the base of either one drives it into conduction and produces a positive pulse output.

The logic symbols most commonly used to represent the OR gate are shown in Fig. 5-11. Sym-bols A and B are the most popular. We will use symbol A throughout this chapter to symbolize an OR gate.

AND Gate. The AND gate is a logic circuit which has an output when all its inputs are present but no output when one or more of its inputs are missing. If the input pulses to an AND gate begin at the same time but do not have the same duration, the output pulse will be only as long as the shortest input pulse.

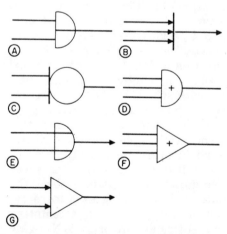

Fig. 5-11. Logic symbols for the OR gate.

Fig. 5-12 is the diagram of a 2-input diode AND gate which operates on positive pulse inputs. The name "positive AND gate" is, therefore, applied to this type of gate. Notice the similarity between this gate and the diode OR gate in Fig. 5-9B. The diodes have been reversed and a positive bias +V has replaced the negative bias used in the OR gate. You will find, if you examine the OR gate closely, that

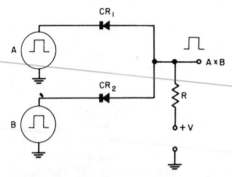

Fig. 5-12. Diode positive AND gate.

when negative pulses are applied to it instead of positive pulses, the OR gate works exactly the same as the positive AND gate in Fig. 5-12. That is, a negative diode OR gate and a positive diode AND gate are exactly the same circuit. The logical function which the circuit performs is determined by the input pulse polarity which is chosen to represent a binary 1. Similarly, a positive diode OR gate and a negative diode AND gate are also exactly alike in every respect. In view of the ability of one circuit to serve two duties, we must first check the pulse polarity being used to represent a binary 1, before attempting to identify an OR or an AND gate in a digital system. Furthermore,

the polarity chosen by the system designer sometimes changes from one section of the system to another. An arrangement of this type is often used, especially in special purpose computers and in digital control systems, to simplify design and to reduce the number of necessary components. While the pulse polarity changes do not alter the general operation of the system, they do necessitate a careful check of pulse polarity at the inputs to each logical circuit before determining the exact function of the circuit.

The operation of the AND gate in Fig. 5-12 can be described as follows. In the static condition, current flows in both of the input branches of the AND gate from ground through the low impedance input circuits to the load R. The two parallel branches together with their corresponding input circuits form low impedance paths to place the output at some slightly positive level above ground.

In actual practice, the input pulses are usually a little less positive than bias voltage +V. To simplify our discussion we will consider the inputs as equal to the bias voltage. When input A is applied to the gate, the cathode of CR_1 is driven positive with respect to ground. Combined with the bias voltage, the net voltage across CR_1 drops to zero, so current through branch A stops. This effectively opens the circuit through branch A. However, since the resistance of CR_1 and CR_2 is small compared to the resistance of R, the total resistance of the circuit changes very little. Thus, the current through R and the voltage drop across it remain essentially unchanged, so the gate does not have an output.

When input pulses A and B are applied to the gate simultaneously, currents through branches A and B are cut off because of the zero bias placed on the diodes. Hence, current through R also stops, and the output level rises to the value of +V. A positive input pulse on each of the inputs at the same time has thus produced a positive output pulse from the gate.

The action of the AND gate indicates that the input pulses must be at least as large as the bias voltage to reproduce an output that resembles the input pulses.

If the input pulses exceed +V, the output cannot rise above +V, due to isolation of reverse biased diodes. However if one input is less than +V, the output pulse will have the magnitude of the smallest input.

A transistorized positive AND gate is shown in Fig. 5-13. Three NPN transistors are used in series with their bases normally negative with respect to their emitters. This holds all three transistors beyond cut off; there is no current through the circuit and the output is at ground through resistor R. A positive input pulse on the base of one of the transistors places a forward bias on its emitter-base junction but, unless this condition also exists on both of the other two transistors, the static condition will remain. A positive pulse input to all three transistors simultaneously places the correct bias on each of them and a current appears through R and the three transistors in series. The voltage drop across R raises the output from ground to +V,

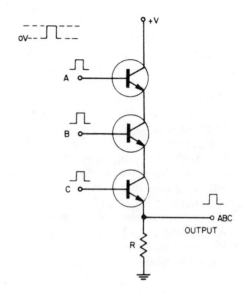

Fig. 5-13. Transistorized positive AND gate.

forming a positive pulse. Thus, coincident positive inputs A AND B AND C produce a positive output from the AND gate.

A vacuum tube AND gate which produces a negative-going output when negative inputs A, B, and C are present is illustrated in Fig. 5-14. The triodes are normally conducting, so the output level is essentially at B+. A negative input

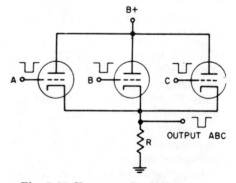

Fig. 5-14. Vacuum tube AND gate.

to two of the triodes simultaneously will cut them off, but the third will continue to conduct, holding the output at B+. Three simultaneous inputs to the gate will cut off all three tubes. A negative-going pulse will then appear as the output drops to ground.

By now, you can see that the duration of the input pulses has an effect on the output. As a rule, the output pulse lasts only as long as the shortest input pulse.

The logical symbols used for the AND gate are shown in Fig. 5-15. We will use the most widely accepted symbol, Fig. 5-15A.

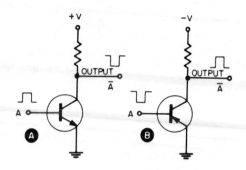

Fig. 5-16. Basic transistorized NOT or inverter circuits.

If a negative pulse is used to represent a binary 1, a PNP transistor can be used as a logical inverter. This arrangement is illustrated in Fig. 5-16B. Here a negative input A produces a positive output $\overline{A}$.

You are thoroughly familiar with the operation of a vacuum tube as an inverter. A negative pulse on the control grid of a normally conducting tube decreases tube current. This causes the potential at the plate to rise, producing a positive pulse at the output while a positive pulse on the grid increases tube current causing the plate potential to drop and to produce a negative pulse at the output.

Some of the logical symbols used to represent a NOT or inverter circuit are shown in Fig. 5-17. The symbol which we will use is Fig. 5-17A.

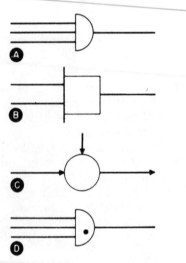

Fig. 5-15. Logic symbols for the And gate.

NOT Circuit. Most NOT circuits are simply inverter amplifiers. In transistor circuitry, the common emitter configuration with the output taken from the collector is the most popular. When a positive pulse represents a binary 1, and an NPN transistor is used as shown in Fig. 5-16A, the positive input A produces a negative output $\overline{A}$.

Combination Circuits

Any Boolean operation can be performed with the proper combination of the basic OR, AND and NOT circuits. It is necessary, then, to use only these three basic circuits in assembling any digital system. However, two other Boolean functions are found almost as fre-

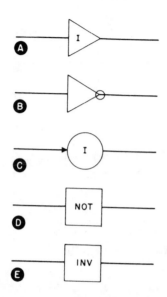

Fig. 5-17. Logic symbols for the NOT or inverter circuit.

quently among OR, AND, and NOT circuits as basic functions themselves. These functions are sometimes taken as basic in the assembly of digital systems. Sometimes, one of these functions can be implemented with fewer electrical components directly than with combinations of basic circuits. Thus, it is desirable to represent the function with its own logical symbol and to employ the simplified circuitry rather than the combined circuits whenever possible. The circuit which fills this description is the INHIBIT gate, or Anticoincidence gate, or INHIBITOR circuit.

The second combination circuit which we will consider is the EXCLUSIVELY OR gate which does not have any simplified arrangements in circuitry. Thus, a special symbol is not entirely appropriate. The gate is always represented by some proper combination of OR,

AND, and NOT symbols.

We will now see how the logical functions of these two gates can be produced with combined OR, AND, and NOT circuits. We will also examine a simplified circuit which produces the Inhibit function.

INHIBIT Gate. The Inhibit function can be represented algebraically by $\overline{A}B$ (read "A AND NOT B"). When input A is applied to an INHIBIT gate in the absence of input B, a gate output is produced. However, if input B is also applied, no output appears at the gate. Input B is said to "inhibit" the gate output, so B is called the inhibit input. The significance of this terminology becomes more apparent in the case of a multiple-input INHIBIT gate. Such a gate could have the output $ABC\overline{D}$. Here, the inhibit input is D whose presence inhibits the gate to prevent an output even though inputs A, B, and C may be present.

Fig. 5-18A is the logic diagram of an INHIBIT gate composed of a NOT circuit and an AND gate. With inputs A and B both present, A and B are applied to the AND gate, and no output appears. However, when A and B are applied, A and $\overline{\overline{B}}$ (read "NOT NOT B") appear at the respective AND gate inputs. Input $\overline{\overline{B}}$ is the same as B, due to double inversion of B, so an output is produced.

The transistor circuit which corresponds with the INHIBIT gate of Fig. 5-18A is illustrated in Fig. 5-18B. A vacuum tube circuit with the same function is shown in Fig. 5-18C.

Fig. 5-19 is an Inhibit circuit which uses only two transistors.

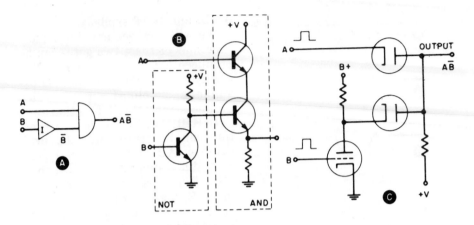

Fig. 5-18. Inhibit gates composed of basic circuits.

Without input B to Q_2, the PNP transistor will conduct when the proper positive potential is applied to its emitter. A positive input A to the base of Q_1 places the proper operating bias on NPN transistor Q_1. This makes the emitter of Q_2 positive with respect to its base so both transistors conduct and the output swings positive. Thus, the input combination AB produces a

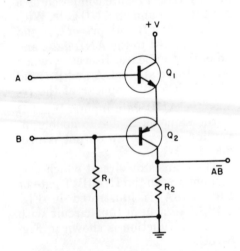

Fig. 5-19. Simplified two-transistor Inhibit gate.

gate output. If a positive input is applied to Q_2, the base becomes positive with respect to the emitter and the PNP transistor remains cut off. The output in this case is zero.

This circuit in Fig. 5-19 is not composed of a NOT circuit and an AND gate. Instead, it is a basic circuit which performs the Inhibit function. Circuits of this type, and "NOT-AND" circuits in general, are commonly represented by one of the logical symbols in Fig. 5-20. We will use the symbol in Fig. 5-20A to represent INHIBIT gate.

EXCLUSIVELY OR gate. The second of our two combination gates is the EXCLUSIVELY OR gate. Its function can be stated as "A OR ELSE B". If either A or B is present, there is an output; but if neither A nor B is present, or if both A and B are present, there is no output. Algebraically, the function can be written $A\overline{B} + B\overline{A}$ (read "A AND NOT B, OR B AND NOT A.") You can see immediately that $A\overline{B}$ and $B\overline{A}$ are functions of IN-HIBIT gates. An EXCLUSIVELY

OR gate is, then, two Inhibit gates, whose outputs are connected by an OR gate, as illustrated in Fig. 5-21A.

By manipulating the relationship $A\overline{B} + B\overline{A}$ according to the laws of Boolean algebra, we can find two alternative ways of stating the expression. We can implement each alternate expression with corresponding circuits.

To obtain the first alternative, let us examine the second law of distribution, (restated here in different letters to avoid confusion).

$$p + qr = (p + q)(p = r) \qquad (1)$$

Next, we will let $p = A\overline{B}$, $q = B$, and $r = \overline{A}$. After substituting these equalities into equation (1), we have

$$(A\overline{B} + B)(A\overline{B} + \overline{A}) \qquad (2)$$

The right hand side of Eq. 2 can be treated separately. Obviously, each expression in parenthesis is identical with the left hand side of Eq. 1. Therefore, we rearrange the first expression in parenthesis of Eq. 2 and apply the principles of Eq. 1 to get

$$A\overline{B} + B = B + A\overline{B} =$$
$$(B + A)(B + \overline{B}) \qquad (3)$$

A similar operation on the second expression in parenthesis gives us

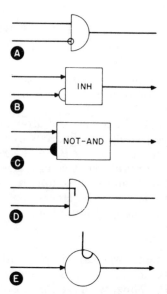

Fig. 5-20. Logic symbols for the Inhibit gate.

$$\overline{A} + A\overline{B} = (\overline{A} + A)(\overline{A} + \overline{B}) \qquad (4)$$

Substituting Eqs. 3 and 4 into their proper parenthesis in Eq. 2, we get

$$A\overline{B} + B\overline{A} =$$
$$[(B + A)(B + \overline{B})] \times$$
$$[(\overline{A} + A)(\overline{A} + \overline{B})] \qquad (5)$$

Observe that $(B + \overline{B})$ and $(A + \overline{A})$ are both equal to 1 from the relations given in the discussion on the logical complement. We can simplify Eq. 5 to

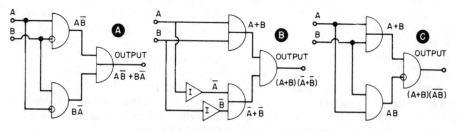

Fig. 5-21. The Exclusively OR circuit.

$$A\overline{B} + B\overline{A} =$$

$$[(B + A)\ (1)]\ [(1)\ (\overline{A} + \overline{B})] =$$

$$(B + A)\ (\overline{A} + \overline{B}) \qquad (6)$$

The logic diagram for the right han side of Eq. 6 is shown in Fig. 5-21B.

To obtain the second alternative, we can apply the first law of dualization, $\overline{A} + \overline{B} = \overline{AB}$, to the result of the first alternative of $A\overline{B} + B\overline{A}$. In Eq. 6 one expression in parenthesis is $(\overline{A} + \overline{B})$. Hence, substitution of the first law yields

$$A\overline{B} + B\overline{A} = (B + A)\ (\overline{AB}) \qquad (7)$$

Again, we can implement the right side directly, as shown in Fig. 5-21C. Thus, we have three Boolean expressions for the EXCLUSIVELY OR gate and three ways to implement the gate with OR-AND-NOT logic circuitry. To show the actual circuitry for any of these EXCLUSIVELY OR combinations is unnecessary since you have already seen the individual circuits for the OR, AND, NOT, and IN-HIBIT components.

You should note that the EX-CLUSIVELY OR circuit does not have an output unless $A \equiv B$, (read "A identically equals B," or "if and only if A equals B.") This restriction means that A and B must occur at the same time and that they have the same magnitude. Thus, this circuit may be used to test for the equality between two binary words. This property is used advantageously to check or monitor the operation of digital computers. For example, a digital computer may be constructed to have two identical digital systems which operate side by side on the same problem. Cor-responding points in the two computers are coupled to the two inputs of an EXCLUSIVELY OR circuit. If the words at these positions are not identical, an output is obtained to provide an error signal.

Primitive Circuits

The title "primitive" is given to each of two logical circuits—the NOR gate and the Sheffer Stroke circuit. The reason for being primitive lies in the adaptability of these two gates to produce any possible Boolean relationship. Using only NOR gates, for example, AND, NOT, INHIBIT and EXCLUSIVE-LY OR functions can be produced to name only a few. In addition, the flip-flop and the binary counter functions can also be produced. The same is true for combinations of Sheffer Stroke circuits, sometimes called STROKE gates for short.

Most popular circuit configurations used for these two gates are very similar. As a result of circuit similarity, many books and publications do not make a clear distinction between the two gates. However, a definite Boolean difference exists between them, as we will see later.

The titles applied to the two gates frequently differ from one technical publication to another. We will try to clear up this difference in terminology so that you will be able to recognize the gates by the several names associated with them. The real key is, of course, to recognize a logic circuit by its Boolean function rather than by its title. You should concentrate on this point when you study the two primitive circuits.

The NOR and STROKE gates in popular use employ transistor circuitry. However, only one transistor per gate is used even with multiple inputs to keep the number of active elements in a complete system at a minimum. This increases reliability because fewer parts can cause trouble than in an OR-AND-NOT system. In addition, every gate has gain. This eliminates the undesirable pulse attenuation often present in diode gating systems and the accompanying necessity for intermediate stages of amplification between adjoining logic circuits. Also, the transistor in each gate is either completely cut off (logic 0) or fully saturated (logic 1), so the gate is almost completely insensitive to ambient noise voltages.

Perhaps the biggest advantage of a system which uses primitive circuits is the economy of spare parts. This feature is based on the probability theory which, for our purposes, implies that the larger the number of operational circuits of a particular type, the smaller is the percentage of necessary spares.

For example, consider a system which uses 100 OR gates, 150 AND gates, and 200 NOT circuits. Twenty spare OR gates, 24 AND gates, and 28 NOT circuits are required. The OR spares represent 20% of the operational gates of that type, the AND spares 16%, and the NOT circuits 14%, for a total of 72 spares, or 16% of the 450 operational circuits. The percentage of necessary spares for an equivalent system with the same number of NOR gates may be only 10%, or 45 spares. This represents a saving of 27 spare logic circuits.

Coupled with the generally lower cost per module, a system using primitive circuits can, therefore, be relatively economical to assemble and to maintain.

Unfortunately, primitive circuits are not usually used in general-purpose digital computing systems. One of the primary reasons is the rather large number of individual circuits necessary to implement the types of functions which a general-purpose computer must perform. As a side effect, the size of the computer is also undesirably increased when primitive circuits are used.

However, in special-purpose digital computers and especially in digital control systems, the NOR and STROKE circuits are enjoying wider and wider application. You can expect to see primitive logical circuits used in an increasing number of applications as computer and digital control technology advances. We will consider here the basic concepts of "NOR logic" and "Sheffer Stroke logic" to prepare you for later contact with these logical systems in technical journals or in actual use.

NOR Gate. A NOR gate is a logical circuit which produces an output when none of its inputs are present. For a 3-input NOR gate, there is an output when neither A, nor B, nor C is present. This relation gives rise to the title "NEITHER-NOR," which is sometimes used to identify the gate. Another name for this circuit is the Pierce gate. One or more inputs close the gate and remove the output.

The logical operation of the NOR gate may also be stated as the Boolean expression $\overline{A + B + C}$, read

"NOT A OR B OR C." As you might expect, this is simply the inverted output of an OR gate. Consequently, the NOR gate is frequently called an "OR-Inverter" or an "OR-NOT circuit."

A transistorized NOR gate which uses the inverted output of a basic OR circuit is shown in Fig. 5-22.

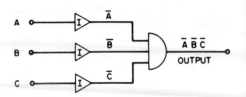

Fig. 5-23. NOR gate for the Boolean relation $\overline{A}\overline{B}\overline{C}$.

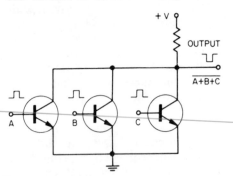

Fig. 5-22. Three-transistor NOR gate.

A positive pulse (1) at any input will cause the related transistor to conduct, changing the positive (1) level at the output to ground (0), assuming negligible transistor internal resistance during conduction.

The second law of dualization shows that the NOR relation $\overline{A + B + C}$ may also be expressed as $\overline{A} \times \overline{B} \times \overline{C}$. This suggests that NOT A, NOT B, and NOT C might be applied to an AND gate to produce the NOR functions, as shown in Fig. 5-23. While this implementation is entirely valid from an algebraic standpoint, the number of circuit components involved is too large to make its use practical.

The popular NOR gate, unlike the two we have seen, does not require a separate transistor for each input. Instead, a simple voltage

divider consisting of one resistor in series with each input and one and resistor in series with the bias supply is used. The resistors are joined at a common point and tied to the base of a transistor. This arrangement is illustrated in Fig. 5-24.

In Fig. 5-24 we use ground as the reference level or 0 condition, and a negative pulse as the 1 condition. This choice of polarity is quite common in NOR systems. Input resistors R_1, R_2, and R_3 are small in value compared with R_4, so the potential at the base of the transistor is at some small positive level.

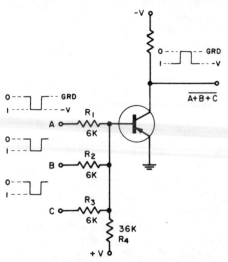

Fig. 5-24. Standard transistorized NOR gate circuit.

This places a reverse bias on the emitter-base junction to cut-off the PNP transistor. Then, the output without an input is -V or binary 1.

A negative pulse at any input increases the current through the related input resistor and through R_4, driving the base of the transistor negative. As a result, the transistor goes into heavy conduction. This causes the collector to rise toward ground, so the pulse at the output is a binary 0. The same process takes place for any combination of inputs.

However, the operating speed of the circuit decreases as the number of coincident inputs increases. The reason for this can best be understood through an examination of the transistor base potential with various input conditions to the gate. With one input applied, the input resistance is 6K ohms. Current through the input resistor actually takes two paths from the junction at the base of the transistor. Part of the current goes to ground through the two unused input resistors in parallel, and part goes to +V through R_4. For this explanation we will consider only the path to +V.

The ratio between the input resistance and R_4 is 6K:36K, or 1:6. This means that six times the voltage dropped across the input resistance will be dropped across R_4. Therefore, the base of the transistor will be at some negative level.

When two inputs are applied simultaneously, the input resistance becomes the parallel resistance of the two involved input resistors, or 3K ohms. The ratio between the input and R_4 becomes 3K:36K, or 1:12. The voltage dropped across

R_4 is now twelve times as great as that dropped across the input resistors, so the potential at the base of the transistor becomes more negative than before. The transistor is thus driven more deeply into the saturated state when two inputs are applied. With all three inputs applied, the saturation becomes even more pronounced.

The time required for the transistor to recover from this state after the inputs are removed is greater than the recovery time with one input. Hence, the operating speed of the gate is reduced somewhat. This is usually not a serious disadvantage in most NOR gate applications, but it does represent a limitation on the possible use of NOR circuits in high-speed switching operations. A few of the more popular logic symbols for the NOR gate are shown in Fig. 5-25.

STROKE Gate. The Sheffer Stroke gate gets its name from a nineteenth century logician who used a type of slash or "stroke" notation to represent certain Boolean functions. For example, the relation $\overline{AB}$, (read "NOT A AND B")

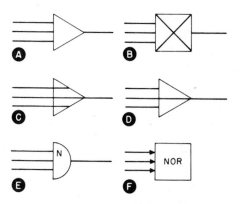

Fig. 5-25. Logic symbols for the NOR gate.

was A/B (read "A stroke B") in Sheffer's notation. The slash is still used in discussions of modern logic and occasionally in the design of electronic STROKE logic systems. However, we will use the more popular method of notation, the Boolean expression $\overline{AB}$.

The output of a STROKE gate is a binary 1 when at least one of the inputs is missing. If all inputs are present, the output is a 0. From the relation $\overline{AB}$ you can see that the output of the STROKE gate is essentially the inverted output of an AND gate. This fact has attached to the gate the titles "AND-Inverter," and "AND-NOT". A contraction of the AND-NOT title has lead to one of the STROKE gate's most popular names, the "NAND gate."

The inverted AND gate arrangement for the Stroke function is illustrated in Fig. 5-26. In this case, the basic logic circuit is an AND gate using a similar arrangement

of NPN transistors in series. Contrary to the AND gate, the output is taken from the collector of the top transistor to produce 180° phase inversion of the input. A positive input pulse on each of the transistor bases places a forward bias on the transistors. As a result, the transistors go into conduction to drop the positive level (1) at the output toward ground (0).

The first law of dualization gives us an alternate way to express the STROKE gate's function as

$$\overline{AB} = \overline{A} + \overline{B}$$

The new relation $\overline{A} + \overline{B}$ shows that the combination of logical circuits in Fig. 5-27 may be used to produce

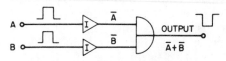

Fig. 5-27. Logic diagram of a STROKE gate with the specific function $\overline{A} + \overline{B}$.

the Stroke Function. The values $\overline{A}$ and $\overline{B}$ are separately produced by NOT circuits whose outputs are sent to an OR gate where they are combined to form the final output $\overline{A} + \overline{B}$.

The most popular STROKE gate, however, like the NOR circuit, uses a voltage dividing network rather than transistors in its input. In fact, the configuration of the STROKE gate is identical with that of the NOR gate. Comparing the STROKE gate in Fig. 5-28 with the standard NOR gate in Fig. 5-24, the difference lies only in the choice of input pulse polarity. With the

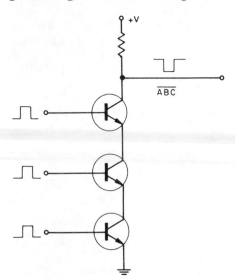

Fig. 5-26. STROKE gate using a transistor for each input.

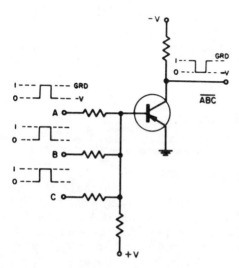

Fig. 5-28. Standard transistorized
STROKE gate circuit.

NOR gate, our binary 0 was ground, and binary 1 was a negative pulse. To make the same circuit function as a STROKE gate, we simply let the negative pulse level represent our binary 0 and any pulse which rises to ground represent our binary 1.

With this choice of polarity, the transistor is saturated without inputs applied; the output is at ground (1). A negative level at each input of the NAND gate is comparable to a NOR gate with all inputs applied. A positive-going pulse at any of the inputs to the STROKE gate is equivalent to the removal of one output from the NOR gate; the output remains unchanged. However, a positive-going pulse on all inputs to the STROKE gate simultaneously produces the same output that the NOR gate produces without inputs applied; the output falls to -V (0).

The comparative analysis on the operation of the STROKE gate and the NOR gate shows the electrical action of the circuit. However, emphasis on the different choice of input polarities clearly identifies the logical function of the STROKE gate as $\overline{ABC}$.

The logical symbols used to represent the STROKE gate are shown in Fig. 5-29. Notice that Fig. 5-29A is the same symbol as the symbol for the NOR gate in Fig. 5-25A. The identity is valid for two reasons: the circuitry is alike for both gates, and a system generally uses only one type of gate. Therefore, as long as the type used is identified as either NOR or NAND, confusion should not arise.

Arithmetic Switching Networks

We have now seen how Boolean functions can be implemented with logical circuits, but the primary concern in digital computers is arithmetic, not algebra. To adapt logical circuits for arithmetic operations, we simply combine them into special switching networks in the same way we combined basic circuits to form the EXCLUSIVE-

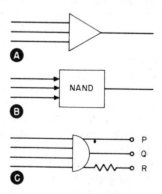

Fig. 5-29. Logic symbols for the
STROKE gate.

LY OR gate, for example. Our interest here, however, is to obtain an output which is some arithmetic function, such as the sum or the difference, of the inputs.

Besides the purely arithmetic operations, switching networks are used also in the control portion of digital computers and in many machines and automatic devices, such as elevator controls, telephone switchboards, code and cipher machines, and railway signaling systems, which are not computers in the usual sense of the word at all.

Very complicated switching networks usually may be quite easily assembled in a straightforward manner. The difficult part of the task is finding an arrangement which has a minimum or reasonable number of components, or which meets some other requirements, such as speed of operation or minimum cost. We will discuss only some of the more elementary networks here.

In general, to add two numbers we must be able to add the two numbers and any carry from a previous position. Thus, three inputs are needed. The three inputs can be obtained with a three input adder called a full adder, or with two two-input adders called half adders. We are going to discuss the half adder first.

Half Adder. A half adder receives any combination of two binary digits as inputs, as shown in Fig. 5-30. The output of the half adder consists of a sum digit and a carry digit to the next higher column. Several other types of half adders can be designed by using various combinations of the basic circuits and by conforming to the rules of

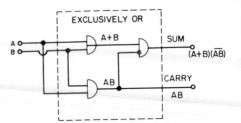

Fig. 5-30. Half adder based on the Boolean expression $(A + B)(AB)$.

binary arithmetic.

Table 5-9 presents the truth table for a half adder. By analyzing this table, we find that if $A = 1$ and $B = 0$, we have 1 for the sum; and if $A = 0$ and $B = 1$, we also have 1. However, if $A = 1$ and $B = 1$, we have 0 for the sum and 1 for the carry. Thus, for the sum we have (A OR B) AND NOT (A AND B) which is written $(A + B)(\overline{AB})$ which is the Boolean function EXCLUSIVELY OR. We have a carry of 1 when $A = 1$ and $B = 1$ and hence the carry is written AB.

The sum may be written as $A\overline{B} + \overline{A}B$ by operating De Morgan's Theorem on $(A + B)(\overline{AB})$. In this case a different half adder can be designed to produce the same results.

Half Subtractor. The half subtractor receives two binary inputs in any combination and produces an output which is their difference. The rules of operation for the half subtractor are presented in Table 5-10. The difference digit is exactly the same for A minus B as it is for

TABLE 5-9

A	0	1	0	1
B	0	1	0	1
Sum	0	1	1	0
Carry	0	0	0	1

TABLE 5-10

A	0	1	0	1
B	0	0	1	1
Difference	0	1	1	0
Borrow	0	0	1	0

B minus A. The difference for each combination is also the same as the sum digit which appears in Table 5-9. It follows that the logic diagram for the half subtractor is similar to that for the half adder. The only difference is the generation of the correct borrow instead of a carry.

The borrow we will need can be described as "B AND NOT A." You will recall that this is the Inhibit function. Therefore, the half subtractor in Fig. 5-31A can be assembled. The difference of the inputs is produced by the half adder from Fig. 5-30; the carry is produced by an added INHIBIT gate.

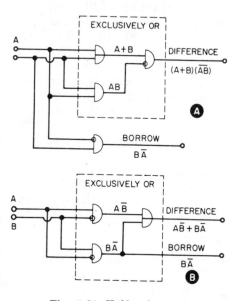

Fig. 5-31. Half subtractor.

The simpler half subtractor in Fig. 5-31B uses an alternate configuration of the EXCLUSIVELY OR gate which inherently generates the borrow BA. However, the output at the difference terminal of both half subtractors is algebraically (Boolean) identical.

The construction of a computer with half adders and half subtractors as the only arithmetic units is entirely possible. Multiplication, for example, may be performed by appropriate programming; that is, the computer may be given instructions telling it how to use the half adders repeatedly to find the product of two numbers. Division can be performed similarly through repeated use of the half subtractors.

Full Adder. The full adder is a combination of two half adders. It has three inputs to include two digits, A and B, and a carry digit C_i from the next lower order. It has two outputs: a sum digit on the same order as A and B, and a carry output digit to the next higher order.

The logic diagram for a full adder is illustrated in Fig. 5-32. Notice how the sum for the first half adder is added to input C_i in the second half adder to produce the total sum. The combination is straightforward. The carry from both adders is sent to an auxiliary OR gate to produce the total carry. This combination of individual carries is valid from an arithmetic standpoint because, from the rules for a full adder given in Table 5-11, a carry results for $AB + BC + AC + ABC$. The carry relationship given in Fig. 5-32 will reduce to this form when operated on with the proper Boolean laws and relations.

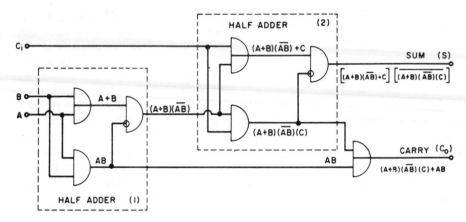

Fig. 5-32. Full adder.

Summary

The treatment of the subjects in this chapter is on an elementary level but thorough. It is our sincere belief that you should be well acquainted with these topics. With a good foundation in the principles, you can adopt this knowledge to diversified digital systems, each with its own own characteristics. However, they all depend on the same "language" and "reasoning"—binary arithmetic and Boolean algebra.

You may feel unduly burdened with new terminologies. Remember, you will be working closely with the engineers and mathematicians who will use these terms and symbols. For instance, assume an assignment that includes making a circuit board from a Boolean equation, such as $\overline{AB}$. With your trained background, you will not set up a circuit to correspond with $\overline{A}\overline{B}$ instead of $\overline{AB}$. We notice also that compound circuits can be done in several different ways to give the same electrical results but are represented by different Boolean equations. For example, a full adder can be implemented with more than eight methods. All of them have different circuits yet retain their individual characteristics. If you were to set up a full adder with the knowledge of electronic circuits only, you would likely have the schematic diagram covered with electronic circuits of the AND, OR, and NOT functions. With Boolean algebra you can simplify the full adder on paper and then make up the circuit to suit your needs. This latter method saves you time and energy.

Boolean algebra is also a very convenient shorthand for writing computer circuit functions. For instance, if we have a NOR gate with

TABLE 5-11

A	0	1	0	0	1	1	0	1
C_i	0	0	0	1	0	1	1	1
SUM	0	1	1	1	0	0	0	1
Carry	0	0	0	0	1	1	1	1

five inputs, we can say that the output F is present when all five inputs are missing; no output if one or more inputs are present. We could write the output $F = \overline{A + B + C + D + E}$. The latter is clearly a shorter expression for the longer verbal one. If you have to explain the function of a particular circuit in a digital system, Boolean expressions are less apt to have double meanings and use less words.

5-6. Review Problems

1. Convert the following numbers. (a) 13.5625 to binary number. (b) (1011.101)$_2$ to decimal number.

2. Perform the following subtraction in an eight-digit machine. Use 1's complement. Show work. 1010.111—10111.01.

3. Solve the following problems. Show work. (a) Multiply 10.101 by 111.011 by the floating-point method and add partial products by accumulation. (b) Divide by using the fixed binary point and subtract by direct subtraction. Dividend = 1011.111; divisor = 10.1.

4. Define: (a) digital computer; (b) "bit" and "word."

5. What happens to an AND gate if you reverse the diodes and bias voltage connections? (See Fig. 5-12)

6. (a) What are the two primitive circuits? (b) Are they alike?

7. Draw the logic symbols, one for each of the five logic circuits that are not primitive. Use the most common symbols.

8. Briefly explain the difference between serial and parallel operation.

9. (a) What is the decimal equivalent of the largest binary number that an eight-digit computer can hold? (b) If the eight digits are held in flip-flops connected as two series decade counters, what is the largest decimal number the series decade counters can hold?

10. Match the terms in the right column of those in the left column.

   (a) Output of INHIBIT Gate with 3 inputs.   (1) Output of EXCLUSIVELY OR gate with 3 inputs.

   (b) (A + B)C   (2) 3 input STROKE function

   (c) difference output of half subtractor   (3) ABC

   (d) Output = A + B + C   (4) ABC

Index